"The Pen's Excellencie"

*Treasures from the Manuscript Collection
of The Folger Shakespeare Library*

This volume has been published in conjunction with the exhibition, *"The Pen's Excellencie": Treasures from the Manuscript Collection of The Folger Shakespeare Library*, presented at The Folger Shakespeare Library,® Washington, DC, from February 6 through June 8, 2002, on the occasion of The Folger Library's seventieth anniversary.

Werner Gundersheimer
Director

Richard Kuhta
Librarian

Rachel Doggett
Andrew W. Mellon Curator
of Books and Exhibitions

The exhibition and the catalogue have been funded by The Winton and Carolyn Blount Exhibition Fund of The Folger Shakespeare Library and by a gift from the George Frederick Jewett Foundation.

Distributed by University of Washington Press, Seattle and London.
ISBN 0-295-98266-7

Photographs by Julie Ainsworth.

"The Pen's Excellencie"

*Treasures from the Manuscript Collection
of The Folger Shakespeare Library*

Compiled and edited by Heather Wolfe

The Folger Shakespeare Library
Washington, DC
2002

Distributed by University of Washington Press
Seattle and London

Dedicated to
Laetitia Yeandle
Curator of Manuscripts
Emerita

upon the occasion
of her retirement
after forty-four years
of dedicated service
to The Folger
Shakespeare Library

Contents

Contributors

J. Leeds Barroll, *Folger Shakespeare Library*
Peter Beal, *Sotheby's (London)*
S. P. Cerasano, *Colgate University*
James Daybell, *University of Reading*
Germaine Greer, *University of Warwick*
Grace Ioppolo, *University of Reading*
Barbara Kreps, *University of Pisa*
Mairi A. Macdonald, *Shakespeare Birthplace Trust*
Leah S. Marcus, *Vanderbilt University*
Steven W. May, *Georgetown College, Kentucky*
Janel M. Mueller, *University of Chicago*
Lee Piepho, *Sweet Briar College*
Dorothy Rouse-Bottom, *Hampton, Virginia*
Sara Jayne Steen, *Montana State University*
Alan Stewart, *Birkbeck College*
H. R. Woudhuysen, *University College, London*

Folger Shakespeare Library Staff
Erin Blake
Rachel Doggett
Werner Gundersheimer
Jim Kuhn
Richard Kuhta
Rosalind Larry
Frank Mowery
Dever Powell
Susan Scola
Suellen Towers
Betsy Walsh
Heather Wolfe
Georgianna Ziegler

Foreword

WOLFGANG SCHMIEDER, the scholar whose famous system of numbering is used to identify the works of Johann Sebastian Bach, was also a learned librarian with a particular interest in manuscripts. In that regard, he would have been able to boast some sort of kinship with Laetitia Yeandle, the Folger's Curator of Manuscripts Emerita, whose careful stewardship of our collection extends back over forty-four years. And Laetitia, whose mastery of English paleography is the stuff of legend, would surely agree with Wolfgang's view of the special and rarified pleasure of studying manuscripts. He wrote:

> Handwritings of the departed are like illuminated windows in the night of the past. It is in these manuscripts, if anywhere, that something tangible of the corporeal-spiritual being of their authors confronts us. We look over their shoulders, so to speak, and take part in their revelations, their troubles, their joys. And while we become absorbed in such a page, our book knowledge of the particular man's life, as well as the times which surrounded him and often heavily oppressed him, becomes a living experience.

Happily, since the present exhibition was conceived in honor of Mrs. Yeandle on the occasion of her recent retirement, not all our manuscripts bear quite the weight of *Sturm und Drang* that so appealed to Herr Schmieder.

In fact, the present exhibition provides a window onto a vast landscape of experience, much of it rather pleasant, seen over the past seven centuries. Perhaps the only common feature of these remarkable texts is that someone wrote them with his or her own hand. Since they are notable examples carefully culled from many thousands of manuscripts, the writers tend to be reasonably well known. In that respect, perhaps, they are not altogether typical of our holdings, which also include much work by that most prolific of authors—"Anonymous."

By catering just a bit to the modern fascination with celebrities, literary and otherwise, we mean to convey the excitement and power of manuscripts to a growing audience. Indeed we hope, and even expect, that visitors to this exhibition will be surprised as well as delighted, both by the variety of this somewhat unrepresentative sampling of the Library's holdings, and by the abundance and significance of the many nineteenth-century manuscripts included here. After all, one more or less expects the Folger to be able to produce some specimens of the handwriting of such Tudor and Stuart worthies as John Donne, Edmund Spenser, and Thomas Traherne. But what about the commonplace books of James Boswell, George Eliot, and Robert Southey, not to speak of letters by Wordsworth, Coleridge, Verdi, Dickens, Twain, Whitman, Wilde, and Cody? Yes, Buffalo Bill!

It is worth noting, at least in passing, that the Folger's manuscript collection is for the most part archival in nature. Much of it consists of long runs of family papers, mundane legal and financial transactions, commonplace books, miscellanies, theatrical records, and the like. While these sources may speak eloquently to the patient investigator, such documents do not a thrilling exhibition make. So ours is unabashedly a view of manuscripts with star power, chosen to honor one of the brightest lights in the Folger's firmament.

In a sense, this exhibition is also a tribute to Heather Wolfe, Laetitia Yeandle's successor. During her brief tenure, Dr. Wolfe has developed an impressive familiarity with our manuscript resources, reaching well beyond her principal area of scholarly expertise in seventeenth-century English literature. A paleographer who is very much in the Folger tradition, she has also reached out to many of her predecessor's colleagues and friends, who have brought their expert knowledge to the challenging task of briefly summarizing the significance of the documents selected. The Library is grateful to all who contributed to this enterprise—to the scholarly contributors; to the conservators who safeguard these fragile artifacts; to Mr. and Mrs. Folger, who started it all; to the generations of wise librarians who have greatly expanded the original collection; to the many donors who have assured the Library's ability to grow; and to Laetitia Yeandle— scholar, teacher, and curator *extraordinaire*.

Werner Gundersheimer
Director

Acknowledgments

THIS CATALOGUE WAS TRULY a collaborative effort. I am grateful to the many scholars and staff members who generously contributed catalogue entries: Leeds Barroll, Peter Beal, Erin Blake, Susan Cerasano, James Daybell, Rachel Doggett, Germaine Greer, Grace Ioppolo, Barbara Kreps, Jim Kuhn, Richard Kuhta, Rosalind Larry, Mairi MacDonald, Leah Marcus, Steve May, Frank Mowery, Janel Mueller, Lee Piepho, Dever Powell, Dorothy Rouse-Bottom, Susan Scola, Sara Jayne Steen, Alan Stewart, Suellen Towers, Betsy Walsh, Henry Woudhuysen, and Georgianna Ziegler. Their specialized knowledge has enriched the catalogue tremendously. Peter Beal was very helpful in the planning stages and was kind enough to describe some of his favorite Folger manuscripts in "A Personal View." Bethany Bryant, my summer intern, conducted preliminary research on a number of manuscripts in the exhibition. Thank you to the Folger conservators, Frank Mowery, Linda Blaser, Linda Hohneke, Rhea Baier, and interns Moena Zeller and Jana Dambrogio, for their preparation and presentation of the manuscripts in the exhibition, and to Julie Ainsworth for the wonderful reproductions in the catalogue. Being a relative new-comer to the Folger, I could not have curated the exhibition without the collective institutional knowledge of Richard Kuhta, Librarian, and the entire library staff. Werner Gundersheimer was the inspiration behind this first-ever display of the Folger's manuscript treasures, so it is fortuitous and fitting that it coincides with his final pre-retirement months at the Folger. I am most grateful to James Daybell for his careful reading of the entire catalogue in its final stages, to Susan Scola for assisting with the index and other tasks, and to Erin Blake, Jim Kuhn, and Georgianna Ziegler for taking on extra responsibilities as the catalogue deadline approached. I am especially indebted to Rachel Doggett, Andrew W. Mellon Curator of Books and Exhibitions, who worked tirelessly to edit and otherwise prepare the catalogue for publication. It should be noted that any errors are of course my own.

My greatest debt is to Laetitia Yeandle, curator emerita of manuscripts. Anyone whose work has been furthered by her meticulousness, curiosity, and caution, knows that Laetitia is one of the Folger's true treasures. Her modesty and generosity have earned her the respect and admiration of scholars throughout the world, and her forty-four years of service at the Folger have played a large part in fostering the library's reputation for supporting and encouraging the research of its readers. It was a privilege to apprentice under Laetitia in her final year as curator of manuscripts, and I am fortunate in that I continue to benefit from her unparalleled knowledge of the manuscript collection. This catalogue is a small token of the Folger Shakespeare Library's appreciation for her immeasurable contributions.

Heather Wolfe

Introduction

To be briefe, the Art of *Writing* is so excellent,
  and of such necessary use, that none ought to be
  without some knowledge therein.[1]

1. Martin Billingsley, *The pen's excellencie or The secretaries delighte* (London, 1618), B4v.

SELECTING ONE HUNDRED MANUSCRIPT TREASURES for this exhibition from the roughly 55,000 manuscripts at the Folger Shakespeare Library was not an easy task. The manuscript collection ranges in date from the late thirteenth century to the present day and includes a vast range of handwritten documents such as deeds, court documents, political treatises, account books, devotional works, sermons, poetry, plays, music, correspondence, journals, miscellanies, commonplace books, scrapbooks, receipt books, scientific, military, and mathematical manuals, heraldic manuscripts, forgeries, and scholars' papers. The collection also houses items less typically thought of as manuscripts, such as locks of hair, tickets, signed photographs, unpublished typescripts, printed books with marginal annotations, menu cards, pressed leaves, coins, and wax seals. My definition of what constitutes a manuscript "treasure" changed a great deal as I prepared for this exhibition, as I debated between the merits of showing manuscripts that are priceless in terms of literary or historic interest but of less value in aesthetic terms, and manuscripts that are fascinating or beautiful to look at but not as interesting from a scholarly point of view. For the purposes of this exhibition, both categories fit into my criteria for inclusion. Is the manuscript of literary, historical, or political significance? Is it written or corrected in the author's hand or does it in any way provide insight into the author's life or creative process? Does it contain an important signature or has it been associated with or presented to a well-known personage? Is it a rare, interesting, or beautiful example of a particular kind of manuscript? And finally, and perhaps most importantly, does the manuscript have the potential to surprise or delight the viewer?

Since the Folger's collection is designed for library use rather than museum display, many of the manuscripts included in this exhibition are not your typical "blockbuster" items. While there are a handful of colorful, attention-grabbing manuscripts, most are deceivingly humble at first glance, written in inscrutable hands in brown ink. The earliest item, a copy of twelve works by Aristotle, is from the early fourteenth century. The latest item, from 1928, is a short poem by A. A. Milne. Within this six hundred year span is a wealth of unique material that relates in some way either to Shakespeare, the theater, or the early modern period. While many of the Folger's manuscript "treasures" are well known to scholars, the majority of the manuscripts in this exhibition are either on public display for the first time, or the first time in many years. The "Dowland manuscript," containing lute tablature written and signed by the Elizabethan lutenist John Dowland, was last shown in 1971. Most of the Shakespeare-related manuscripts were last seen in 1979 during the *Shakespeare, the Globe, and the World* exhibition; the Mendelssohn overture, the John Donne letter, the sixteenth-century German military manual, and James I's warrant releasing Sir Walter Raleigh from the Tower were shown in the *Folger's Choice* exhibition of 1987; a handful of the manuscripts signed by the Tudor and Stuart kings and queens appeared in the *Royal Autographs* exhibition in 1989; and Sir Edward Howard's *Change of Crownes* was shown in the *Five Years of Acquisitions* exhibition in 1990. Only the Macro Plays, the Trevelyon Miscellany, the letter from Robert Dudley, earl of Leicester, to Elizabeth I, Thomas Fella's *Divers Devices*, Hugh Alley's *Caveat*, and Esther Inglis's calligraphic manuscripts have been shown in the past five years. A deed of bargain and sale of the rooms which were to become Blackfriars Theatre (sold by Sir William More to James Burbage in 1596), an unpublished poem by Thomas Traherne, a copy of a letter in Edmund Spenser's hand, a holograph letter from Elizabeth I to James VI of Scotland, and the New Year's gift roll of Henry VIII have never before been shown according to Folger exhibition records. An unexpectedly rich group of letters and original works by writers, dramatists, and poets from the eighteenth, nineteenth, and twentieth centuries are also shown here for the first time.

For the most part, the exhibition is organized chronologically. It begins with examples from the Folger's collection of medieval manuscripts and then progresses on to Tudor and Stuart royal documents signed or written by Henry VIII, Edward VI, Lady Jane Grey, Mary I, Elizabeth I, James I, and Henry, prince of Wales. The next section consists of legal, historical, and dramatic manuscripts relating to Shakespeare and his fellow players and dramatists. The Shakespeare-related manuscripts are followed by manuscripts in the autographs of John Donne, Edmund Spenser, Thomas Traherne, John Dowland, and Gabriel Harvey; pastoral works by Sir Philip Sidney, Mary Wroth, John Barclay, and William Basse; books of emblems and epigrams by Esther Inglis, Henry Peacham, Sir John Harington, Thomas Fella, and Thomas Trevelyon; and Restoration plays, including two controversial plays thought lost until the twentieth century—*The Change of Crownes* by Edward Howard and *The Country Gentleman* by Sir Robert Howard and the second Duke of Buckingham. Filling out the seventeenth century are a few "curiosities"—an Elizabethan fold-out toy with portraits and verses made out of parchment, a ca.1620 German military manual with vividly-colored paintings of a wide range of weapons, and an equally colorful book condemning illegal practices in the London markets. The last third of the exhibition focuses on the letters, original works, notebooks, and literary criticism of dramatists and literary figures from the eighteenth century through the early twentieth century. Manuscripts in the hands of James Boswell, Jonathan Swift, Samuel Johnson, David Garrick, Elizabeth Inchbald, Hannah More, and Sarah Siddons, and the Romantic poets (Wordsworth, Coleridge, Lamb, Southey, De Quincey) are followed by a number of less expected manuscripts, including Mark Twain's autograph copy of his controversial work, *Is Shakespeare Dead?*, a notebook compiled by George Eliot while she was researching her novel *Middlemarch*, theatrical manuscripts by Charles Dickens, and autograph works by Louisa May Alcott, Elizabeth Barrett Browning, Washington Irving, A. A. Milne, Dante Gabriel Rossetti, George Sand, Robert Louis Stevenson, Bram Stoker, Algernon Charles Swinburne, Alfred Tennyson, Walt Whitman, and Oscar Wilde. Thus, we see the authors of *Little Women* and *Treasure Island* adapting characters from *A Midsummer Night's Dream* and *The Winter's Tale* into their fiction, the author of *Dracula* writing a loving biography of his closest friend, the Shakespearean actor Sir Henry Irving, the author of "The Legend of Sleepy Hollow" speculating on the influence of an ill-fated voyage to Virginia on Shakespeare's *The Tempest*, the author of *The Adventures of Huckleberry Finn* challenging Shakespeare's identity, Oscar Wilde chastizing Shakespeare for privileging life over art in his plays, George Sand discovering Hamlet as personified by the actor William Charles Macrcady, and Walt Whitman proposing that Shakespeare's historical plays represent the seeds of modern democracy. While other libraries have the manuscripts of the works that gave these authors canonical status, the Folger has the manuscripts of these very same authors that show them in an entirely different light—as they engaged with and related to Shakespeare—essentially, the seeds for a prosopographical history of Shakespeare's readers over the past four hundred years.

Out of necessity, many important manuscripts have been excluded from the exhibition, and the richness of many parts of the collection is woefully underrepresented. Among the theatrical manuscripts exhibited, only seven are from the sixty manuscript plays from the sixteenth and seventeenth centuries. Peter Beal describes some of these manuscripts in the following essay. Only ten manuscripts (out of seven hundred) are from the Loseley collection. The Loseley collection, purchased in six batches between 1938 and 1954, comprises the papers of Sir Thomas Cawarden, the first Master of the Revels and Master of the Tents, and his executor, Sir William More of Loseley Park, Surrey, and his family, and constitutes one of the largest collections anywhere of documents relating to the logistics of court entertainments and to the use of tents for royal progresses and military campaigns in the sixteenth century. The manuscript treasures in the David Garrick (1717–1779) collection—letters, journals, account books, plays, prologues, epilogues, poems, scrapbooks, promptbooks, and a run of Drury Lane records which encompasses his tenure as manager (nightly accounts, ledgers, paybooks, agreements, inventories)—are represented here by only a handful of items. A recent grant from the Delmas Foundation has allowed the Folger to provide detailed online catalogue records and conservation work for the Garrick material, some of which will be displayed in a David Garrick exhibition at the Folger in the next few years. The only items from the approximately two thousand letters and documents saved and collected by Augustin Daly (1838–1899), playwright, producer and lessee of the Fifth Avenue Theatre and Daly's Theatre in New York City from 1869 to 1899, are the letter from Buffalo Bill and the manuscripts concerning Daly's production of Alfred, Lord Tennyson's *The Foresters*. Other collections are not represented at all. The already strong collection of manuscripts relating to the dramatic editor for the *New York Herald Tribune*, William Winter (1836–1917), which includes letters to and from Winter, his diaries, and theatrical memorabilia relating to many of the leading American and British theatrical figures from the late nineteenth century, has grown extensively in the past year thanks to donations and purchases from Winter's great-grandson, Robert Young. The William Henderson (1831–1891) collection includes over five hundred autograph letters of actors, authors, composers, and artists. In fact, nearly all of the leading American and British Shakespearean actors and dramatists from the eighteenth through twentieth centuries are well-represented in the Folger's manuscript collection, including Frances Abington, Viola Allen, Junius Brutus Booth and his son Edwin Booth, Colley Cibber, Susannah Maria Cibber, Kitty Clive, George Colman, the younger and elder, Charlotte Cushman, Edwin Forrest, Helena Modjeska, Hannah More, Elizabeth Inchbald, Sir Henry Irving, Edmund Kean, his son Charles Kean, Charles Kean's wife, Ellen (Tree) Kean, the Kemble dynasty, including siblings Sarah Siddons, John Phillip Kemble, and Charles Kemble, and Charles' daughter Fanny Kemble, William Charles Macready, Samuel Phelps, Ada Rehan, Richard Brinsley Sheridan, and Ellen Terry.

As I cast my net into the post-1700 collection, I was surprised to find that Henry and Emily Folger had collected literary manuscripts by numerous American, British, and continental authors and poets who engaged with Shakespeare in one way or another, whether it be to adapt, imitate, criticize, defend, doubt, or admire him. For every author included in the exhibition, many others have been excluded, such as W. H. Auden, Thomas Carlyle, Lewis Carroll, Wilkie Collins, William Congreve, Ralph Waldo Emerson, Goethe, Thomas Hardy, Nathaniel Hawthorne, Victor Hugo, Henry Wadsworth Longfellow, Alexander Pope, Samuel Richardson, John Ruskin, Sir Walter Scott, George Bernard Shaw, Mary Shelley, Leslie Stephen, William Makepeace Thackeray, Henry David Thoreau, Oliver Wendell Holmes, Voltaire, and Emile Zola. Their letters provide wonderful insight into the ubiquity of

Shakespeare in both the common parlance and literary development of innumerable Augustan, Romantic, and Victorian writers.

The Folger also has the papers of numerous Shakespeare scholars, editors, and collectors, including Mary Cowden Clarke, Frederick Fleay, James Orchard Halliwell-Phillipps, Clement Mansfield Ingleby, Sir Sidney Lee, Edmund Malone, Caroline Spurgeon, and George Steevens, and the manuscripts of the Shakespearean forgers William Henry Ireland (1777–1835) and John Payne Collier (1789–1883). A complete run of the *Gentleman's Magazine* annotated by the editors, the Nichols family, as well as boxes of correspondence from their contributors relating to the publication of *Gentleman's Magazine*, have been invaluable for identifying many of the unsigned articles in the periodical. Also at the Folger are the papers of various Baconians, that is, people who believe that Francis Bacon was the author of Shakespeare's plays, chief among them, Delia Salter Bacon (1811–1859), but also Isaac Hull Platt and Ignatius Donnelly.

Some of the Folger's greatest treasures are not represented here because their value lies in their connectivity to other manuscripts within an "archive" of family papers, affording scholars a generous glimpse into family relationships, patronage networks, and life at the Court and in the country in the early modern period. Larger collections from the sixteenth and seventeenth centuries include the Bagot papers, the Bacon-Townshend papers, the Rich papers, the Ferrers of Tamworth papers, the Cavendish-Talbot papers, the Newdigate newsletters, and the two hundred volumes of transcripts from the papal and Venetian archives formerly owned by the Strozzi family. Some of the finding aids for these collections are already online, and others are in the process of being converted for online publication.

What constitutes a "treasure" has changed over the decades, as literary and history scholars have expanded the canon and incorporated previously marginalized lives and activities into their research. What has often been considered the detritus of everyday life has now become invaluable to uncovering the interplay between the public and domestic spheres in early modern England. Letters, miscellanies, and receipt books are probably the most heavily used early modern manuscripts at the Folger. The difference in the ways that manuscripts are described in catalogues at the beginning and at the end of the twentieth century indicates this shift in value. A group of two thousand manuscripts at the Folger, originally catalogued as a collection of watermarks on otherwise "valueless" manuscripts, has turned out to contain extensive records of the Hale family of King's Walden, Essex, providing a valuable record of the daily operations of a local lord of the manor. Manuscripts written by women historically have been catalogued under their husbands' names, and letters have been calendared in terms of their references to politics or literature, so that content relating to domestic matters is obscured. One of the great assets of the manuscript collection is the fact that it contains multiple copies of many poems, letters, and politically-sensitive tracts. Despite the advent of printing in the fifteenth century, early modern England was as much in the throes of a thriving manuscript culture as it was a print culture—the impetus to produce and read texts in manuscript was as strong as the impetus to produce and read texts in print. Comparison of these documents to other printed and manuscript copies in order to discern the interesting and suggestive variants between them, whether they be the result of carelessness, poetic license, or censorship, often helps to unravel how and why a work might have been transmitted from one person to another, showing its political, social, and literary significance.

Many of the manuscripts at the Folger Shakespeare Library are treasures merely because they *survived*. My two favorite items in this category are medieval vellum manuscripts used to stiffen bindings, and letters ending with the pleading post-script: "Burn this letter."[2] Laetitia Yeandle has played a major role in the growth and cataloguing of Folger manuscripts during her tenure at the Folger, realizing the long-term scholarly value and significance of even the most insignificant-looking and ephemeral manuscripts, and caring deeply about the manuscript writings and compilations of writers both known and unknown, famous and infamous, talented and aspiring, organized and disorganized. Thus, it is fitting that the manuscript purchased by the Folger in honor of her retirement is an unwieldy and dilapidated 300+ page disbound manuscript written and compiled by the merchant Michael Lok (b. 1532) and indexed and added to by his stepson, Sir Julius Caesar (1558–1636), Master of the Rolls (Folger MS Add 1100). Written in multiple hands and languages, it is the first numbered manuscript in Caesar's library catalogue (now at the British Library, Lansdowne 123, fol. 7), where it is described as "The Contents of the Booke in fol. Signed 1. touch. Nobility." In addition to pedigrees of English and continental aristocratic and ruling families, it contains, among other items, extracts from deeds, indexes to various letter books, an index of books in the Herald's office, and three sets of opinions regarding banks, drains, and sluices. The precise function and importance of this manuscript are yet to be discovered.

Heather Wolfe

2. The most famous binding fragment is in fact no longer part of the collection—a seventh-century Irish manuscript fragment of Eusebius found in a sixteenth-century binding at the Folger in 1984. Since it was deemed beyond the scope of the collection, it was auctioned at Sotheby's on June 25, 1985, and an endowed fund for the acquisition of books and manuscripts was created from the proceeds. Originally purchased by the British Railway Pension Fund, it was later sold to Sir Paul Getty, KBE.

The Folger Manuscript Collection: A Personal View

WHEN MOST PEOPLE THINK OF THE FOLGER LIBRARY they think of its incomparable collection of Shakespeare First Folios (three of them with original corrected proof sheets), its other Shakespeare Quartos and Folios, and its vast range of further sixteenth- and seventeenth-century books relating to Shakespeare and his contemporaries. For my part, though, the treasures of the Folger are nowhere more apparent than in the truly remarkable number and quality of its sixteenth- and seventeenth-century literary and historical *manuscripts*, the collection which Laetitia Yeandle has helped to build and has promoted so well for the past forty-four years. This is a resource into which I have had the privilege of delving on numerous occasions, principally since 1974 when I began the virtually lifelong task of compiling the 1450–1700 section of the *Index of English Literary Manuscripts*.

Not surprisingly, for the supreme American "Shakespeare Library," we have dramatic texts for a start. We find manuscripts, some of them authorial, of plays or masques by Shakespeare himself (the Dering transcript of *Henry IV*; a later-seventeenth-century manuscript of *Julius Caesar*), Thomas Middleton (*A Game at Chess*, twice, and *Hengist King of Kent*), Ben Jonson (*Christmas his Masque*, etc.), Thomas Randolph (*Aristippus*), Thomas Killigrew (*Cecilia and Clorinda*), John Wilmot, Earl of Rochester (*Lucina's Rape*), John Dryden (*The Fall of Angels*, adapted from *Paradise Lost*), his brother-in-law, Sir Robert Howard, and the Duke of Buckingham (*The Country Gentleman*), Edward Howard (*A Change of Crowns*), and Roger Boyle, Earl of Orrery (*Henry V* and *Mustapha*), as well as plays in the Beaumont and Fletcher canon (*Beggars' Bush*, *The Woman's Prize*), various university entertainments, and much else besides. We find, too, the "Harbord volume" of six printed plays by Philip Massinger annotated in the playwright's own hand, and numerous promptbooks of plays by Shakespeare and others, including James Shirley's *The Sisters* used ca.1669 by the King's Company. And these are only the items which come immediately to mind.

Such manuscripts and annotations in printed books enrich our knowledge of playwrights' texts and throw light on compositional, transmissional and, occasionally, playhouse practices. They also contribute significantly to what might be called a common international pool of textual resources and scholarship. For no collection exists as a sealed entity, self-contained and insulated from the rest of the world. Indeed, one measure of its importance may be the very links that can be established with other resources.

One illustration of this in the field of drama is the Folger's printed copy of the play often attributed to Middleton, *Blurt, Master-Constable* (1602), which has two missing leaves supplied in manuscript. As long ago as 1945 the former Folger librarian James G. McManaway established that, instead of being transcribed from another printed copy as one would expect, these leaves were almost certainly copied by a playhouse scribe from a contemporary playhouse promptbook. In fact, this established a trail that reaches to other libraries in Britain and opens up considerable research possibilities. For the same scribal hand can now be recognized in pages of a similar kind added to a copy of George Chapman's *May Day* (1611) at Worcester College, Oxford; in the British Library's unique manuscript of *Dick of Devonshire* (ca.1626), sometimes attributed to Thomas Heywood; in a substantial 1630s verse miscellany in the British Library (Add. MS 33998), including poems by Beaumont, Jonson, Davenant and Shirley; and in at least one other dramatic text elsewhere. Recognizing this scribe's contribution to the transmission of poetical and dramatic literature in the 1620s–30s opens up intriguing possibilities about the nature and authority of his sources, his affiliations to particular companies and employers, and the methods by which certain kinds of text either may have been controlled or disseminated in this period.

Similar links can be established for certain of the Folger's anthologies of dramatic extracts. A number of the Library's seventeenth-century manuscript miscellanies contain extracts and quotations from plays—which provide a valuable insight into the nature of taste, readership, and interpretation in this period. None is larger, however, than V.b.93: a 900-page anthology, including literally hundreds of quotations from Shakespeare, entitled *Hesperides, or the Muses Garden*. Not only does this turn out to be a compilation apparently by one John Evans that Humphrey Moseley intended to publish in 1655, but the Folger has part of what can be identified as a second manuscript of the same work. Folger V.a.75, 79, and 80 are pages taken by J. O. Halliwell-Phillipps from that manuscript, the rest of which he chose, for reasons of his own, to cut up into strips that he pasted into more than sixty of his Shakespearean scrapbooks now preserved in the Shakespeare Centre, Stratford-upon-Avon. He did the same thing with a set of four music partbooks of John Playford. Folger V.a.411 comprises five leaves with songs from *The Tempest* by John Wilson. For the rest of the manuscripts from which these were excised we must consult, once again, Halliwell-Phillipps's scrapbooks at Stratford and also the main partbooks at the University of Glasgow (MSS R.d.58–61).

Fortunately, other links and identifications which the Folger's resources provide are less redolent of Victorian vandalism. Not the least of the Folger's treasures is its huge collection of seventeenth-century manuscript miscellanies and commonplace books, especially poetical ones. Much ink could be spent listing these marvelous compilations, chiefly in the V.a. and V.b. series, witnesses to a vigorous and flourishing manuscript culture among the educated classes, especially in the 1620s–40s, with all their texts of poets such as John Donne, Ben Jonson, Richard Corbett,

Thomas Carew, Robert Herrick, Richard Crashaw, Henry King, and numerous other writers of the period. Inspired by the pioneering work of Mary Hobbs, one can relate many of these items to compilations found in other British and American libraries. Such links help to define points of origin, reading communities, patterns of distribution—local and family networks, particular universities, colleges, or London Inns of Court circles—and may even help to determine the nature of particular texts before they were subject to the vagaries of multiple recopying or printing. Here, too, identification of hands plays a part. To take a single instance, Folger V.a.103, an anthology of poems by Donne and his contemporaries, formally arranged according to genre, can be matched to one in the Portland Collection at the University of Nottingham (MS PwV 37). Thus the network of widely dispersed and seemingly numberless manuscript texts of this kind may draw closer and the patterns and affinities which explain them begin gradually to be revealed.

This celebration has not yet included important manuscripts of works by particular poets. Readers will have their own favourites—and there are plenty to choose from. If I mention having a particularly soft spot for Folger V.a.249, Sir John Harington's collection of 408 of his epigrams, it is not only because of its attractive physical presentation, complete with a drawing of a lantern, and because (like certain other of Harington's carefully produced manuscripts now in other repositories) it was prepared as a gift for Prince Henry, but also because I can't help feeling what a wonderful challenge this artifact (seen in relation to its cousins elsewhere) offers to a modern editor. Perhaps soon we shall have a scholar present these epigrams to a modern audience in the form they deserve, with a sufficiently clear explanation of the context and jokes they embody that made them such a source of merriment to their privileged Elizabethan and Jacobean readers.

Other equally distinguished manuscripts come to mind—the Clifford Manuscript of Sidney's *Old Arcadia* (H.b.1); the Harmsworth Manuscript of poems chiefly by the martyred Jesuit priest Robert Southwell (Bound with STC 22957); the transcript of a letter on poetry and Latin verses which can now be identified as written in Spenser's hand in his own copy of Sabinus's *Poemata* (X.d.520); the recently identified manuscript of Thomas Traherne's *The Ceremonial Law* (V.a.70); the verse miscellany which proves to be compiled by Rochester's protégé, the satirist John Oldham (V.a.169). Notable manuscripts by women include exquisite calligraphic tours de force by Esther Inglis (V.a.91–94); poems of Sidney's niece Mary Wroth (V.a.104); the Works of Lady Anne Southwell (V.b.198); poems by Anne Finch, Countess of Winchilsea (N.b.3); and *Poems* by Katherine Philips (V.b.231, whose apparently humble status as a transcript of the 1669 printed edition is belied by the light it sheds on contemporary reception of this publication).

Nor must we forget the profusion of sixteenth- and seventeenth-century scribal transcripts of political tracts and discourses, state papers, and the like—including works by Sir Philip Sidney, Francis Bacon, Viscount St. Albans, Sir Walter Raleigh, Samuel Daniel, Sir John Davies, Sir Robert Cotton, Sir Charles Cornwallis, George Puttenham, Sir Henry Wotton, and many others. Here we have abundant evidence of a flourishing manuscript culture in which discussions of topics of current interest were circulated in manuscript long before they ever saw the light of print, especially in those years of intellectual ferment leading up to the English Civil War. The Folger collection of manuscript verse miscellanies allows us to establish at least some patterns of dating and distribution, especially when the hands of the same scribes can be recognized. I might be forgiven for mentioning my own favorite here—the ubiquitous "Feathery Scribe" (in G.b.9, V.b.50, X.d.210, X.d.337)—but he is only one of many represented. It is also a pleasure when one discovers that what might seem at first sight to be a routine collection of transcribed materials on state affairs proves to have a more interesting provenance. Thus, for instance, Folger V.b.142, partly relating to the threat to Queen Elizabeth posed by Mary, Queen of Scots, turns out to have been produced almost certainly by the secretariat of Robert Beale, a principal Secretary of the Queen's Privy Council itself, not to mention the man who had the dubious privilege of reading out Mary's execution warrant at the actual execution.

These random examples are a reminder of what a huge manuscript literary culture flourished in Britain in this period; of how the traditional bibliographical concentration on printed books alone offers cultural historians only part of the picture, and a possibly distorted one at that; and of the enormous potential which a collection such as the Folger's offers to scholars for the study of that culture. Laetitia Yeandle has been in the vanguard of those promoting that study, in encouraging so many scholars for so many years to avail themselves of the Library's manuscript resources to that purpose. Even so, given the wealth of material available, she and her successor would no doubt be among the first to say that the detailed and penetrating exploration of those resources has scarcely begun.

Peter Beal
Sotheby's (London)

Textual Conventions and Dating

All transcriptions from manuscripts maintain original spelling, capitalization, and punctuation. Abbreviations have been expanded with the added letters in italics and superscript letters silently lowered. In early modern England, the letters *i* and *j* and the letters *u* and *v* were often interchanged and *ff* was used instead of *F*. These conventions have been maintained here. In a few instances, letters or punctuation have been supplied in square brackets for clarification. When referring to dated documents, the New Year is taken to begin on January 1, even though documents in early modern England were often dated with the New Year beginning on March 25 (Lady Day).

Unless otherwise noted, reproductions are from the first or only page of the manuscript, and transcriptions are taken from the page reproduced.

Catalogue of the Exhibition

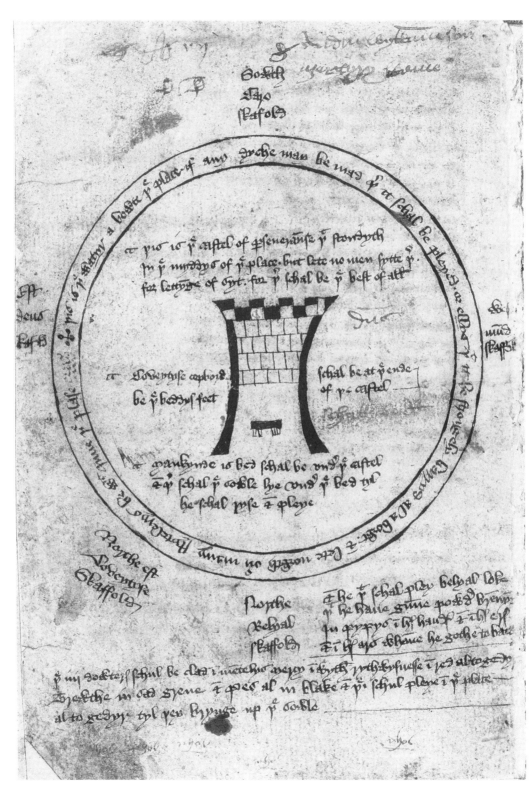

The Castle of Perseverance, V.a.354, fol.191

Macro manuscripts: Three morality plays

THIS HUMBLE MANUSCRIPT is one of the most treasured items of the Folger Shakespeare Library. Without it our knowledge of the early history of the once flourishing genre of English morality plays would be scanty, since it contains the full texts of three of the four surviving morality plays written in English before 1500.[1] Named after its eighteenth-century owner, the Reverend Cox Macro, the Macro manuscript consists of three distinct manuscript plays written at different times and brought together by Reverend Macro.[2]

Morality plays were largely allegorical, using outward representations of good and evil as a means to reveal man's inward spiritual qualities. The plot of *The Castle of Perseverance* (composed ca.1400–25, copied ca.1440) involves the hero Mankind struggling to maintain his virtuous character even as he faces the Coming of Death, the Debate of Body and Soul after his death, and the Parliament in Heaven. *Wisdom* (composed in the 1460s, copied ca.1475), also called *Mind, Will, and Understanding*, examines the soul from a theological perspective. The Folger's copy of *Wisdom* contains an unusually large number of stage directions and marginal annotations. The comical *Mankind* (composed in the 1460s, copied ca.1475, but slightly later than *Wisdom*) is the first English play to show that actors took up a collection from the audience.

The leaf shown here is the last page of *The Castle of Perseverance*. It is the earliest known stage diagram for an English play, and as such provides invaluable insight into how morality plays were performed. It shows a stage in the round with the Castle in the center, surrounded by a water-filled ditch and five scaffolds on the outer perimeter. The scaffolds to the east and west represent God and the World, with the other three scaffolds representing the Flesh, Covetousness, and the Devil. Underneath the Castle is a bed, with Mankind underneath the bed until "he schal ryse & pleye" (he shal rise and play). A "Coveytyse copbord" is located at the foot of the bed. The character playing the Devil is instructed to look like he has gunpowder brimming out of his hands and eyes when he goes to battle. According to this diagram, Mercy, Justice, Truth, and Peace were to be clad in mantles of red, red, green, and black, respectively, and were to remain together in one place until they brought out the soul of Mankind.[3]

The dialect, stage directions, and ownership marks indicate that the manuscripts originated and remained in East Anglia for quite some time. A monk named Hyngham, from the abbey at Bury St. Edmunds, identifies himself in two places as the owner of *Wisdom* and *Mankind*. On fols. 121v and 134 he writes (in Latin): "O book, if anyone should by chance ask to whom you belong, you shall say, I belong above all to monk Hyngham." Richard Beadle has identified the monk as Thomas Hyngham, and through paleographical, codicological, and linguistic analysis,

Wisdom, or Mind, Will and Understanding (ca.1475)

Mankind (ca.1475)

The Castle of Perseverance (ca.1440)

[73] fols., foliated 98–121, 122–134, 154–191; 210 x 142 mm.

Cox Macro - Hudson Gurney manuscript 1820; purchased via Quaritch at the Gurney sale at Sotheby's, March 30, 1936, no. 170

V.a.354

1. The only play of these three that exists in more than one manuscript is *Wisdom*, for which a large fragment survives in the Bodleian Library (Digby MS 133). At some point before 1820 the Macro Plays were bound with three other unrelated manuscripts (Gurney sale, lots 143, 145, and 73).

2. This manuscript is published in facsimile as *The Macro Plays*, ed. David Bevington (New York, 1972).

3. For a discussion of the iconography of the *Perseverance* stage diagram, see Clifford Davidson, *Visualizing the Moral Life* (New York, 1989), 131–63.

Mankind, V.a.354, fol. 123v

argues that the texts of *Mankind* and *Wisdom* are very possibly in the hand of Hyngham himself.[4] The two plays seem to have passed into the hands of one Robert Oliver in the Tudor period. Other names in the margins of *Wisdom* are also in Tudor handwriting: Richard Cake, rector of Bradfield near Bury St. Edmunds; Rainold Wodles of Ipswich; Thomas Gonolde of Croxton; and John Plandon of Eriswell.

It seems as if one or more of *Wisdom*'s owners or readers used the manuscript for other purposes. Some of the marginal annotations are in cipher, such as the inscription which translates "This book belongs to me Robert Oliver." The key for one of the codes is explained in a verse on the back cover of *Wisdom*; another cipher can be cracked by using the key on fol. 104. There are also examples of mirror-writing and words spelled backwards (such as "Thus me to cummande to wryght with my left hande" in mirror-writing and "thomas gonnolld" in backward spelling). The fragment of a ballad, elaborate flourishes, and drawings of men and dragons, also contend for space in the margins. The back cover of *Mankind* was apparently used for a sixteenth-century schoolboy's translation of a passage into Latin.

H. W.

4. Richard Beadle, "Monk Thomas Hyngham's hand in the Macro manuscript," *New Science Out of Old Books*, eds. Richard Beadle and A. J. Piper (Aldershot, 1995), 315–41.

Aristotle

Physica, and
eleven other works
ca.1300?

353 fols.; vellum; 290 x 230 mm.

Purchased with the Smedley
Collection in 1924

V.b.32

THIS 706-PAGE MANUSCRIPT of Aristotelian works is one of the Folger Shakespeare Library's oldest manuscripts. It includes twelve works by Aristotle: *Physica*; *De anima*; *De sensu*; *De memoria*; *De somno*; *De vita et morte*; *De plantis*; *De generatione animalium*; *De coelo*; *De causis*; *De meteorologica*; and a new Latin translation of *Metaphysica*. Written in a round gothic bookhand on parchment by an unidentified scribe or scribes, the manuscript originated in Italy in the early part of the fourteenth century. Some of its rubricated initials are flourished in purple, blue, and red, while others are more elaborate, historiated with animals and human beings. A corrector has added missing words and phrases to the text.

Aristotle was a staple for scholars in the medieval period. Nearly half of the pages of this manuscript are either densely annotated with scholarly notes in the wide margins and between the lines or marked with notational symbols. The student who annotated this manuscript used many kinds of little pointing hands, or *manicula*, including some with particularly long fingernails and some with very elaborate cuffs, to highlight important passages. He did not limit himself to hands, however. The margins are littered with dogs (dog heads and whole bodies; leashed and unleashed; one-headed and two-headed), birds, serpents, dragons, fish, a rabbit, swords, men with pointing beards, men with pointing tongues, standing men, kneeling men, profiles of faces, hands holding flowers, a woman with a bow and arrow, and other marks of emphasis. Some of the non-rubricated capital letters have human and cat faces drawn in them.

Henry Folger purchased this manuscript in 1924 as part of the collection belonging to Mr. W. T. Smedley of London. Smedley believed that Francis Bacon had annotated this and many other manuscripts and books he sold to Folger, and brashly says of this one: "It may be asserted with confidence that the marginal notes, especially the pointers are the work of Bacon."[1] No proof exists for Smedley's assertion, and the annotations appear to be in a fourteenth-century hand. However, this manuscript and the others in the Smedley collection are of considerable interest and value independent of Smedley's collecting impetus.

H. W.

1. Catalogue of Smedley Books and Manuscripts, unpublished, Folger Shakespeare Library.

Book of Hours

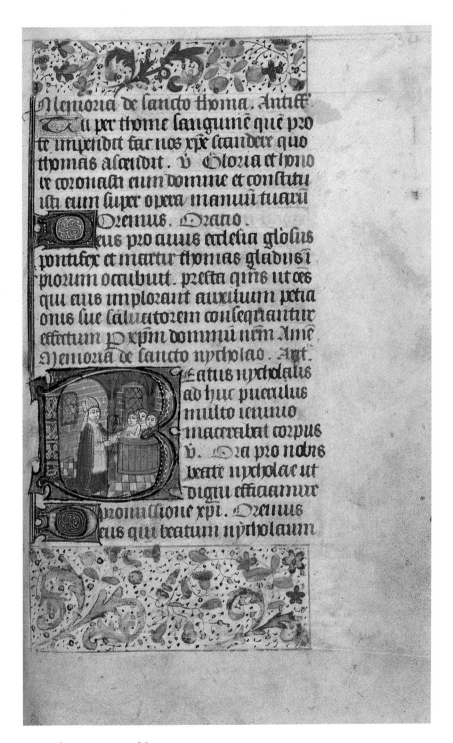

Book of Hours, V.a.228, fol. 34r

Book of Hours
ca.1450–1460

[2] 116 fols.; vellum;
190 x 130 mm.

Owned by Thomas Wakefeld;
Scott of Harden - Boies
Penrose II - Harmsworth
manuscript; purchased with
the Harmsworth collection
in 1938

V.a.228

1. For an excellent survey of
Books of Hours, see Roger
Wieck, *Time Sanctified: The
Book of Hours in Medieval Art
and Life* (New York, 1988). Also
see the introduction to Victor
Leroquais, *Les Livres d'Heures
manuscrits de la Bibliothèque
Nationale* (Paris, 1927).

2. On the value of Books of
Hours for study, see L. M. J.
Delaissé, "The importance
of Books of Hours for the
history of the medieval book,"
*Gatherings in Honor of
Dorothy R. Miner,* ed. Ursula
McCracken, et al. (Baltimore,
MD, 1974), 203–25.

3. For a study of a Rouen-made
Book of Hours of the same
period as Folger V.a.228, see
Rowan Watson, *The Playfair
Hours: A Late Fifteenth Century
Illuminated Manuscript from
Rouen* (London, 1984).

4. Wieck, 28.

BOOKS OF HOURS, ILLUSTRATED PRAYER BOOKS intended for use by the laity, were the most popular books of the late Middle Ages.[1] In the west, more manuscript Books of Hours were produced during this period—the fourteenth to the early sixteenth centuries—than any other type of book.[2] The book takes its name from its primary section, the Hours of the Virgin, a series of prayers divided into the eight canonical hours of a day: Matins, Lauds, Prime, Terce, Sext, None, Vespers, and Compline. These prayers, with accompanying images from the life of the Virgin Mary, were recited and reflected upon throughout the course of each day. In a time when laymen and women sought to imitate the clergy and be in closer daily communion with their God, Books of Hours were both practical devotional tools—read, annotated, preserved, and passed within families from one generation to the next—and prized possessions frequently of great artistic beauty.

The owners of Books of Hours ranged from royalty and the nobility to the emerging literate urban middle classes. Kings and queens commissioned the most famous artists of their times—Jean Pucelle, the Limbourg brothers, Fouquet, Bourdichon, among the best known. In the period following the invention of print by movable type in the mid-fifteenth century, less wealthy patrons increasingly turned to the growing number of anonymous artisans producing and illustrating Books of Hours or to bookshops selling printed and less-expensive exemplars, with woodcut or engraved images often printed on vellum and hand-colored to imitate costlier manuscript illumination.

Folger V.a.228, a late-fifteenth-century manuscript Book of Hours for use in England, was made in France, possibly Rouen, by an undetermined workshop.[3] In fact, France produced more Books of Hours, both manuscript and printed, than any other country in Europe during the early modern period.[4] The contents of Books of Hours, including, for example, the specific saints commemorated in the suffrages or the calendars, vary from volume to volume and diocese to diocese, reflecting local traditions and possibly the tastes of the patrons. Illuminated images, such as the numerous historiated initials found throughout the manuscript shown here, were employed in Books of Hours as aids to reflection, to be used either in tandem with the texts or, for those who could not read the Latin texts, on their own. Iconography also served in books without tables of contents as modes of bookmarking texts; for example, the immediately recognizable annunciation scene always precedes Matins.

Books of Hours are often mines of contemporary provenance; each one can speak to us not only of the religious devotions and art of the time but also of the lives of people who once owned, opened, and used the books. Folger V.a. 228 offers an expansive look into the past. It was owned by one Thomas Wakefeld

(1500?–1575), who was appointed by Henry VIII as the first Regius Professor of Hebrew at Cambridge University.[5] In the tradition of present-day family histories inscribed in Bibles, Wakefeld's sixteenth-century family history was written on the front flyleaves and in the calendar of his Book of Hours. We know from the moving contemporary inscriptions that Wakefeld, born at Pontefract in Yorkshire, was first married to Agnes Tilney, who died between 9 and 10 o'clock on the night of August 19, in the year "an*no* sec*u*ndo Edwardi Sex [i.e. 1548]," and was buried at Chesterton in Cambridgeshire. His second wife was Alice Jacobs. We know the names of the guardians of his son Thomas and daughter Alice and the dates, and very hours, when these children were born.

Historians have noted that Wakefeld apparently adhered to Catholicism during the turbulent decades of the Reformation, his association with King Henry VIII notwithstanding.[6] Wakefeld's Book of Hours may lend further credence to this supposition. In 1538 Henry VIII issued a proclamation decreeing the removal, destruction, or erasure of all images and references to Thomas Becket throughout England. This decree extended to personal books: the Folger Library collection contains early-sixteenth-century printed Books of Hours for use in England in which former owners, dutiful Protestants, obliterated images, feast days, and suffrages of Saint Thomas with black ink or white chalk.[7] Significantly, the image and feast days of Thomas Becket in Wakefeld's Book of Hours remain untouched to this day, as if in centuries-long defiance of the Tudor fiat. In fact, each carefully written note on marriage, birth, and death, along with the good condition of the manuscript, attests to the personal hold this Book of Hours must once have had on the man who owned, wrote in, and prayed from it, like so many other men and women did their own, half a millennium ago.

Dever Powell
Folger Shakespeare Library

5. James Bass Mullinger, *The University of Cambridge from the Royal Injunctions of 1535 to the Accession of Charles the First* (Cambridge, 1884), 416–17. According to Mullinger, Wakefeld was appointed to the office for life in 1547.

6. Mullinger, 416: "It seems most probable that [Wakefeld] continued to adhere to the ancient faith, for we find that, although his ability and learning were unquestioned, during the reign of Edward, and again in that of Elizabeth, readers were appointed to lecture [at Cambridge] in his stead."

7. See, for example, the calendar of a Book of Hours, or Primer, for English use printed in Paris in 1530, Folger STC 15968.

tatem: luxurie deformitatem: qui eo tñſ
it / deſcendit: qui deſcendit cadit. Oech
nemus itaq egyptiu homine & nõ deu.
Viciis enĩ ſuis eciã ipe rex egyptioru
in poteſtate eſt datus, cuius coparatio
ne Moyſes deus o iſtimatus eſt: impe
rans regnans: ſubiiſtiens ſibi poteſtates.
Vnde ei dictũ legimus: Faciã te in de
u regi Pharaoni. Vale & nos vt
facis quaſi filius dilige:

Omnipotenti deo: Chriſtifere vir
gini Marie: toti celoꝗ exercitui: ſit
laus honor & glã: quoꝗ adiutorio
conſcptus eſt preſens is libellus ſup
tibus & expenſ Rᵐⁱ dñi Chriſtopho
ri Vrſwyke Wyndeſore Decani: arte
& induſtria Petri Meghen monoculi
theutonis brabantini oppidi Buſchi
ducen. Aⁿ Sereniſſimi Regis Henrici
vii Nonodecimo:

Annoꝗ Domini . 1504 .

Añꝗ Domini . 1504 .

Apologeticus, V.a.84, fol.66

Peter Meghen, scribe (1466–1540)

THIS MANUSCRIPT WAS WRITTEN by the one-eyed Flemish scribe Peter Meghen, whom Erasmus playfully called "Cyclops" and "Petrus Monoculus," among other names. Erasmus, who employed Meghen as a courier and amanuensis, makes mention in his correspondence of Meghen's traveling, over-working, and over-consumption of alcohol. These descriptions occur particularly in his letters to John Colet, dean of St. Paul's, whom Erasmus visited in 1505–06. Meghen's courier trips on Erasmus's behalf between England and the Low Countries, and his scribal duties for the circle of humanists in London, laid the groundwork in part for the increasing popularity of Erasmian thought in England in the 1530s.[1]

Meghen matriculated at the University of Louvain in 1497 and was *the* scribe for London humanists at the beginning of the sixteenth century. His elegant and unadorned humanistic book script appealed to the likes of Henry VIII, John Colet, Cardinal Wolsey, and Christopher Urswick, who commissioned him to make copies of the writings of Savonarola, the early fathers of the Christian church, and parallel texts of Erasmus's version of the New Testament and the Vulgate, among other writings.[2] Meghen also made copies for Colet of Colet's own commentaries and expositions. He is thought to have worked as a scribe in England from 1504 until his death in 1540. For the last ten years of his life he was Writer of the King's Books.[3]

Christopher Urswick (1448–1522), grand almoner to Henry VII and dean of York and Windsor, commissioned the work shown here, Rufinus's Latin translation of the *Apologeticus* of St. Gregorius Nazianzenus with extracts from sermons 37 and 42 of St. Maximus of Turin and St. Ambrose's *Epistola ad Irenaeum*. A tract on personal holiness and the duties of religious men, *Apologeticus* was apparently one of Urswick's favorite texts, since Meghen copied it for him on three different occasions. The first page of the text bears Urswick's arms and motto. On the last page, Meghen adopts Erasmus's nickname for him, signing himself "Petri Meghen monoculi theutonis brabantini oppidi Buschiducen."

The Meghen manuscript at the Folger and a manuscript at Princeton are the only two confirmed examples of his work in U.S. libraries—the roughly twenty-nine other copies reside almost exclusively in London, Oxford, or Cambridge.[4] Seven of these surviving Meghen manuscripts were commissioned by Urswick.

H. W.

St. Gregorius Nazianzenus, Patriarch of Constantinople (ca.329–ca.389) *Apologeticus*, translated by Rufinus, and other texts 1504

73 fols.; vellum; 200 x 138 mm.

Owned by Christopher Urswick; given by John Mellerius to Thomas Makernes, 1674; Palmer library, 1747 - Verney - Smedley manuscript; purchased with the Smedley Collection in 1924

V.a.84

1. See J. K. McConica, *English Humanists and Reformation Politics under Henry VIII and Edward VI* (Oxford, 1965), 69–72. For biographical information see *Contemporaries of Erasmus*, ed. Peter G. Bietenholz (Toronto, 1986), 2:420–22.

2. Meghen copied almost exclusively from printed works. For Urswick, Colet, and Meghen, see J. B. Trapp, *Erasmus, Colet, and More: The Early Tudor Humanists and Their Books*, The Panizzi Lectures 1990 (London, 1991), 13–29, 80–96. A page from V.a.84 is reproduced on p. 25.

3. For the stylistic evolution of Meghen's hand, see Andrew J. Brown, "The Date of Erasmus' Latin Translation of the New Testament," *Transactions of the Cambridge Bibliographical Society*, 8 (1984): 351–80.

4. See the inventory by J. B. Trapp, "Notes on Manuscripts written by Peter Meghen," *The Book Collector*, 24 (1975): 80–96.

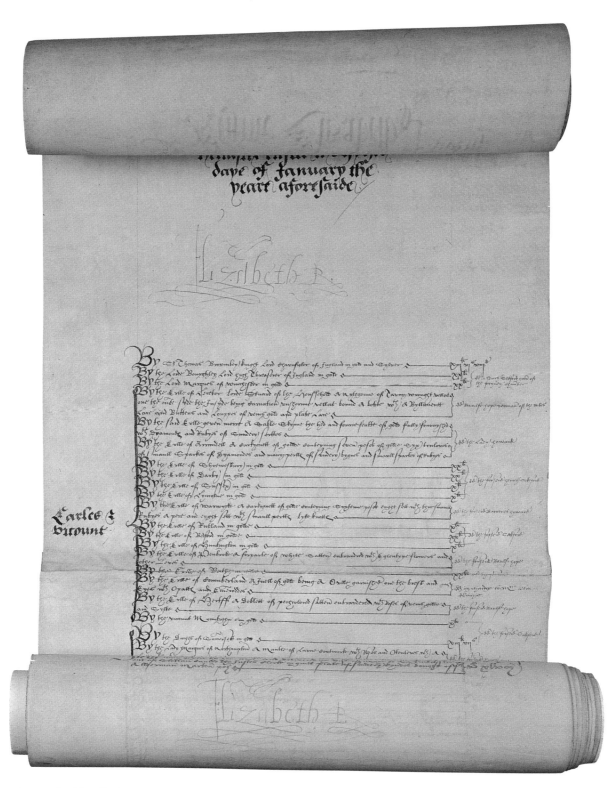

New Year's Gift Roll of Elizabeth I, Z.d.16

Henry VIII (1491–1547)
Elizabeth I (1533–1603)

THE LONG-STANDING CUSTOM OF GIVING GIFTS to the monarch on New Year's Day was a highly ritualized social and political act in early modern England. The Master of the Jewel-House and his assistants carefully recorded gifts received from and given to high-ranking nobility and members of the royal household on "gift rolls," sheets of paper or membranes of vellum stuck or sewn together and then rolled and kept in the Jewel House.

The New Year's Gift Rolls featured here represent two of the seven gift rolls held at the Folger, which themselves are almost a third of the original rolls extant for the Tudor period. Henry VIII's gift roll, signed on both sides, is written on paper and measures eight and one-half feet in length, while Elizabeth I's gift roll, written on vellum, extends to eleven feet and is signed by her at the top and bottom of each side. The names of the gift-givers and their gifts are recorded on one side of the roll, grouped in descending order according to rank and position.[1] In the margin opposite each entry is noted the name of the person or officer to whom the gift was delivered, or the office to which it was consigned.[2] The reverse side of the gift roll lists gifts presented by the sovereign.

The gift roll of Henry VIII is from January 1, 1539—a year before his marriage to Anne of Cleves. Overwhelmingly Henry expected gifts to be in gold. Most of the bishops and chaplains, and many of the lords and knights gave money, often presented in velvet or leather purses; the majority of the dukes and earls gave goldsmiths' work, including "a swerde the pomell and hilt gilt." Examples of this work still survive. Other forms of gifts were not uncommon: the marquis of Dorset gave "a brase of greyhoundes," and Lord Morley presented "a boke covered withe grene veluet." Henry also received numerous gifts of richly embroidered garments: the countess of Hampton gave "a night cap *with* cheynes & buttons of golde," Lord Richard Grey "a shirte of camericke wrought in silke."

Elizabeth I's gift roll is from 1585, the twenty-seventh year of her reign. By the mid-Elizabethan period, gold and silver plate was no longer as common among the New Year's gifts. In December 1585, Elizabeth Wingfield counseled the countess of Shrewsbury that a gift of money would be "ell liked" [ill-liked].[3] Of greater prominence in 1585 were gifts of clothing, personal jewelry, and trinkets. Sir Francis Walsingham gave the queen "a French goune of Russett Satten Floryshed with Leves of Sylver bound Aboute with A passamayne of venis golde with pendante sleves Lyned with Cloth of Sylver," Mrs. West "A Doblett of blacke Satten enbraudered with Fethers of golde and Sylver and smaull sede perlles," and the earl of Cumberland "A Juell of gold being a Oulle garnished one the brest and Eyes with Opalles and Emeroddes." The gifts of gentlemen and gentlewomen were less elaborate, sometimes no more than a scarf or a handkerchief, while apothecaries

HENRY VIII

New Year's Gift Roll
January 1, 1539

Paper roll; 2620 x 310 mm.

Rev. F. Hopkinson collection; purchased by Pearson for Folger, Sotheby sale June 1, 1905, no. 731

Z.d.11

ELIZABETH I

New Year's Gift Roll
January 1, 1585

Vellum roll; 3320 x 400 mm.

Purchased from Maggs Bros. in 1928

Z.d.16

1. In the 1585 roll, the order is as follows: earls and viscounts, duchesses, marchionesses and countesses, bishops, lords, baronesses, ladies, knights, gentlewomen and gentlemen. The Henrican roll lists bishops before earls, which may well reflect something of the declining status of bishops during Elizabeth's reign. While the 1539 roll contains a section for chaplains, this is absent from the 1585 roll; earlier Elizabethan gift rolls list chaplains separately, but these rarely number more than three names (Z.d.12–15).

33

Laetitia Yeandle holding
New Year's Gift Roll
of Elizabeth I in 1983

2. This side of the roll, as does the back, features the monarch's signature (Elizabeth's appears at the head and foot; Henry's only at the head), and the countersignatures of the Master of the Jewel-House, which was Sir John Williams in 1539, and John Astley in 1585. Also accompanying Astley's signature are those of four of his staff. At the bottom of the 1585 list is a statement of the total amount of gifts of money (£828 7s od); the 1539 roll contains no such total.

3. Folger X.d. 428 (131).

4. A. J. Collins, *Jewels and Plate of Queen Elizabeth I: The Inventory of 1574, edited from Harley MS 1650 and Stowe MS 555 in the British Museum* (London, 1955), 101–10, 247–53.

customarily gave items such as preserved fruits, "pottes of greene Gynger," and "boxes of peches of Janua." Striking in both rolls is the intimacy of many of the gifts to the monarch.

The return gifts from the monarch, less elaborate and imaginative, were always of gilt plate, the weight and value of which depended on the rank of the recipient, though both monarchs on occasion rewarded favorites more substantially. The Henrician roll records the giving of standing cups, bowls, or even simpler cruses (two-handed drinking vessels); the 1585 roll records only gifts of "guilt plate." The names of recipients, again arranged in sections according to rank, are those of the gift-givers recorded on the other side. In general, entries give the name or initial of the goldsmith who supplied the gift, and the weight of the plate is noted in the margin. A sample entry reads, "Too Mrs Hopton in guilt plate k . . . 10 oz." The 1585 roll also lists recipients of "free guiftes," and "gyftes gyven and delyvered at sundry tymes." The latter was a record of all gifts presented from the queen to ambassadors and other foreign visitors, and at weddings and christenings since the compiling of the last gift roll. They include a gilt bowl delivered at the christening of Lord Thomas Howard's child, and a gold chain given to the Danish Ambassador Mathias Budde. Elizabethan gift rolls also record gifts presented to maids of honor, which reflects the increased ceremonial importance of these young women during the reign of a female monarch: they were absent from the male-dominated Henrician Privy Chamber. Overall, the monarch benefited financially from the exchange of gifts; New Year's gift-giving was one of the main ways by which the crown accumulated plate.[4] Nevertheless, those of limited means and relatively low status at court could stand to gain from the exchange: John Dudley, Sergeant of the Pastry to Elizabeth I, in return for "a fayre Pye Orringed" received gilt plate weighing 6 oz.; Marke Antonio gave the queen "A glas of Swete water" and received in return plate weighing 5 oz.

Presentation of gifts to the sovereign was a public ceremony of political and social importance, which took place in the presence chamber at court: those out of favor were not allowed to take part in the ritual exchanging of gifts.[5] The manner by which gifts were given is markedly different for Henry VIII and Elizabeth I. In the Henrician roll, gifts in most cases were recorded to be "with the kings grace," although others were sent "to the juel house" and in the case of geldings "to the stable." A 1538 letter from John Husee, Lord Lisle's court agent, provides a snapshot of the personal nature of gift-giving during Henry VIII's reign, and sheds light on the way in which gifts were recorded: "The King stood leaning against the cupboard, receiving all things; and Mr. Tuke at the end of the same cupboard, penning all things that were presented."[6] By contrast, presentation of gifts to Elizabeth was indirect to a court officer. Gifts are recorded being delivered to "John Astelley esquire Master of the Juelles & Platte," "Mrs Blanch parry" and "Raulfe hope yeoman of the Robes."

James Daybell
University of Reading

5. Philippa Glanville, "Plate and Gift-Giving at Court," in *Henry VIII: A European Court in England*, ed. David Starkey (London, 1991), 131–35.

6. *The Lisle Letters*, ed. Muriel St. Clare Byrne (Chicago, 1981), v:10.

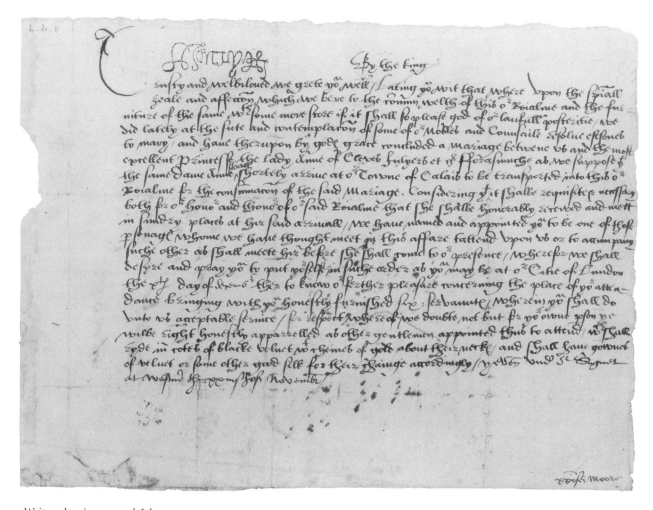

Writ under sign manual, L.b.1

Henry VIII (1491–1547)

. . . we did lately at the sute and contemplacion of some of our Nobles and Counsaile resolue eftsones to mary / and haue therupon by godes grace concluded a mariage betwene vs and the most excellent Princesse the lady Anne of Cleves . . . we suppose *that* the same Dame Anne ∧shall∧ shortely arriue at our Towne of Calais to be transported into this our Roialme [realm] for the consum*ma*cion of the said Mariage. . . .

Writ under sign manual to Christopher More Westminster, November 24, [1539]

1 fol.; 210 x 285 mm.

Loseley Collection - purchased via William H. Robinson Ltd., in 1938

L.b.1

THIS SIGNET LETTER OR WRIT from Henry VIII to Sir Christopher More concerns the imminent arrival into England of the king's future bride, Anne of Cleves, with whom he had entered into a marriage contract in October 1539.[1] Henry VIII was impatient to meet the princess, whom he knew only through a portrait miniature painted by Hans Holbein.

In the writ, Henry VIII informed Christopher More (ca.1483–1549), a wealthy country gentleman from Loseley Park, Surrey, that he was one of "those *personages* whome we haue thought meet" either to attend the king at his first meeting with Anne of Cleves, or to meet her beforehand on her journey from Calais to London.[2] Because her arrival date was uncertain, More was instructed to be present in London on December 10 to receive further instructions. He was to bring six "honestly furnished" servants and was himself to be "honestly apparelled" in a black velvet coat with a chain of gold around his neck, and to have velvet gowns or "some other good silk for their chainge accordingly."

Anne of Cleves reached Calais on December 11, where she was greeted by hundreds of gentlemen in satin damask coats and yeomen in red and blue cloth. After a seventeen-hour crossing of the Channel, she arrived in Dover and then proceeded onward to Canterbury, where she was welcomed by the Archbishop of Canterbury, the Bishop of Ely, and three hundred gentlemen. On New Year's Eve, escorted by one hundred horsemen in velvet coats and gold chains, Anne of Cleves traveled to the Bishop's Palace in Rochester. Henry VIII in his impatience "to nourish love," met her there for the first time. She then traveled to Shooter's Hill at the foot of which was set up "a very gorgeous tent or pavillion." Here, she again met the king who "marched through the park to meet her"; Christopher More was among the esquires and knights in attendance.[3]

Henry VIII was unhappy with the appearance of his bride, and although he wed her in a ceremony at Greenwich on January 6, 1540, within six months the marriage was annulled, on July 9. Henry VIII proceeded to marry Katherine Howard on July 28, the same day that his chief minister, Thomas Cromwell, who had arranged the king's marriage to Anne of Cleves, was executed for treason and heresy.

1. A writ is a written command or formal order issued on behalf of the sovereign.

2. For biographical details of Sir Christopher More, see S. T. Bindoff, ed., *The House of Commons, 1509–1558* (London, 1982), 2:616–17.

3. *Letters and Papers Foreign and Domestic, of the Reign of Henry VIII*, ed. J. S. Brewer, et al. (London, 1864–1932), xv:14:6. For a narrative of these events, see also R. M. Warwicke, *The Marrying of Anne of Cleves: Royal Protocol in Early Modern England* (Cambridge, 2000), ch. 6.

4. On the development of the sign manual, see David Starkey, *The Reign of Henry VIII: Personalities and Politics* (New York, 1986), 135–36.

Henry VIII's signature, or sign manual, appears to have been made with a crude wooden stamp (the "wet stamp") pressed first in ink and then applied to paper. For a monarch averse to paperwork and bureaucratic routine, the sign manual stamp allowed him to avoid what he saw as the tedious task of authenticating official documents with his signature. After 1545, this system was replaced with the "dry stamp," applied uninked to the page (perhaps as David Starkey suggests with the use of a screw mechanism) to make an indentation of the king's signature, which the Clerk then went over in ink in order to form a near-perfect facsimile of the royal signature. Throughout Henry's reign the sign manual, which ministers such as Cromwell were authorized to use, was an important "motor of government."[4]

James Daybell
University of Reading

Heather Wolfe
Folger Shakespeare Library

Edward VI (1537–1553)

...That of suche olde stuf remayning in your custodie within your office of the Revelles, ye deliuer or cawse to be deliuered ... Suche and somuche of the said stuf or ∧otherwyse∧ as shall be by them and yow thought moost meetest and sufficient for the ffurniture of their bases. and as shall appertaigne vnto their horses accordingly. . . .

ON NOVEMBER 17, 1551, EDWARD VI NOTED in his *Chronicle* that John Dudley, earl of Warwick, Sir Henry Sidney, Sir Henry Neville, and Sir Henry Gates, had challenged all comers at a tilt to be held on January 3 and a tourney on January 6.[1] A week later, the fourteen-year-old king of England signed this warrant to Sir Thomas Cawarden, commanding him to deliver "bases" for the horses of the four challengers.[2] Sir Thomas Cawarden, Master of the Tents and Master of the Revels, was responsible for supplying equipment needed for tournaments, masques, and coronations, as well as for military purposes.

The Christmas entertainments of 1551/52 were more extensive than usual, possibly to divert attention away from the trial of Edward Seymour, duke of Somerset, who had been Edward VI's Protector and who was later executed on January 22, 1552. Edward VI had participated in his first tournament in April 1551 and clearly enjoyed both watching and participating in jousts, tournaments, and other sporting displays.[3] The king recorded in his *Chronicle* on January 3 that eighteen defendants each ran against the challengers noted above six times. On January 6, he noted that two additional defendants joined the tourney "and fought right well, and so the challenge was accomplished." As this was Twelfth Night, he and his courtiers also watched a play, an interlude, and two masques, followed by a banquet of 120 dishes. [4]

In addition to official documents relating to Edward VI, the Folger has an incomplete manuscript copy of Sir John Hayward's *Life and Reign of King Edward VI* which contains material not included in the 1630 printed edition or the other manuscript copies.[5]

H. W.

Warrant under sign manual to Sir Thomas Cawarden Westminster, November 24, 1551

1 fol.; vellum; 155 x 315 mm.

Loseley Collection - purchased via William H. Robinson, Ltd., in 1938

L.b.16

1. *The Chronicle and Political Papers of King Edward VI*, ed. W. K. Jordan (Ithaca, NY, 1966), 97. A tilt consisted of mock combat between two men on horseback armed with lances.

2. Bases were the clothing worn by horses in tournaments and were often ornately decorated.

3. Jennifer Loach, *Edward VI* (New Haven, CT, 1999), 153–58.

4. *Chronicle*, 103–5.

5. Folger V.b.164.

Lady Jane Grey (1537–1554)

Detail from warrant under sign manual, L.b.24

Warrant under
sign manual to [Sir
Thomas Cawarden]
Tower of London,
July 19, [1553]

1 fol.; vellum; 310 x 410 mm.

Loseley Collection - purchased
via William H. Robinson Ltd.,
in 1938

L.b.24

Jane the Quene. By the Quene. Trusty and welbeloued we grete you well and let you wit our will and pleasure is that you shall delyv*er* or cause to be delyvered vnto the bearer hereof for the vse of our right dere and trusty and right entierly beloved father and counsellor the Duke of Suffolke, fowre [tents] out of suche our store as remayneth in your custody for the plasing and lodging of [*ms. damaged*] attending here in o*ur* tower abowt o*ur* service and these our *lettr*es shalbe y*our* sufficient wa*rr*ant and discharge in that behalf. Yeeven vnd*er* o*ur* Signet at our Tower of London the xixth day of Iuly in the fyrst yere of our Reigne.

THE REIGN OF SIXTEEN-YEAR-OLD LADY JANE GREY lasted a mere ten days. On what was to be her final day as Queen, she issued this warrant to an unnamed addressee, probably Sir Thomas Cawarden, Master of the Tents and Master of the Revels, under her sign manual, or signature, "Jane the Quene."[1] The warrant orders that four tents be delivered for the use of Lady Jane's father for lodging those attending her in her apartments in the Tower.[2] The Tower of London, incorporating some eighteen acres of land inside its walls, was begun under William the Conqueror, and the buildings were expanded and enlarged under later monarchs, notably Henry VIII. Long used as a state prison, the Tower also served as a royal residence until the time of James I. The royal apartments in the Tower were not spacious, so it is quite likely that some of those attending the young queen were lodged in tents on the grounds.

1. See the *Seventh Report of The Royal Commission on Historical Manuscripts*, Pt. I, Appendix (London, 1879), 596–98.

2. Ibid., 610. Damage to the margins of the document at some time in the past now obscures what was to be delivered, but the partial abstract in the 1879 *Report* identifies the articles as four tents.

Lady Jane Grey's mother, Lady Frances Brandon, was the eldest daughter of Henry VIII's sister, Mary, Queen of France, and therefore a cousin to King Edward VI. She married Henry Grey, duke of Suffolk. Beginning in 1551, Lady Jane was frequently at Edward's court with her parents. The powerful duke of Northumberland, John Dudley, contrived to marry Jane to his son, Lord Guildford Dudley, and was influential in persuading Edward VI to designate Jane his successor.[3] Lady Jane's devout Calvinism was a deciding factor. Determined to maintain the Protestant religion in England, Edward had already signed a 'devise' excluding his half-sisters Mary and Elizabeth from the succession.

Although Edward VI died on July 6, 1553, his death was not publicly announced until July 8. On July 9, Lady Jane Grey was proclaimed queen, and on July 10 she entered the royal apartments in the Tower. Edward's sister, Mary Tudor, was gathering support, however; on July 19, the date of this warrant, she successfully claimed the throne. The following November, Lady Jane and her husband were arraigned for high treason and sentenced to death. They were beheaded on February 12, 1554, on Tower Green.[4]

Rachel Doggett
Folger Shakespeare Library

3. David Loades, *John Dudley, Duke of Northumberland, 1504–1553* (Oxford, 1996), 238–41.

4. David Mathew, *Lady Jane Grey: The Setting of the Reign* (London, 1972), 126–61.

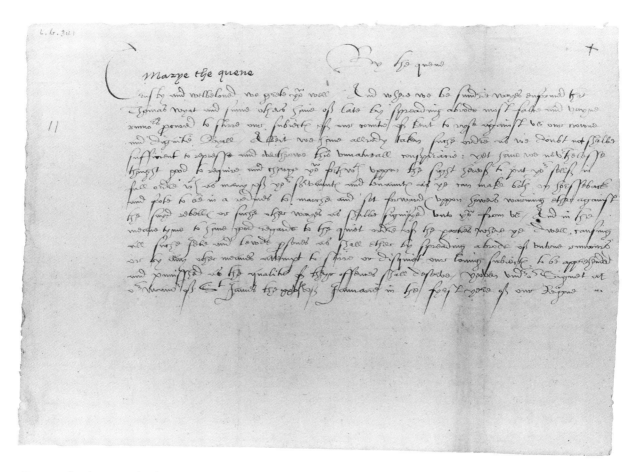

Letter under sign manual, L.b.341

Mary I (1516–1558)

THERE IS AN OMINOUS UNDERTONE in this letter from Mary I to Sir Thomas Cawarden, Master of the Tents and Revels. Normally, monarchs wrote to Cawarden requesting costumes, tents, and supplies for masques, plays, tilts, and other court entertainments. Mary, however, had other business to pursue with him.

Mary, a Roman Catholic who became queen in July 1553 after the short reign of Lady Jane Grey, had just agreed upon the terms of her marriage to the Roman Catholic Philip II of Spain, whom she intended to marry against the wishes of some of her closest advisors. As a result, Sir Thomas Wyatt (ca.1521–1554), son of the poet and privy councillor to Henry VIII, published a proclamation against the queen's marriage to a foreign power, calling for supporters to join him in his crusade.[1] Since Cawarden was known to be a staunch Protestant interested in reform, a supporter of Mary's half-sister Elizabeth, and the possessor of a large arsenal at Blechingly, he was viewed as a potential threat to the Crown.

On the day before this warrant was issued, Cawarden had been arrested at his house at Blechingly and brought before Star Chamber for questioning. On January 26, he was set free by the Privy Council, and as he departed he was handed two letters. The first letter commanded him to discharge the sheriff who had been guarding Blechingly since the arrest. The second letter, shown here, informed Cawarden of Wyatt's "unnaturall conspiracie" and directed him to be prepared with as many of his servants and tenants as possible, both on foot and horse, so that he could be called upon at an hour's notice to defend the queen from the rebels, "or suche other wayes as shalbe signyfied unto you from us." In the meantime, he was told to remain quiet and watchful at Blechingly and to punish all "idle and lewde" individuals who had spread false rumors or incited trouble. On January 27, he was again arrested by the Lord Admiral William Howard.[2] This time his arsenal was seized for the queen's use and he was not released until after Wyatt's march on London and eventual defeat on February 7. On February 24, the eighteen wagonloads of weapons and supplies that had been carted away were ordered to be returned to Cawarden. Cawarden only received some of the confiscated goods, and for many years struggled to have the remainder returned.[3]

On the same day as this warrant, Mary summoned princess Elizabeth to court, but Elizabeth demurred, not arriving until February 23, the same day that the duke of Suffolk was beheaded for treason. Seventeen days after this warrant, Lady Jane Grey and her husband, Lord Guildford Dudley, were beheaded. On April 11, Sir Thomas Wyatt himself was beheaded. Although Cawarden was never charged with complicity in the rebellion, he remained under constant scrutiny until Mary's death.[4]

H. W.

Letter under sign manual to Sir Thomas Cawarden St. James, January 26, 1554

1 fol.; vellum; 205 x 300 mm.

Loseley Collection - purchased via William H. Robinson, Ltd., in 1939

L.b.341

1. For biographical accounts of Sir Thomas Wyatt and his father of the same name, see S.T. Bindoff, ed., *The House of Commons, 1509–1558* (London, 1982), 3:669–72.

2. D.M. Loades, *Two Tudor Conspiracies* (Cambridge, 1965), 56–59.

3. See William B. Robison, "The National and Local Significance of Wyatt's Rebellion in Surrey," *The Historical Journal*, 30 (1987): 769-90, for a detailed account of Cawarden's involvement in the affair. Other Loseley manuscripts, Folger L.b.32, 44, 45, 53–80, relate to Cawarden's efforts to have his goods returned, and include details concerning his arrest and release.

4. Cawarden was arrested and interrogated on several occasions, ostensibly for reasons unrelated to the events of January 1554. W.R. Streitberger, *Court Revels, 1485–1559* (Toronto, 1994), 208–13.

Elizabeth I (1533–1603)

Warrant under
sign manual to
Sir Thomas Cawarden
Westminster,
January 3, 1559

1 fol.; vellum; 190 x 320 mm.

Loseley Collection - purchased
via William H. Robinson, Ltd.,
in 1938

L.b.33

1. This manuscript is described
and contextualized in David
M. Bergeron, "Elizabeth's
Coronation Entry (1559): New
Manuscript Evidence," *English
Literary Renaissance*, 8 (1978):
3–8. For an account of the
procession, see *The Quenes
Maiesties Passage through the
Citie of London to Westminster
the Daye before her Coronacion*
(London, 1559) [STC 7590], and
Richard Grafton, *An Abridge-
ment of the Chronicles of
England* (London, 1562), fols.
166–67.

2. They were most likely
returned on that date so that
they could be used in a masque
on the day after the coronation
(Bergeron, 7).

3. Folger L.b.109.

4. Folger L.b.4.

Thies shalbe to will and commaunde yow imediatlie vpon the sight hereof that you deliuer or cause to be deliuered vnto John Gresham and John Elyot citizins of our Citie of London suche and so muche of the said apparrell as they shall require for the setting forthe of those pagentes whiche be appoynted to stande for the shewe of our Cytie at the tyme we are to passe through thesame towardes our Coronation wherein you shall vse your discretion to deliuer suche percelles as may most convenientlie serve their torne and therewithall take lest hurte by vse. . . .

ON JANUARY 3, 1559, six weeks after her accession to the throne and less than two weeks before her coronation (January 15), Elizabeth I commanded Sir Thomas Cawarden to ensure that the city of London had an ample supply of costumes for the civic pageant to be held during her coronation procession on January 14.[1] The pageants, organized and funded by the city of London and the guilds, would consist of a series of allegorical tableaux along the procession route, including children dressed up as the eight Beatitudes at Soper's Lane; Father Time and his daughter Truth at the Little Conduit in Cheapside; and a representation of Deborah, judge and restorer of the house of Israel at the Conduit in Fleet Street.

Sir Thomas Cawarden, who as Master of the Revels supervised and financed court entertainments, delivered the costumes on the day before the pageant, with the stipulation that they be returned on January 16.[2] An indentured note at the Folger documenting this transaction lists a wide array of costly silks and velvets, such as: "a kirtell for a woman of yelowe cloth of gold vpperbodied with tynsell and sleves of gold," "a womans garment of tynsell vpperbodied with skalop'shelles," 3 "garmentes of blewe cloth of gold with sleves of flat siluer," 2 "longe garmentes of cloth of gold with black tynsell sleves and capes," and "a cloke of yelowe cloth of gold turfed with white & a sword."[3]

The warrant shown here is one of the earlier examples of Elizabeth I's sign manual, or signature, at the Folger. The earliest of the Folger's approximately thirty documents signed by Elizabeth is a letter to Cawarden dated ca. 1550, prior to her accession to the throne.[4]

H. W.

Elizabeth I (1533–1603)

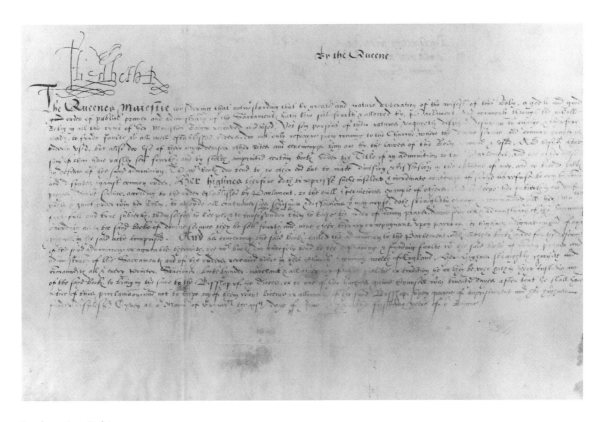

Proclamation, X.d.87

1. Elizabeth I, c. 2, 1559,
Statutes of the Realm 4:355.

2. *An Admonition to
the Parliament* ([Hemel
Hempstead? printed
by J. Stroud? 1572]).

3. W. H. Frere and C. E.
Douglas, eds., *Puritan
Manifestoes. A Study of
the Origin of the Puritan
Revolt* (London, 1954).

4. British Library Lansdowne
MS 17 Art. 37, quoted in E.
Arber, ed., *A Transcript of the
Registers of the Company of
Stationers* (London, 1875),
1:217b.

. . . her highnes straightly chargith and com*m*aundith all & euery Printer,
Stacioner, bookebynder, marchant & all other men of what qualitie . . . who
hath in theyr custodie any of the sayd book*e*s, to bring in the same to the
Bisshop of the dioceese, or to one of her highnes priuie Counsell w*ith*in
twenty dayes after that he shall haue notice of this proclama*c*ion, and not to
keepe any of them w*ith*out licence or allowance of the sayd Bisshop, vpon
payne of imprisonment and her highnes furder displess*u*re. . . .

COMPROMISES OFTEN DISAPPOINT. The Elizabethan religious settlement
was no exception. When Elizabeth Tudor ascended the throne in 1558, following the
death of her Catholic half-sister Mary, the realm was sharply separated along religious lines. In an attempt to discourage dissension, the new regime sought a middle
road between the practices of Catholicism and those of Protestantism. A modified
version of the Edwardian *Book of Common Prayer*, authorized by statute in 1559,
served as a signature piece of this settlement.[1]

The Catholics who had prospered under Mary's rule were the expected adver-
saries. However, many of the returning Marian exiles—Protestants who had fled to
the Continent during Mary's reign and had been exposed to the reformed religions
taking hold in cities such as Geneva and Frankfurt—were hostile to certain aspects
of the Church of England. To them the *Book of Common Prayer* especially was
suggestive of popish superstitions. After Parliament failed to address requests for
additional reform of the *Book of Common Prayer*, John Field and Thomas Wilcox
published *An Admonition to the Parliament* in 1572.[2] Anonymous and printed
secretly in England, this attack on the liturgy and episcopal government of the
Church of England served as a veritable "puritan manifesto."[3]

Shown here is a manuscript copy of the proclamation issued by Queen
Elizabeth to reinforce the supremacy of the *Book of Common Prayer* and to halt the
distribution of the *Admonition* and other publications, such as *A Reply* issued by
Thomas Cartwright in 1573 as a defense of the *Admonition*. At the head is the sign
manual of Elizabeth I. Since the beginning of printing in England, forms of state
censorship that enlisted the assistance of members of both the church hierarchy
and the book trade had been utilized to silence criticism of regimes. This proclamation exhibits those same tendencies.

Even though the authors of the *Admonition*, Field and Wilcox, were imprisoned,
albeit briefly, contemporary accounts report a failure of compliance. In a letter
dated July 2, 1573, and addressed to Lord Treasurer Burghley, Edwin Sandys, the
bishop of London, complained that although the tracts had been widely disseminated in London, and the time limit had expired, still no copies had been brought to

him.[4] Nevertheless it was not until 1617 that the *Admonition* was reprinted.[5] It was then produced abroad, at the Pilgrim Press in Leiden, and thus retained its status as a fugitive tract. This was not surprising as the *Admonition* broke new ground when its authors cast aspersions on the role of bishops; in this sense it presaged the emergence of presbyterianism as a force in England.

Sometimes proclamations are preserved only in manuscript. However, a copy of the official printed version of this proclamation resides at the Folger, as part of two volumes of Elizabethan proclamations collected and issued in 1618 by the notary public Humphrey Dyson.[6] This Folger set of proclamations has been deemed "from a bibliographic standpoint, probably the finest copy known."[7]

Roughly twenty-eight (or seven percent) of Elizabeth's known proclamations were of a religious nature and of these, twelve were related to problems with books.[8] More typical of the struggle with seditious printing during the first years of Elizabeth's reign is another manuscript proclamation at the Folger. This one was issued in March 1569, at the height of Elizabeth's struggles with the Pope and with her Catholic subjects.[9] Aimed specifically at Catholic books, this manuscript copy bears the royal sign manual and has been identified as the copy which served as the chancery warrant.[10]

Suellen Towers
Folger Shakespeare Library

5. *An Admonition to the Parliament* ([Leiden, William Brewster], 1617).

6. Folger STC 8063 bound in STC 7758.3 vol. 1, fol. 176.

7. W. A. Jackson, "Humphrey Dyson and his collections of Elizabethan Proclamations," *Harvard Library Bulletin,* 1 (1947): 80.

8. "A Royal proclamation was a royal command . . . validated by the royal sign manual, issued under a special Chancery writ sealed with the Great Seal, and publicly proclaimed." F. A. Youings, Jr., *The Proclamations of the Tudor Queens* (Cambridge, 1976), 9–10, 13.

9. Folger X.d.85.

10. For discussions of the proclamation shown here and the controversy surrounding the *Admonition*, see also: P. L. Hughes and J. F. Larkin, eds., *Tudor Royal Proclamations* (New Haven and London, 1969), 2, no. 597; P. Milward, *Religious Controversies of the Elizabethan Age* (London, 1977), 29–30; and F. Youings, 204-6.

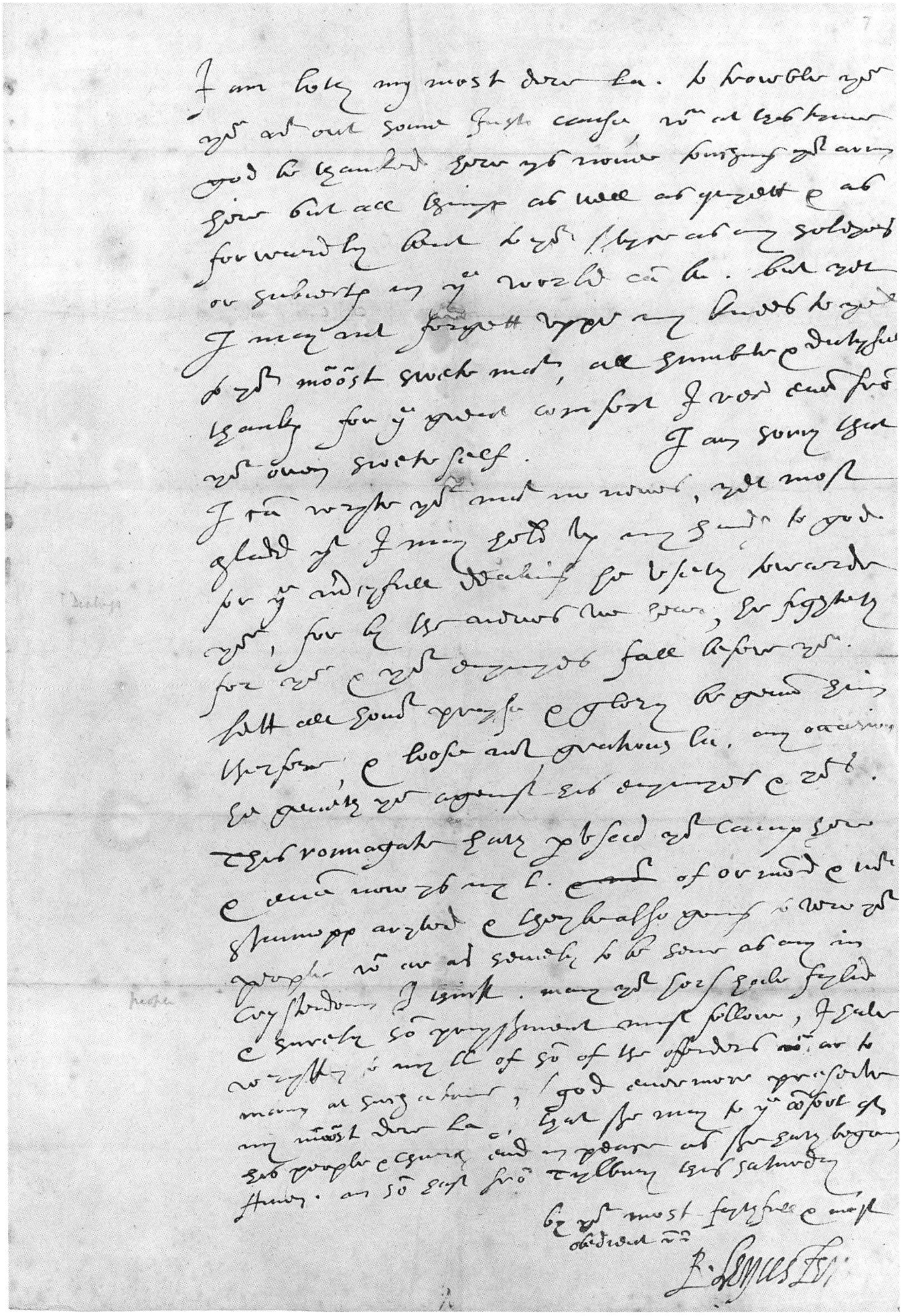

Autograph letter, signed, to Elizabeth I, MS Add 1006

Sir Robert Dudley, earl of Leicester (1532?–1588)

IN THE SUMMER OF 1588, Spain prepared to punish the heretic nation that once had been its ally. In the not so distant past, the marriages of King Henry VIII to Catherine of Aragon, and of Queen Mary to King Philip II, ensured some measure of political and religious congruity between England and Spain. Elizabeth's coronation, however, brought not only a Protestant ruler to the throne, but also a self-possessed woman who refused Philip's offer to marry. Her government defied Spain's imperial claim to the distant lands of the Americas and to the nearby states of the Low Countries. Her captains prowled Atlantic sea-lanes to rob Philip's treasure fleet and to raid his harbors. As a result, a vast armada of Spanish ships was making for England's coasts when Robert Dudley, earl of Leicester, Lieutenant and Captain-General of the Queen's Armies and Companies, wrote to Queen Elizabeth from the English military camp at Tilbury on Saturday August 3.[1] Across the Channel, the duke of Parma, commanding thousands of seasoned soldiers, awaited only wind and tide to begin the invasion. When or where the combined Spanish forces would land was the subject of frenzied speculation.

As Leicester penned this letter, troops were marshalling close by his tent for the defense of London. But to Elizabeth, his "mōōste dere Lady," he displayed no hint of alarm. Rather, with words of reassurance and endearment, he reported that her camp was quiet and well ordered, her soldiers as "forwardly bent" as any in the world, and the news he heard was that God "fighteth for you & your enymyes fall before you." Though he scribbled in haste, his tone was leisurely and playful: it bespoke the amity of time-tested lovers whose regard for one another, rooted in youthful friendship, evolving from dalliance to reckless ardor, surviving political pressure and personal betrayal, had come round at last to bedrock devotion. "I may not forgett," he wrote, "vppon my knees to yeld to your mōōste swete maiestie, all humble & dutyful thankes for the great comfort I receive euer from your owen swete self." Leicester closed the letter using the mark signaling her nickname for her "most faythfull & most obedient ˜ ˜." Twice within the text Leicester draws eyebrows over the letters *o* in the word "moost," in reference to the queen's nickname for him, which was "Eyes." This coded and private reference within a letter of conventional courtly love certainly suggests a degree of intimacy between Leicester and Elizabeth.

On August 9, Elizabeth joined Leicester at Tilbury, the site of one of her most famous speeches, the courageous and defiant words that ring down the centuries of English memory: "I am come . . . resolved in the midst and heat of battle to live and die amongst you . . . I know I have the body but of a weak and feeble woman, but I have the heart and stomach of a king and of a king of England too—and take foul scorn that Parma or any prince of Europe should dare to invade the borders of my

Autograph letter, signed, to Elizabeth I
Tilbury, August 3, 1588

1 fol.; 332 x 235 mm.

Part of the Hulton Papers

Gift of Dorothy Rouse-Bottom, 1996

MS Add 1006

1. The date was suggested by Dr. Simon Adams, who transcribed the correspondence of Elizabeth and Leicester at the British Library for the Navy Records Society.

2. For a version of Elizabeth's Tilbury speech, see *Elizabeth I: Collected Works*, Leah S. Marcus, Janel Mueller, Mary Beth Rose, eds. (Chicago, IL, 2000), 325.

3. Public Record Office, SP 12/215/65, August [29], 1589.

4. *Calendar of Letters, and State Papers, relating to English Affairs of the Reign of Elizabeth*, ed. M. A. S. Hume (London, 1899), IV:432.

5. For details of the items offered at auction, see *Elizabeth and Essex: The Hulton Papers*, Monday, 14th December 1992 (London: Sotheby's, 1992).

realm." She promised that her lieutenant general "shall be in my stead" in battle, adding, "than whom never prince commanded a more noble or worthy subject." By the valor of her troops and their "obedience to myself and my general," they would "shortly have a famous victory over these enemies of my God and of my kingdom."[2]

Within days, superior English naval strategy combined with violent storms had thrown the Invincible Armada into disarray. While his troops disbanded, the visibly ailing lieutenant-general departed Tilbury. On September 4, traveling toward a rest-cure at Buxton, Leicester died unexpectedly in Cornbury. Elizabeth, when told of his death, is said to have fled into her private chamber, and "for some days," "mourned alone and inconsolable."[3] After her death in 1603 a bejeweled box was found by her bedside. Within it lay a letter addressed in Leicester's distinctive hand. Across the envelope she had written, "His last letter."

Folger MS Add 1006 was not that last letter.[4] It is nonetheless a powerful reminder that Elizabeth and Leicester were not only larger-than-life political figures, but also a man and woman who lived real lives. That this fragment of their story now resides among Folger's treasures owes everything to the real person being honored by the present occasion. Because of Laetitia Yeandle's good offices, a paleography student, pursuing research on Leicester's wife, was permitted to view an extraordinary collection of letters known as the Hulton Papers. Consisting largely of correspondence of Leicester's stepson Robert Devereux, earl of Essex, they had been sent by their owner, Sir Geoffrey Hulton, for auction at Sotheby's.[5] When they failed to achieve their 1992 reserve prices, they were withdrawn from market and disappeared from sight. It was at Mrs. Yeandle's suggestion that the aforesaid researcher, traveling to London in 1996, rang Sotheby's to inquire their whereabouts. Dr. Peter Beal of Sotheby's Manuscripts Department answered guardedly that he might know where to find them. Only when the caller uttered three magic words—"Laetitia Yeandle" and "Folger"—did Dr. Beal add, "They are right here on my desk." An hour later he handed her the Hulton Papers, and allowed her not only to inspect but also to bid on particular items instead of entire groups. Through Mrs. Yeandle's agency and Dr. Gundersheimer's enthusiastic partnership the Leicester letter was acquired for the Folger, along with a letter by Essex and twenty letters sent to the third earl of Essex by his cousin Henry Rich, earl of Holland. It is likely that none of these prizes would have come to the Folger but for a gifted teacher's lifelong habit of encouraging her students' work. Because Dudley's letter was similarly supportive, its inclusion in this exhibit seems an apt tribute to Laetitia Yeandle.

Dorothy Rouse-Bottom
Hampton, Virginia

Elizabeth I (1533–1603)

Autograph letter, signed, to Henri IV, V.b.131, p. 2

Autograph letter, signed,
to Henri IV of France,
in French
ca.1590

2 pp. (bifolium); 305 x 189 mm.

Alfred Morrison collection
(his sale London, December
10, 1917, I, no. 326) - to
Throgmorton; purchased
from Maggs Bros. in 1922.

V.b.131
See Appendix, p. 233, for full
text and translation

---

1. English translation of the
opening phrases of her original
French, preserved as Hatfield
House, Cecil Papers 133/101, fol.
157r, in a secretary's copy that
significantly shows one change
in Elizabeth's hand. The text
of this letter is accessible in
the Folger microfilm holdings
of the Cecil Papers; it will be
printed as No. 87 in *Elizabeth I:
Autograph Compositions and
Foreign Language Originals*, ed.
Janel Mueller and Leah S.
Marcus (Chicago, IL, 2002).

2. This letter in a modern
English translation is printed as
No. 82 in *Elizabeth I: Collected
Works*, ed. Leah S. Marcus,
Janel Mueller, and Mary Beth
Rose (Chicago, IL, 2000),
363–64.

HENRI IV OF FRANCE (1533–1610), also known as Henri de Navarre, was one of Elizabeth I's most important Continental allies, particularly before his public conversion to Catholicism in July 1593, which she was to lament in a letter to him that began, "Ah what griefs, O what regrets, O what groanings felt I in my soul at the sound of such news . . . !"[1] According to legend, Henri admitted that the conversion was a matter of political expedience: "Paris is worth a mass."

The present letter comes from an earlier and happier stage in the alliance, when England was helping Henri as leader of the Protestant cause in the French civil wars.[2] Beauvoir la Nocle, the "Monsieur de Beauvois" of the first sentence, had reportedly persuaded Elizabeth to aid the Huguenots with 4000 troops, powder, munitions, and a loan of 20,000 pounds. The date assigned this letter is based on allusions—to Henri's dwelling so near his enemies, to the preservation of his person, and to the necessity of securing Paris—that evoke the English expedition of October 1589–December 1590 sent to relieve the embattled, not yet publicly confirmed or crowned, King of France.

Most of the letter, in fact, is taken up with Elizabeth's fears that her aid will come to naught if Henri is killed during the conflict. From her point of view, his noteworthy bravery in leading his troops needs a "bridle" for reasons of state. What she terms his "invincible magnanimity" is sufficiently evident to all that he should not need to risk his life in support of what she calls "the whole cause"—international Protestantism. In a characteristic closing, she applies the same lesson to herself, who, though a "woman" and therefore to be suspected of a "fearful heart," has shown similar magnanimity in her own brushes with death by assassination. Her postscript expresses the anger and urgency that simmer beneath the surface throughout: "What use is it for Paris and the king to perish?"

The letter bears remnants of Elizabeth's seals. It is written in her idiosyncratic, mainly italic script, used in virtually all of her autograph compositions from the last twenty-five years of her reign. Elizabeth's italic includes a few staple letter-forms (*e*, *g*, and *y*) taken over from secretary hand.

Leah S. Marcus
Vanderbilt University

Janel M. Mueller
University of Chicago

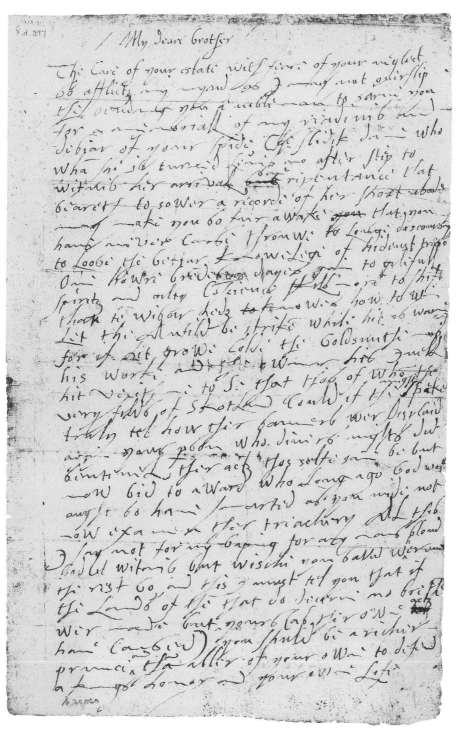

Autograph letter, signed, to James VI, X.d.397

Autograph letter, signed, to James VI of Scotland ca. March 1593

2 pp. (1 fol.); 306 x 197 mm.

Purchased from Maggs Bros. in 1925

X.d.397
See Appendix, p. 236, for full text

1. This letter, written on both sides of a folio half-sheet, is printed in a modern English transcription as No. 85 in *Elizabeth I: Collected Works*, ed. Leah S. Marcus, Janel Mueller, and Mary Beth Rose (Chicago, IL, 2000), 368–69. The second half of the letter is reproduced in facsimile in Jean F. Preston and Laetitia Yeandle, *English Handwriting, 1400–1650* (Binghamton, NY, 1992), 65.

2. This letter's partially legible endorsement reads: "delivered by the Lord Borto . . . gh xvj merche 1592[3]." Borough's name is only partially legible because the ink has faded. Borough's letter of credence, written in Elizabeth's hand and dated February 12, 1592 [1593], bears this endorsement: "Deliuerd by the lord Borrough the xvj. of Marche 1593." Its text has been printed in *Letters of Queen Elizabeth and King James VI of Scotland*, ed. John Bruce, Camden Society, 46 (London, 1849), 79–80.

JAMES VI OF SCOTLAND (1566–1625), who would become Elizabeth's successor in 1603 as James I of England, was only in his twenties at the time of the present letter, but already a seasoned monarch. As an infant and then a boy under the control of successive regents, he had held the Scottish throne since 1567, after the abdication of his mother, Mary, Queen of Scots. Although he and Elizabeth never met, they had been in close communication since at least the beginning of 1584 in letters penned by themselves, and, before that, they had regularly exchanged written and oral messages through their ambassadors.

Here, as in many of her letters to James, Elizabeth expresses horror and outrage at what she perceives to be his tenuous and diffident hold on his sovereignty.[1] The context of writing was the aftermath of the plot known as "the Spanish blanks"—initiated by Scottish Jesuits and revealed under torture by a captured Scottish messenger. Several of James's Catholic earls—Huntly, Crawford, Angus, Errol, and others—had signed blank letters addressed to the King of Spain; their intent, evidently, was to give the Spaniards carte blanche in carrying out a Catholic invasion of their homeland. The plot had been to land 30,000 Spanish troops from The Netherlands, 4000 to establish Catholic control in Scotland, and the rest to proceed south against England.

Despite the manifest treason of the Catholic lords, James did not take strong measures against their chronic lawlessness—most recently, their murder of the earl of Murray in November 1592, which brought on them nothing more than expulsion from court. James considered the Catholic lords useful as a check on an equally ungovernable Protestant lord, Francis Stewart Hepburn (d. 1624), fifth earl of Bothwell, and nephew of the Bothwell who had married Mary, Queen of Scots, and forced her abdication. The fifth earl headed the extreme faction of Scottish Protestants. During the early 1590s he made a series of increasingly humiliating raids against James, penetrating the royal palace in 1591 and coming close to seizing the king.

The "noble man" whom Elizabeth mentions sending in the opening phrases of this letter was Thomas, Lord Borough, later Governor of the Brill and Lieutenant of Ireland. She appointed him in February 1593 as her special emissary to James for negotiating about the errant Scottish lords, both Protestant and Catholic. James had accused Elizabeth of harboring Bothwell in England and otherwise abetting his dangerous insubordination. Borough was charged with assuaging James's suspicions of Elizabeth, on the one hand, and with inciting him to take military action against the Catholic lords, on the other.

Lord Borough presented his letter of credence to James in Edinburgh on the same day that he presented this letter in Elizabeth's hand.[2] The queen's outspoken urgency tallies in every point with her emissary's special commission. She exhorts James to deal sharply with the Catholic lords who, with "guileful spirits and guilty conscience," have both contrived secret rebellion and raised open rebellion on "the very fields of Scotland"—"those . . . who long ago, God wot, ought so have smarted as you need not now examine their treachery." But she denounces Bothwell in equally heated terms as "a lewd, unadvised, headsick fellow, a subject of mine . . . that so boldly attainted your doors." It is a "foul infamy," laments Elizabeth, to be suspected of permitting such a gross offender to "enter my territory" or to "trust my hands to be his safe refuge." Such baseless suspicions disparage both her rule and her truthfulness, supposing her to be "of less government than mistress of her word." Turning the tables, she accuses James's own delaying tactics of providing Bothwell with the latitude he uses so turbulently. To conclude, Elizabeth admonishes James to imitate her own resolute authority in words and actions—"be your doings as sound as my profession staunch"—and thus to assert his true sovereignty, "*regis regula,*" in the manner of a king.

Elizabeth remarks, "Methinks I frame this letter like to a lamentation," but it reads equally like a scolding. Perhaps because so much of its phrasing seems close to speech, the text is particularly rich in characteristic spellings that may suggest certain features of Elizabeth's spoken English. For example, she may have pronounced word-final *s* like *z* in such words as "afflicts," "spirits," "mars," "acts," "bids," and "hands," for she spells all of these with terminal *z*. Other consonants may have been sounded more plosively than they are today: witness her spellings "slidik" (sliding) and "Anfild" (anvil).

In the postscript to this letter, Elizabeth also remarks tellingly on her handwriting. Her "skribled Lines," she fears, "cumber" James's reading, so she ends her text—having run out of space anyway—in the lower left corner of this folio half-sheet.

Leah S. Marcus
Vanderbilt University

Janel M. Mueller
University of Chicago

great wickednes of the people · on the ane pairt
procuris this horrible defection wherby God ust
he punishes sinne be a greater iniquitie: and on
the vther pairt the consummation of the worlde
and our delyuerance drawing neir makis Satan
to rage the maire in his instrumentis knawing
his kingdome to be so neir ane end. And so
faire weill for this tyme.

5

Revela^{on} 12

+ 9 Jan 1778

// godd hauing appointed that secreate ~~miraculous~~ supernacurall signe for
tryall of that secreate unnaturall cryme, sa it appearis
that godd hes appointed for a supernaturall signe of the
monstruouse iniquitie of the witches) that the uatter
sall refuse to reissaue thaime in her bossome that haue shaken
of thaime the sacred uatter of baptisme & willfullie refused
the benefite thairof na not sa mekle ~~greater~~ as thair
eyes are able so shedd the teares (threattens to ture thame
as ye please) quhill first thay repent (godd not permitting
thame to dissembill thaire obstinacie in sa horrible a cryme)
albeit the uemen kynde especiallie be able to shedd teares
at euerie occasion quhen thaye will yea albeit it uare dissimu-
lichie lyke the crocodiles.

James I (1566–1625)

JAMES VI AND I WAS THAT RARE PHENOMENON, a king who set down in writing his current interests, be they the art of being a king (in his *Basilikon Doron*) or the ill effects of tobacco (*A Counterblaste to Tobacco*).[1] In 1590, his attention was caught by the series of sensational witchcraft trials in North Berwick, in which various supernatural attempts on his life were revealed.[2] According to contemporary commentators, James was himself involved in the interrogations, "by his owne especiall travell [travail]," drawing "the great witch," Agnes Sampson "to confess her wicked doings."[3] His observations were written up, probably in 1591 or 1592, in a treatise entitled *Daemonologie*, a dialogue in which "Philomathes" and "Epistemon" debate what is known about witchcraft.[4] The dialogue was first published in Edinburgh in 1597, subsequently issued three times in London on his accession to the English throne in 1603, made available in Dutch and then Latin for international consumption over the following year, and finally incorporated into his *Workes* of 1616.[5]

Daemonologie affords us a rare glimpse into the composition of James's writings. In common with many Renaissance authors, the king did not work in isolation.[6] Early versions of two sections of *Daemonologie*, drafted in James's own hand, survive as nos. 17 and 18 of MS Bodley 165 in the Bodleian Library, Oxford. James then authorized a clean copy of his treatise to be made, perhaps by his childhood friend Sir James Sempill—the manuscript that is now Folger V.a.185. This copy, however, also bears the signs of revisions by two persons, one of whom has been identified as James Carmichael, the Minister of Haddington,[7] and the other as James himself. James makes over one hundred amendments to the manuscript, ranging from deletions and insertions of single words, to the addition of entire passages. The vast majority of these amendments were incorporated into the 1597 printed edition, although experts believe that that volume was set from a further, interim manuscript copy.[8] The longest of these amendments is also the last, in the final opening of the manuscript, as James adds in the margin a characteristically gruesome discussion of how witchcraft can be detected by the tell-tale signs it leaves on the corpses of its victims:

& besydes that thaire are ∧tua∧ other goode helpis that maye be used for thaire tryall the ane is the finding of thaire marke & the ~~ty~~ trying the insensiblenes thairof the other is thaire fleiting ~~in~~ ∧on∧ the uatter for as in a secreate murther if the deade carcage be at any ∧tyme∧ thairefter handled by the murtheraire it will gushe out of bloode as if the bloode uare crying to the heauen for reuenge of the murthcrer godd hauing appointed that secreate ~~miraculouse~~ ∧supernaturall∧ signe for tryall of that secreate unnaturall

Daemonologie in form of a dialogue
ca.1592

Autograph corrections

[14] 110 pp.; 197 x 155 mm.

John Pinkerton - Beckford - Phillipps MS 2713; purchased from Quaritch in 1923

V.a.185

1. The first editions of these writings were Βασιλικον δωρον. *Deuided into three bookes* (Edinburgh: R. Walde-graue, 1599) [STC 14348]; *A counter-blaste to tobacco* (London: R. B[arker], 1604) [STC 14363].

2. For the fullest account see *Witchcraft in Early Modern Scotland: James VI's* Demonology *and the North Berwick Witches*, ed. Lawrence Normand and Gareth Roberts (Exeter, 2000).

3. Robert Bowes to Lord Burghley, December 7, 1590. *Calendar of State Papers Relating to Scotland, 1589–1593* (London, 1936), 430.

4. For this dating, see Rhodes Dunlap, "King James and Some Witches: The Date and Text of the *Daemonologie,*" *Philological Quarterly,* 54 (1975): 40–46.

5. *Daemonologie, in forme of a Dialogue* (Edinburgh: R. Walde-graue, 1597) [STC 14364]; *Daemonologie, in forme of a Dialogue* (London: R. Wald-grave, 1603) [STC 14366]; *Daemonologie, in forme of a Dialogve* (London: W. Aspley and W. Cotton, 1603) [STC 14365 and 14365.5, two issues]; *Daemonologia, dat is, Eene Onderrichtinghe teghen de Tooverie* (Amsterdam: Vincent Mevsevost, 1603);

Daemonologia; hoc est, adversus incantationem siue Magiam, institvtio, Forma Dialogi concepta, & in Libros III. distincta (Hanoviæ: apud Guilielmum Antonium, 1604; another edn., Hanoviae: apud Gulielmum Antonium, 1607); *The workes of . . . James . . . King of Great Britaine* (London: R. Barker and J. Bill, 1616) [STC 14344]. Important modern editions include *Minor Prose Works of King James VI and I*, ed. James Craigie (Edinburgh, 1982), 147–77; and *Witchcraft in Early Modern Scotland*, 327–52.

6. See David H. Willson, "James VI and his literary assistants," *Huntington Library Quarterly*, 8 (1944): 35–58.

7. The suggestion is by Dunlap, "King James and Some Witches," 43.

8. Private correspondence of James Craigie to Laetitia Yeandle, 1977 ("The *Daemonologie* of King James VI and I; A Note on MS V.a.185"), Folger Shakespeare Library curatorial files.

cryme, sa it appearis that godd hes appointed (for a supernaturall signe of the monstruouse impietie of the uitches) that the uatter sall refuse to ressaue thame in her bosome that haue shaken of thaime the sacred uatter of baptisme & uillfullie refused the benefite thairof na not sa mekle (~~threaten~~ as thaire eyes are able ~~fo~~ to shedd ~~tre~~ teares (threatten & tortoure thame as ye please) quhill first thay repent (godd not permitting thame to dissembill thaire obstinacie in sa horrible a cryme) albeit the uemenkynde especiallie be ∧other uayes∧ able to shedd teares at euerie ∧liche∧ occasion quhen thaye uill yea allthoch it uare dissimulatlie lyke the crocodiles.

Alan Stewart
Birkbeck College

Liber Amicorum

Est nobilis ira leonis
Parcere Subiectis & debellare Superbos.
              Jacobus R.
Tout gist en la main de dieu.
              Anna Royne decosse

Liber Amicorum
1564, 1590–1609
Kept by Theodoricus
von Bevernest
(1546–1608)

[6] 164 pp.; 154 x 93 mm.

Purchased from J. Pearson &
Co. in 1928

V.a.325

THIS *LIBER AMICORUM*, BOUND IN ITS ORIGINAL RED VELVET with gilt and gauffered edges, was most likely commenced by Theodoricus von Bevernest of Lüsewitz during the wedding celebrations of James VI of Scotland and Anne of Denmark in 1590. Bevernest, envoy of the duke of Mecklenburg to the Queen Mother of Denmark, Sophia of Mecklenburg, was a regular at the Danish court. He had traveled to Copenhagen in 1588 at the proclamation of Christian IV as king of Denmark and in 1590 to the marriages of Christian IV's sisters, Anne of Scotland and Elizabeth of Brunswick-Luneburg. In 1596 and 1602, Bevernest accompanied Anne's younger sisters Augusta and Hedwig to their respective husbands, Prince John Adolph, duke of Slesvig-Holstein, and Christian II, duke elector of Saxony.[1]

The first signatures in the album belong to James VI and his new wife, Anne, who was sixteen years old at the time. James VI's first motto translates "The rage of the lion is noble," while the second, from Book VI of Virgil's *Aeneid*, translates: "To spare the subject and subdue the proud."[2] In English, Anne's French motto is: "All things rest in God's hand." After a proxy marriage in Copenhagen on August 20, 1589, James VI and Anne were married in person in Oslo on November 23, 1589, followed by a third ceremony on January 21, 1590, in Copenhagen, where they remained until April 1590.[3]

On the page facing the signatures of James and Anne are the signatures of the Queen Mother of Denmark and Christian IV, the fourteen-year-old king of Denmark. Anne's other brothers, Hans and Ulric, and her aunt also signed the album. In addition to the signatures and epigrams of many German nobles, the book was signed by Peter Munch, Admiral of Denmark and one of the regents during the minority of Christian IV. Munch had tried to deliver Anne to Scotland in September 1589 but was turned back by severe storms, which he attributed to sorcery. The signatures of two of Munch's co-regents, Nicholas Kaas, chancellor of Denmark, and George Rosencrantz, also appear (Peter Guildenstern was the fourth regent). The signature of Sir Peter Young, who had been one of James VI's tutors and was involved early on in the marriage negotiations, is written on a piece of paper glued to a page in Bevernest's album.

1. For a discussion of this manuscript, see Leonard Forster, "Das Album Amicorum von Dietrich Bevernest," *Wolfenbutteler Forschungen*, 11 (Munich, 1981), 165–76. See also Leonard Forster's edition of the same title, published in 1982.

2. This is the translation of Sir John Harington, made for James's son, Henry, prince of Wales. See *The Sixth Book of Virgil's Aeneid, translated and commented on by Sir John Harington (1604)*, ed. Simon Cauchi (Oxford, 1991), 58.

3. Anne had attempted to reach Scotland after the proxy marriage, but storms diverted her ship to Norway. James VI, impatient for the wedding, left Leith in October 1589 to retrieve her himself.

Friendship albums were popular among students in Scandinavia and northern Germany. An album with particularly important names could serve as a kind of passport or letter of recommendation. First pages were generally reserved for nobility, and thus the dates do not progress chronologically. Albums often included mottoes, epigrams, coded references, portraits, and coats of arms, in addition to signatures.

Rosencrantz and Guildenstern are the names of the prince's former school friends in *Hamlet, Prince of Denmark*, and Rosencrantz's signature was undoubtedly the source of Henry Folger's interest in the manuscript when he purchased it in 1928.

H. W.

L.b.654

Goode Sir george I ame extreamelie sorie that youre unfortunate

prisoner turnis all the greate caire I have of him, not onlie against

him selfe, but against me also as farre as he can, I can not blame

you, that ye can not coniecture quhat this maye be for god knowis

it is only a tricke of his ydle braine, hoaping thairby to shifte

his tryall, but it is easie to be seene, that he wolde threatten me,

with laying an aspersion upon me of being in some sorte acces-

sorie to his cryme, I can doe no more (since god so abstractes his

grace from him) then repeate the substance of that lettre quhich

the lorde have sent you yesternight, quhiche is this, if he

wolde writte or sende me any message concerning this ponting

it needis not be privatt, if it be of any other bussienesse thn

quhiche I can not nou with honoure ressaue privatlie, I maye

doe it after his tryall & serve the turne as well for ex

ather his tryall, or confession preceede, I can not heare a

private message from him without laying an aspersion upon

my selfe of being an accessorie to his cryme, & I praye

you to urge him by reason, that I refuse him no favoure with

taking upon me the suspicion of being guiltie of that cryme

quhairof he is accused & so fairwell.

James R

Autograph letter, signed, to Sir George More, L.b.654

Autograph letter, signed,
to Sir George More
ca. May 1616

1 p.; 290 x 194 mm.

Loseley Collection - purchased
via William H. Robinson, Ltd.,
in 1954

L.b.654

Goode Sir george I ame extreamelie sorie that youre unfortunate prisoner turnis all the greate caire I haue of him, not onlie against him selfe, but against me also, as farre as he can, I can not blame you, that ye can not coniecture quhat this maye be, for, god knowis it is only a'trikke of his ydle braine, hoaping thairby to shifte his tryall, but it is easie to be seene, that he wolde threattin me, with laying an aspersion upon me of being in some sorte accessorie to his cryme . . . if he wolde writte or sende me any message concerning this poysoning it needis not be priuate . . . I can not heare a priuate message from him without laying an aspersion upon my selfe of being an accessorie to his cryme. . . .

1. *Calendar of State Papers
and Manuscripts, Venetian*, ed.
Allen B. Hinds (London, 1908),
14:61, 65.

THIS IS ONE OF FOUR LETTERS FROM JAMES I to Sir George More, lieutenant of the Tower of London, concerning the future of the royal favorite, Robert Carr, earl of Somerset. Carr had been a member of the King's Bed Chamber with other young favorites until he was singled out by James, raised to the peerage first as Viscount Rochester, March 25, 1611, and, as he grew in power, as earl of Somerset, November 14, 1613. His aristocratic standing had been complemented by an accession to political dominance several months before when the King had appointed him to the Lord Chamberlainship, one of the most powerful positions in England, on July 10, 1613. On his path to these heights, Carr had also married the wife of Robert Devereux, the young earl of Essex (son of the famous rebel). To marry Carr, Frances (Howard) had secured a divorce on the grounds of Essex's alleged impotence. Accordingly, the couple had made many enemies in the old Essex circle.

During his rise, however, Carr had also alienated a close friend and aspiring courtier, the thirty-two-year-old Sir Thomas Overbury, whose own overconfidence, presumptions of intimacy with Carr, and alleged insolence to the Queen, had angered James enough to commit the unwary malcontent to the Tower, April 21, 1613. Puzzlingly, Overbury died after five months of imprisonment (on September 14). The circumstances were suspicious. In fact, a far-ranging investigation ultimately implicated Carr himself, as well as his new wife, the motive presumably being that former-confidant Overbury's disgruntled and threatening state of mind—and writing of letters—was a danger to Carr's position. Yet Somerset and his wife were not taken into custody until October 17, 1615, when he was told to remain in his own chambers until further notice: he was committed to the Tower on November 3.[1] He came to trial on Saturday, May 25, 1616, and was adjudged guilty by a jury of his peers, remaining in the Tower until his release in 1622.

The date of this letter has disappeared, although the recipient, More, dated the others on this subject that he received from the king at this time. The king was probably writing between November 1615 and May 1616. Because the contents *anticipate* the trial (May 25), and because the king had written More on May 9 and 13 on the same subject, we may suppose this letter was received between May 14 and 25, 1616.

It is clear from the contents that James seeks to avoid Somerset's efforts to entangle him in any sense of complicity regarding Overbury's fate, despite common court knowledge about the royal couple's dislike of the murdered courtier. The complicated situation is described in many contemporary manuscripts listed in Beatrice White's study of the subject.[2]

J. Leeds Barroll
Scholar in Residence
Folger Shakespeare Library

2. Beatrice White, *Cast of Ravens* (London, 1965), 245–48.

Warrant under the Great Seal, L.b.358

James I (1566–1625)

... Whereas Sir Walter Raleigh knight haveing bene heretofore by order of our lawes ... attainted of high treason ... Whereas by le*tt*res vnder our signett to you we com*m*aunded you to suffer Sir Walter Raleigh to goe abroad with his keeper to our Citty of London or elsewhere which accordingly you have donn (as wee are informed) ... Nowe wee out of our princely compassion being graciously pleased that the said Sir Walter Raleigh shalbe noe longer continued prisoner in our said tower, but forthwith be fully enlarged and deliuered out of the same ... and sett at lib*er*tye.

Warrant under the Great Seal, to Sir George More, Lieutenant of the Tower, for Sir Walter Raleigh's release from the Tower January 30, 1617

1 fol.; vellum; 280 x 430 mm.

Loseley Collection - purchased via William H. Robinson, Ltd., in 1939

L.b.358

IN 1603, WITHIN MONTHS OF THE SUCCESSION of James VI of Scotland to the English throne, Sir Walter Raleigh, one of the great gallants of his time, was accused of high treason and sentenced to death. The day before he was to be tortured and executed in a custom of unspeakable cruelty, the sentence was lifted, and Raleigh escaped with his life to the Tower of London, where he spent the next thirteen years, out of the way.

While Raleigh's fall from grace is one of the most spectacular and unjust in Tudor-Stuart England, he did little to help his cause in the years leading up to James's coronation. Raleigh did not anticipate the change of administration very well, or foresee the implications of his courtly, and unfashionable, allegiance to Elizabeth. He underestimated the cunning of Robert Devereux, earl of Essex, the hatred of Lord Henry Howard, and the insecurity of Elizabeth's successor. He failed to perceive that his indifference to public opinion, anachronistic chivalry, and irredeemable obstinacy would leave him without a single ally.

Essex was plotting before James came to power, heated by envy and anger. The earl's fantasies about Raleigh and his supposed scheme to hand over the English throne to Spain compelled Essex to bold and reckless maneuvers that ultimately led to the ill-conceived Essex Revolt in 1601 and his own end, but the contention also sealed Raleigh's fate.

Raleigh's relentless protestations of love and loyalty to Gloriana in the final years of her reign were interpreted by James to be the posturing of an enemy, rather than the gallantry of an Old World order playing itself out. A constellation of things conspired to fix James's mind against Raleigh before he even met the man: Essex's repeated allegations, public mistrust of Raleigh's wealth and the means by which it was acquired, Howard's obsessive complaints, and Raleigh's own astonishing miscues (dismissing one of James's ambassadors).

The Elizabethan era ended on March 24, 1603, and Raleigh became a leftover. He not only had no stock with Elizabeth's successor; he became *persona non grata*. In the shuffle for entitlement and new appointments, Raleigh was left out. Robert

1. For further background to Raleigh's imprisonment, voyages, and execution, see: Robert Lacey, *Sir Walter Ralegh* (London, 1973); V. T. Harlow, *Ralegh's Last Voyage* (London, 1932); John Parker and Carol A. Johnson, *Sir Walter Raleigh's Speech from the Scaffold* (Minneapolis: Associates of the James Ford Bell Library, 1995).

Cecil got his peerage. Francis Bacon became Lord Chancellor. Thomas Howard became Lord Chamberlain and an earl. George Carew was made a baron. Even the followers of Essex were pardoned, while Raleigh tumbled into a void, deprived of his residence, possessions, means of income, position as captain of the guard, and personal freedom. Within four months of James's accession Raleigh was accused and committed to the Tower of London. While he was spared a savage execution, his life was over, or so he thought.

On March 19, 1617, Raleigh, sixty-three years old, was freed from the Tower to go on a gold hunt for James. The document before you, dated January 30, 1617, is the royal warrant ordering Raleigh's release. It is addressed to George More, Lieutenant of the Tower, and carries the Great Seal of James I, made of wax.

Raleigh had been to Guiana (now Venezuela) in 1595 and returned to publish *The Discoverie of the Large, Rich, and Beautiful Empyre of Guiana* (1596). It was an appeal, to anyone who would listen, to seek gold and riches in the New World—he knew the way. In July 1617, with James's consent (but not his pardon), Raleigh led fourteen ships and 900 men on an expedition to restock the royal coffers that were severely in debt. Gold had been the constant theme of Raleigh's repeated petitions, and by 1617 James had nothing to lose in granting the release of the renowned navigator. While James consented to the voyage, he did not fund it. Raleigh had to raise the money to outfit the expedition from prison, composing elaborate entreaties to wealthy Dutch merchants, for example, assuming all risk. The Folger has one of his feverish appeals (MS Add 991).

The voyage was a disaster, ill-fated from the start and plagued to the end. Raleigh encountered storms, illness, hostile Spanish vessels, riots on board, and finally mutiny. His eldest son was killed. He found no riches, only misery. The chivalrous Elizabethan arrived back in Plymouth a year later without an ounce of gold, ruined.

While no crime was committed and no serious offense could be brought before Raleigh regarding the Guiana debacle, the conviction of treason from 1603 had never been removed and, upon his return, he was escorted back to the Tower. On October 24, 1618, Sir Walter Raleigh was sentenced, again, and executed five days later before a large audience. In one of the greatest speeches from the scaffold in English history, Raleigh praised Essex, denied his accusers to the end, and refused a blindfold. The axeman would not pronounce the time-honored words, "behold the head of a traitor."[1]

Richard Kuhta
Folger Shakespeare Library

Henry Frederick, prince of Wales (1594–1612)

. . . Item that perfect bookes be daylie and weeklie kept by the said Auditor
generall as a Counterroll of all the Receiptes and paymentes of his highnes
Treasure by the handes of his Treasorer or Receavor generall, both for
his highnes better satisfaccion, and alsoe for a more perfect charging and
discharging the said Treasorer vppon his Accompt and iustificacion of his
cleere honest and iust dealing in his place and office to his great Credit./

JAMES I'S ELDEST SON HENRY was created Prince of Wales in June 1610. With
this appointment he was given his own household, revenues, and palaces. A year
later, the seventeen-year-old heir to the throne, who exerted tight control over the
running of his household, established detailed procedures for the operation of his
treasury. He requested that, as with his father's treasury ("as in the kynge Maiesties
affares of this kynde, soe likewise in this of his highnes"), he receive certificates of
accounts paid and received on a monthly basis, "By which his highnes shall receave
great benyfitt in knowing whoe is paid and whoe not," not only to be informed
but so that he is better able to "distribute his bountie as shalbe best agreeable to
his wysedome."

Perhaps this handsome manuscript was prompted by a ca.1610 document at
the Folger titled "Observations concerning the duties of the treasurer and receiver-
general to the Prince," in the hand of Sir George More (1553–1632), Henry's receiver-
general.[1] Other documents at the Folger relating to More and to Richard Connock,
Henry's auditor-general, attest to the smooth running of Henry's treasury.[2] In the
year after he established procedures for the treasury, the much-beloved Prince of
Wales died unexpectedly of typhoid fever.

Two bound manuscripts at the Folger were dedicated to Prince Henry: Sir
John Harington's *Epigrams* (1605), shown in this exhibition, and Esther Inglis's
calligraphic masterpiece, *Argumenta psalmorum Davidis* (1608), with an exquisite
embroidered contemporary binding decorated in gold and silver thread and
seed pearls.[3]

H. W.

Memorandum under
sign manual concerning
the Prince's treasury
June 24, 1611

1 fol.; vellum; 480 x 290 mm.

Loseley Collection - purchased
via William H. Robinson, Ltd.,
in 1939

L.b.347

1. Folger L.b.626. This is the
same Sir George More who
sold a house at Blackfriars to
Richard and Cuthbert Burbage
in 1601, which adjoined property sold by More's father to the
Burbages' father in 1596 (where
the King's Men performed
from 1609). The Folger owns
the deeds for both of these sales
(L.b.356, in this exhibition;
L.b.357).

2. Folger L.b.632, 635, 636.

3. Folger V.a.249, V.a.94.

Final concord, Z.c.36 (110-111)

William Shakespeare (1564–1616) and Hercules Underhill

IN MAY OF 1597, WILLIAM SHAKESPEARE, by then clearly a man of substance, bought for himself a family home in Stratford. This was the property known as New Place, allegedly the second largest house in the borough. Described by Leland as "a praty house of bricke and tymbre," it had been built in the late fifteenth century by Sir Hugh Clopton, another Stratfordian who had made his fortune in London, and who owned one of the books now in the Folger Shakespeare Library, a manuscript (ca.1400) of Robert Mannying of Brunne's *Handlyng Synne*.[1]

Shakespeare bought the property from William Underhill, whose father had previously owned New Place. This was at a time when there was no formal registration of title, so Shakespeare entered into a customary fictitious legal action to ensure that the transaction was recorded in offical sources. Under this process, a purchaser would claim in court (through his attorney) that he, or his family, had been dispossessed in the past from the property in question by the vendor, and ask for a judgment recording his right to it. The vendor would admit that this was indeed the case and judgment would be given in favor of the purchaser, and his right to the premises would be recorded. A sum, allegedly the fine imposed for such dispossession, would also be recorded. This judgment, known as a "Final Concord," would be written out three times by the chirographer in the Court of Common Pleas on a single piece of parchment and then divided along wavy, or indented, lines. The third, or "foot," was retained in the court records and the remaining two were handed to the purchaser and vendor. The foot to the two copies shown here is in the Public Record Office.[2] In practice, both copies of the fine would have been kept with the documents of title and would have descended with the property.

Just two months after selling the property to Shakespeare, William Underhill died, supposedly having been poisoned by his son Fulke, who was hanged in 1599 for the crime. This episode may have called into question the legality of the 1597 final concord, leading William Underhill's second son, Hercules (to whom the property would have passed when he came of age in 1602), to reconvey the property to Shakespeare with this new final concord.

In cases where both deed and final concord survive, it would seem that the amount of fine was conventionally about fifty percent of the purchase price; therefore, the £60 mentioned in the fine of New Place probably represents a purchase price of £120 to £150. The three copies of the fines do not name the property in question as New Place but follow a formulaic legal description for the purposes of the case. Thus the premises are referred to as "one messuage, two barns, two gardens, and two orchards."

Interestingly, another version of these New Place fines survives in the collections of the Shakespeare Birthplace Trust in Stratford. This is a larger, certified copy,

Final concord for Shakespeare's purchase of New Place, Stratford-upon-Avon Court of Common Pleas, Michaelmas term, 1602

2 fols.; vellum; each 118 x 397 mm.

J. O. Halliwell-Phillipps collection; purchased with the Marsden J. Perry collection in 1908

Z.c.36 (110–111)

1. Folger V.b.236.

2. PRO CP 25 (2)/237, Michaelmas 44-45 Eliz. I, no. 15.

known as an exemplification, for which Shakespeare would have had to pay. It bears the seal of the court, but the initial letter has not been elaborated, although the space has been left (perhaps Shakespeare scoffed at the cost). This exemplification adds nothing to the validity of Shakespeare's title and perhaps may be seen as indicating either snobbery or insecurity on the part of the rising playwright. In the early nineteenth century, Robert Bell Wheler, a local antiquary, borrowed many of the Shakespeare documents of title when they were in the hands of the agents of the last of the Cloptons (who had re-acquired New Place after the death of Elizabeth Barnard), and the exemplification formed part of his collections when they were left to the Birthplace Trust by his sister.

Mairi A. Macdonald
Shakespeare Birthplace Trust

Ralph Brooke (1553–1625)
and William Dethick (1543–1612)

SOMETIME AROUND 1568, WILLIAM SHAKESPEARE'S FATHER, John, unsuccessfully approached the College of Arms about acquiring a coat of arms for his family. Nearly thirty years later, in 1596, Shakespeare, by now a successful actor and playwright, renewed the application on his father's behalf. William Dethick, the temperamental and controversial Garter king-of-arms, awarded the Shakespeare family with a shield displaying a spear, with a falcon for a crest. Three years later, John Shakespeare applied to have his arms impaled with those of his wife's family, the Ardens, and although permission was granted, the joining of arms never occurred.

In 1602, however, the Shakespeare coat of arms, along with twenty-two others, came under the scrutiny of the York Herald, Ralph Brooke, who accused Dethick of abusing his authority by elevating unqualified persons and assigning arms already in use. The list of twenty-three names, with Shakespeare's name listed fourth, appears in the upper left corner of the flyleaf of Folger V.a.156. Eleven of these twenty-three names are among the colored arms and crests that follow. Ralph Brooke, much disliked by his fellow heraldists, annotated this manuscript in preparation for making a similar manuscript for his attack on Dethick, and added to his "complaint" additional arms granted by the two provincial kings-of-arms, the antiquarian William Camden, Clarenceux king-of-arms, and William Segar, Norroy king-of-arms. Brooke drew attention to the lowly careers of many of the recipients, such as "Parr the Embroderer whose father was a Pedler by occupacion and not able to proue his surname to be Parr," "Fishemonger. . . The Crest is not fitt for so meane a person But Rather for one that pocesseth the Whole worlde," "one Molesworthe whose occupacion is to sell stockings in London," and "John Gibbes, whom the Gibbes of Devon doe denye to be ethere of there name or kynred sainge that they are wronged to haue there Armes geven away to a stranger." Nothing ever came of this dispute. In their joint reply to the charges, Dethick and Camden defended the uniqueness of the Shakespeare coat of arms and described John Shakespeare as "A magestrat in Strafford vpon Avon. A Justice of peace he meryed A daughter and heyre of Ardern. and was of good substance and habelite."[1] After a very controversial tenure, Dethick, who was alleged to have granted the royal arms of England to a plasterer, was finally forced to surrender his office in 1605.

Roughly a century later, Peter Le Neve (d. 1729), who was elected the first president of the revived Society of Antiquaries in 1687 and appointed Rouge Croix pursuivant in 1690, Richmond Herald in April 1704, and Norroy king-of-arms in May 1704, had a copy made of a manuscript recording the earlier dispute, titled "A note of some Coats & Crests lately come to my hands Given by William Dethick when he was Yorke and since he hath executed the Office of Garter King of Armes." On page 28 of this volume, a sketch of Shakespeare's arms is annotated: "Shakespeare the Player by Garter." It has been suggested that the copy was made from the manuscript compiled by Brooke himself from Folger V.a.156, based on

York Herald's Complaint
ca.1600

17 fols.; 204 x 145 mm.

Saville 38 - Phillipps 25925 - W. H. Rylands manuscript; purchased from Henry Young, Liverpool, in 1924

V.a.156

York Herald's Complaint Copy, ca.1700

[2] 30 pp.; 187 x 145 mm.

Peter Le Neve - William Constable manuscript; purchased from Dobell in January 1907

V.a.350

1. Ashmolean Museum, Oxford, MS 846, fol. 50. Facsimile reproduced in Samuel Schoenbaum, *William Shakespeare, A Documentary Life* (New York, 1975), 172.

2. Folger V.a.350 was originally bound together with three other items: William Westby, "A continuation of my memoires or memoranda book" (1688) (V.a.469); an early transcription of George Eglisham, *The forerunner of revenge upon the Duke of Buckingham . . .* (Frankfurt, 1626) (V.a.470); and "Coats of arms in trick of Yorkshire families" (ca.1650) (V.a.471). The volume was disbound in October 1978.

the presence of the derogatory reference to Shakespeare as a "player," a career not generally worthy of a coat of arms. It is not known who drew the coats of arms and crests and transcribed the accompanying comments in Le Neve's copy, but the annotations, and the notations of colors on the coats and crests, are most likely in Le Neve's hand. The order of the coats of arms and crests on pages 7 to 25 of this manuscript are identical to the depictions in Folger V.a.156, and some of the coats of arms and crests on pages 1 to 6 and pages 26 to 30 are among the remaining twenty-three names listed on the flyleaf of Folger V.a.156.[2] These two manuscripts are part of a large collection of heraldic manuscripts, visitations, and pedigrees at the Folger Library.

H. W.

Henry Walker (d. 1616?)
and William Shakespeare (1564–1616)

Bargain and sale, Z.c.22 (45)

Bargain and sale
for Shakespeare's
purchase of the
Blackfriars Gatehouse
March 10, 1613

1 fol.; vellum; 482 x 600 mm.

Rev. Mr. Featherstonehaugh -
Albany Willis - Sir William
Tite - J. O. Halliwell-Phillipps -
Marsden J. Perry manuscript;
purchased in 1908

Z.c.22 (45)

1. S. Schoenbaum, *William
Shakespeare: A Compact
Documentary Life*, rev. ed.
(Oxford, 1987), 272–75.

This indenture made . . . Betweene Henry Walker Citizen and Minstrell of London of thone partie, & William Shakespeare of Stratford vpon Avon in the Countie of Warwick gentleman, William Johnson Citizen and Vintener of London, John Jackson, and John Hemmyng of London gent. of thother partie. Witnesseth that the said Henry Walker for and in consideracion of the somme of one hundred and fortie poundes of lawfull money of England to him in hand before thensealing hereof by the said William Shakespeare well and trulie paid, whereof and wherewith hee the said Henry Walker doth acknowledge himselfe full & satisfied and contented.

THE DOCUMENT SHOWN on page 73 is William Shakespeare's own copy of the deed for his purchase of the Blackfriars Gatehouse in London, on March 10, 1613. According to the deed, the gatehouse was adjoined to the King's Wardrobe on the east side and a plot of ground belonging to the widow Anne Bacon on the west. The third side of the structure was a brick wall, and it faced a street leading to Puddle Wharf. His purchase included free entry through the gate and the yard, and also to "all and singular cellars, sollars [attics], rooms, lights, easements, profits, commodities, and hereditaments whatsoever to the said dwelling house or tenement belonging, or in any wisc appertaining."

Despite its convenient location near the Blackfriars Playhouse, the winter headquarters for the King's Men since 1609, the Gatehouse dwelling was apparently only an investment for Shakespeare, who lived for the most part at New Place in Stratford-upon-Avon. Shakespeare paid £80 of the £140 selling price up front, and on the day after the conveyance he mortgaged the Gatehouse back to Henry Walker, "Citizen and Minstrell," for the remaining £60. The three other names in the deed, William Johnson, landlord of the Mermaid, John Jackson, possibly the shipping magnate from Hull, and John Hemminge, one of the King's Men, acted as trustees in his interest. Two years after Shakespeare's death, his trustees conveyed the Gatehouse to John Greene of Clement's Inn and Matthew Morris of Stratford, "in performance of the confidence and trust in them reposed by William Shakespeare deceased . . . according to the true intent and meaning of the last will and testament of the said William Shakespeare."[1]

The other copy of the deed, with Shakespeare's signature, went to Henry Walker, the seller of the property, and is now at the Guildhall Library in London.

H. W.

Richard Stonley (ca.1520–1600)

This day after morninge p*r*ay*e*r I rode to London dyned at Badnall greene
spent the after noone at home at my book*es* w*i*th thank*es* to god at night. . . .

Book*es*   for the Survey of ffraunc w*i*th
              the Venus & Adhonay p*ar*   xii^d
              Shakspere

THIS DIARY CONTAINS the first recorded purchase of Shakespeare's first publication, *Venus and Adonis*, made less than two months after the narrative poem
was licensed to be printed at the Stationers' Hall on April 18, 1593. Dedicated to the
young courtier Henry Wriothesley, earl of Southampton, *Venus and Adonis* enjoyed
great success, coming out in sixteen editions between 1593 and 1636, few of which
survive today.

The diarist, Richard Stonley, was one of Queen Elizabeth's four Tellers of the
Exchequer of Receipt. Stonley spent his weekdays at his house on Aldersgate Street
in the parish of St. Botolph in London and his weekends at his estate in Dodding-
hurst, Essex. The diaries of Stonley (the Folger has three volumes) reveal a pious
and hardworking elderly man who structured his day around work and prayer.[1]
Stonley's brief daily entries generally included his activities, the date and saint's day,
moral advice in the form of quotations and paraphrases from the Bible, classical
authors, Erasmus, and others, often in Latin *and* English, and his daily expenses. He
made frequent references to his immediate and extended family, mentioned the
names of his minister and friends who were invited to his house after services for
dinner, and occasionally recorded public events, such as Edmund Campion being
taken to Tyburn on December 1, 1581.

The entry for Tuesday, June 12, 1593, follows the same format as most other
entries. On the day he purchased *Venus and Adonis*, which was St. Basilide's Day,
Stonley went to the city of London in the morning and dined at Bethnal Green,
spent the afternoon at home with his books, and gave "thank*es* to God" in the
evening. His quotation for the day was the second distich from Book 4 of the
Distichs of Dionysius Cato ("Commoda naturae nullo tibi tempere deerunt / Si
contentus eo fueris quod postulat Vsus"), which he was recording chronologically
in his diary, distich by distich. While in London, he spent ten shillings on "vittell"
(victuals), twelve pence on books (in addition to *Venus and Adonis* he purchased
John Eliot's *The Survey, or Topographical Description of France*), and three shillings,
twelve pence on apparel.

In 1597, at the age of seventy-seven, Stonley was imprisoned in the Fleet and had
his property seized for the crime of embezzling nearly £13,000 of the Queen's

Diary
May 14, 1593–
May 24, 1594

[2] 92 fols.; 195 x 137 mm.

Bookplate of John Adair
Hawkins (Marlow Place
Library); purchased from
William Wreden in 1972

V.a.460

1. The first volume covers
the period June 15, 1581, to
December 31, 1582 (V.a.459);
the second volume (V.a.460),
shown in this exhibition, May
14, 1593, to May 24, 1594; and
the third volume (V.a.461),
March 14, 1597, to May 18, 1598.

75

2. The list is included in Leslie Hotson, "The Library of Elizabeth's Embezzling Teller," *Studies in Bibliography,* 2 (1949–50): 49–62.

money. The ensuing appraisal of his household goods at his Aldersgate residence listed the titles of 413 books, as well as numerous pamphlets and songbooks, but did not include the items purchased on June 12, 1593.[2] Stonley maintained his diary in prison, recording menus and the names of fellow diners.

While this Shakespeare reference was known to scholars in the late eighteenth century, the diary disappeared from view until 1972, when it was purchased by the Folger. In reading through the diaries, Laetitia Yeandle "rediscovered" the long-lost *Venus and Adonis* entry, which the Folger announced in a press release on Shakespeare's birthday in 1973.

H. W.

John Ward (1629–1681)

Shakespear Drayton and Ben Jhonson had a merry meeting and it seems drank too hard for Shakespear died of a feavour there contracted

I haue heard *tha*t Mr Shakespeare was a natural wit without any art at all. hee frequented *th*e plays all his younger time, but in his older days liud at Stratford: and supplied *th*e stage with 2 plays euery year and for *tha*t had an allowance so large *tha*t hee spent at *th*e Rate of a 1000[¹] a yeer as I haue heard:
> Remember to peruse Shakespears plays and bee versd in *th*em *tha*t I may not bee ignorant in *tha*t matter:

Shakespear had but 2 daughters one whereof Mr Hall *th*e physitian married and by her had one daughter, to wit *th*e Lady Bernard of Abbingdon:

Whether Dr Heylin does well in Reckoning vp *th*e Dramatick poets which haue been famous in England to omit Shakespear:[1]

Diary
1662–1663

179 fols.; 147 x 90 mm.

Medical Society of London manuscript (their sale, Sotheby's, London, April 4, 1928, no. 631)

V.a.292

JOHN WARD, THE VICAR OF STRATFORD-UPON-AVON, was a man of many interests. While he is best known for supplying the only known account of Shakespeare's death, Ward reveals much more than local Shakespearean gossip in the sixteen volumes of his densely-written diaries.[2] After taking his M.A. at Christ Church, Oxford, in 1652, Ward spent a great deal of time in London studying the natural sciences. He became vicar of Stratford-upon-Avon in 1662, was licensed to practice medicine by the Archbishop of Canterbury in 1666, and was appointed rector of Dorsington in Gloucestershire in 1668 (while maintaining his incumbency at Stratford). Since medicine was his primary love, his diaries include details relating to surgery, chemistry, pharmacy, herbs, botany, and astrology, often taken from Latin sources. He visited the laboratories and physic gardens of many of the leading scientists, and collected pharmaceutical recipes, attended lectures, and witnessed operations. Ward's diaries also include notes on theology, ancient and modern history, politics, literature, and travel. Some of the diaries still have their original bindings, stamped in gold with John Ward's initials.

Laetitia Yeandle described Ward in 1960 as an endearingly determined man, eager to expand his horizons in order to be a good doctor and vicar:

> No opening was left unexplored in this quest; he was continually reminding himself of the need to look further into some question, to meet some person, to visit a particular physic garden, to read a certain book. . . . Later as the vicar of Stratford he displayed the same anxiety to fulfill his role,

1. Taken from V.a.292, fols. 150, 140, 138v (all three entries written between January 24 and March 6, 1663); V.a.294, fol. 20 (November 1665). He repeated the Heylin statement in V.a.295, fol. 120 (November–December 1668): "Dr. Heylin in reckoning up *th*e dramatick poets, omits Shakespear."

2. Folger V.a.284-299. Charles Severn published extracts from Ward's diaries in the *Diary of the Rev. John Ward* (London, 1839). Sir D'Arcy Power's manuscript notes and transcriptions of some of the Ward diaries, completed in the early nineteenth century, are divided between the Royal College of Surgeons and the Wellcome Library. The Folger has microfilm copies of Power's notes and transcriptions.

3. A. L. D. Kennedy-Skipton [Laetitia Yeandle], "John Ward and Restoration Drama," *Shakespeare Quarterly*, 11 (1960): 493–94. Laetitia Yeandle contributed a number of Notes to *SQ* concerning the Ward diaries, including *SQ*, 8 (1957): 460, 520, 526 (reproductions of three Shakespeare items in V.a.292); *SQ*, 12 (1961):353 ("A footnote to 'John Ward and Restoration Drama'"); *SQ*, 20 (1969):87–88 ("Shakespeare Allusions").

systematically setting out to familiarize himself with its history and the details of its parochial affairs and making the acquaintance of its more substantial citizens. It is this attitude which makes his comments so invaluable. They are completely disinterested.[3]

Ward qualified his statements about Shakespeare's death and spending habits with "it seems" and "I haue heard." While his reports are most likely the stuff of urban legend, it is not implausible that Shakespeare might have met up with Drayton and Jonson around the time of his death, perhaps at the wedding of Shakespeare's daughter, Judith, to Thomas Quiney on February 10, 1616. Judith, whom Ward refers to as Mrs. Queeny in his diary, was still living during Ward's time in Stratford-upon-Avon, as were other contemporaries of Shakespeare.

H. W.

Sir William More (1520–1600)
and James Burbage (d. 1597)

Bargain and sale, L.b.356

. . . in consideracon of the some of Sixe Hundreth Poundes of Lawfull money of England . . . the saide Sir William More . . . doth fullie and clerelie Bargayne sell alien enfeoffe and confirme to the saide Iames Burbage his heires and assignes forever / All those Seaven greate vpper Romes as they are nowe devided being all vpon one flower and sometyme beinge one greate and entire rome. . . .

Bargain and sale
of seven upper rooms
in the Blackfriars
to James Burbage
February 4, 1596

1 fol.; vellum; 660 x 745 mm.
Pendant seal of beeswax
(fragment)

Loseley Collection - purchased
via William H. Robinson, Ltd.,
in 1939

L.b.356

1. S. Schoenbaum, *William Shakespeare: A Compact Documentary Life* (Oxford, 1979), 264–67.

2. Folger L.b.356.

IN 1596, JAMES BURBAGE, owner of "The Theatre" (the first commercial theater in London, built in 1576), purchased seven upper rooms in the dissolved Dominican monastery-complex at Blackfriars. The deed shown here records the transfer of this property from Sir William More to Burbage. The purchase price was £600, and Burbage spent several hundred more pounds to convert the space into a new theater for the Lord Chamberlain's Men since the lease on the Theatre was going to expire on April 13, 1597, and Burbage and Giles Allen, the landlord, could not agree on the terms for renewal.

But the Lord Chamberlain's Men, including one William Shakespeare, were prevented from performing in the new theater by the aristocratic residents of the Blackfriars neighborhood, who did not want a common playhouse in their midst. As a result, Burbage let the theater to a company of child actors and the Lord Chamberlain's Men continued at the Theatre until the end of 1597, eleven months after James Burbage's death. After a short stay at a rival playhouse, the Curtain, Burbage's two sons, Richard (who performed many of Shakespeare's title roles) and Cuthbert, took matters into their own hands. In the middle of the night of December 28, 1598, they dismantled the Theatre and transported the timber across the river to Bankside, where they built the Globe.

In August 1608, Shakespeare and the other players, now called the King's Men, assumed the lease of the Blackfriars theater, suddenly available because James I had ended the tenure of the company of child actors there after a scandalous performance of Chapman's *Conspiracy and Tragedy of Charles, Duke of Byron*. Richard and Cuthbert Burbage, along with Shakespeare, Thomas Evans, John Heminges, Henry Condell, and William Sly (who died a week later) formed a very profitable syndicate, dividing the lease and the profits between them. The King's Men began performing at the Blackfriars theater in 1609, after the plague restrictions were lifted, and continued to use it until the beginning of the civil wars in 1642 (it was demolished in 1655). Blackfriars was used for the winter season and the open-air Globe theater was used in the warmer months. The King's Men played to a smaller, more selective audience at Blackfriars, which measured just 46 x 66 feet and was illuminated by suspended candles. Tickets at Blackfriars were six times more expensive than the cheapest tickets at the Globe, and all ticket-holders were guaranteed a seat.[1]

The Folger also has a deed dated June 26, 1601, detailing the sale of a property adjoining the Blackfriars theater by Sir George More, the son of Sir William More, to Richard and Cuthbert Burbage, the sons of James Burbage.[2]

H. W.

Edward Alleyn (1566–1626)
Thomas Dekker (1570?–1641?)
Samuel Rowley (d. 1633?)

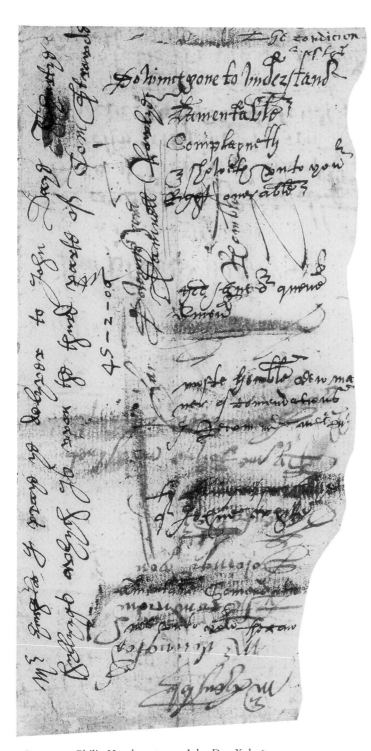

Request to Philip Henslowe to pay John Day, X.d.261

EDWARD ALLEYN

Memorandum relating
to Dulwich College
September 22
and 27, 1626

1 fol.; 300 x 194 mm.

Purchased from Maggs Bros.
in 1923

X.d.255

THOMAS DEKKER

Receipt, for loan of £3
from Philip Henslowe
January 18, 1598 [1599]

1 fol.; 104 x 185 mm.

J. O. Halliwell-Phillipps (his
sale, London, July 1, 1889, no.
1225) - to Pearson - John Boyd
Thacher (Anderson sale, New
York, May 13, 1915, V, no. 312)
- to G. D. Smith for H. C.
Folger, 1915

X.d.319

SAMUEL ROWLEY

Request to Philip
Henslowe to pay
John Day 30 shillings
1601

1 fol.; 202 x 100 mm.

Purchased in 1904

X.d.261

PHILIP HENSLOWE (ca.1555–1616) and Edward Alleyn (1566–1626) were the most financially-successful theater owners of Shakespeare's day. Between them they came to own the Rose Playhouse (built in 1587) and the Hope Playhouse (1613), both located on London's south bank near the Globe. They also owned a bearbaiting arena in the same vicinity. Additionally, north of London wall Henslowe and Alleyn constructed the Fortune Playhouse (1600); and following Henslowe's death, Alleyn built a private playhouse near Puddle Wharf (1617) within the city. Although the latter theater never opened for business, Henslowe and Alleyn turned entertainment into a substantial income. Furthermore, they did so with a social flourish that guaranteed them eminent standing amongst the London citizenry and many noblemen of the period as well.

Edward Alleyn—the son of a porter to Queen Elizabeth I—began his career as an actor who performed major roles in Christopher Marlowe's most popular plays, *Doctor Faustus* and *Tamburlaine the Great*, both staged at the Rose Playhouse. The theater was then owned by Henslowe, a dyer by trade, who descended from a family with an ancient coat of arms and significant political connections at court. In 1592 Alleyn married Henslowe's stepdaughter, and together the men forged the family entrepreneurship that employed many notable actors and playwrights of the time, some of whom (notably Ben Jonson) also wrote plays for Shakespeare's actors. Moreover, Shakespeare's company appears to have performed briefly with Alleyn's troupe during the summer of 1594 at a playhouse outside of London when plague forced the closure of the city theaters.

The three items selected for this exhibition were undoubtedly taken, at some indeterminate time, from the collection of Henslowe-Alleyn papers which was left at Dulwich College upon Alleyn's death. However, there is no reason to believe that all of these manuscripts were removed at the same time or by the same person. Unhappily, the Dulwich collection was much pilfered throughout the years, primarily by scholars such as Edmond Malone and J. P. Collier, who were allowed to borrow and use the manuscripts while they wrote their histories of the Elizabethan theater. Upon the death of Malone many manuscripts were returned to Dulwich College by James Boswell the younger, who was acting as executor of Malone's estate; however, other pieces eventually found their way into the collections of major libraries, including the British Library, the Bodleian Library at Oxford, and the Folger Shakespeare Library.

The three manuscripts featured here exemplify not only the public side of Henslowe's and Alleyn's lives, but also the personal interactions amongst the theater owners and the personnel associated with their playhouses. Folger X.d.319 is a receipt for a loan of £3 from Henslowe, written in the handwriting of Thomas

Dekker, a profligate playwright whose comedies became a staple of the Fortune's acting companies and who himself became notorious for his indebtedness. The condition of the loan is that it is "to bee repayd . . . / at thend of one Moneth next ensuing." Doubtless Dekker was borrowing money from Henslowe (acting as the actors' financier) against future profits due him when one of his plays was performed; or perhaps he was anticipating the future payments he might obtain if he were commissioned to write another play for the company (at the time of this transaction, Dekker was just completing the third part of *The Civil Wars of France* with Michael Drayton). Two fellow actors (Thomas Downton and Edward Juby) witnessed the loan (dated January 18, 1598, but probably 1599). Interestingly, the relationship between Dekker and his patrons turned out to be a longstanding association. As late as 1616, Dekker was writing to Henslowe and Alleyn from the King's Bench prison, where debtors were customarily incarcerated, requesting favors. On the verso of X.d.319 is the cancelled receipt noting that another well-known dramatist, George Chapman, was owed £3 in part payment for a comedy entitled *The World ronnes vpon Wheeles* (January 22, 1598/99, later entitled *All Fools but the Fool*, text now lost). Downton, who had paid Chapman on behalf of the company, and Dekker served as witnesses to the transaction. This particular transaction was noted by Philip Henslowe in his famous "diary," an account book recording various transactions for the Rose and Fortune Playhouses in the period between 1593 and 1604.

Folger X.d.261, a fascinating scrap of paper, contains notes relating to the purchases of playbooks, bits of legal formulae, and other scribbles, including Henslowe's and Alleyn's names. Most of the notes are in Henslowe's handwriting, except one of particular interest: a request from Samuel Rowley, an actor-dramatist who helped to manage the Lord Admiral's players, to Henslowe requesting that the playwright John Day be paid for the third part of a play entitled *Tom Strowde* (alternatively known as *The Blind Beggar of Bethnal Green*, the first part of which was later published in 1659). Rowley writes: "Mr hincheloe I praye ye delyver to John Daye Thurtye / shyllyngs whych Ys vpon the thurd parte of Tom Strowde." The play, a comedy written jointly by Day and William Haughton for the Admiral's Men at the Fortune Playhouse, was popular enough to sustain the audiences' interest through not only the original play, but two full-length sequels as well. In fact, from extant evidence it would appear that the companies performing at the Fortune seemed, more than others, to feature the multi-part play in their repertory.

Philip Henslowe died in 1616, after which the major portion of his estate passed to his son-in-law. With his fortune mounting and no heirs to pass it on to, Alleyn decided to establish "The College of God's Gift at Dulwich" in 1619, a foundation that served initially both as an orphanage and a pensioner's home. The major repository of the Henslowe-Alleyn papers is still located at Dulwich College which, in the nineteenth century, was rebuilt on another part of the Dulwich estate. It is now an elite private school numbering amongst its distinguished alumni such writers as P. G. Wodehouse and Raymond Chandler. Folger X.d.255 is Alleyn's "Memorandum for his Colledge," written on September 22 and 27, 1626, just two months before his death. It consists of two parts, both signed by Alleyn. The first sheet specifies some of the many properties that were to be bequeathed to the College upon Alleyn's death; the second sheet lists debtors who owed money to Alleyn. For most readers the list of debts is the more interesting of the two documents because it names, amongst others, "Mr Gun*n*ell" (Richard Gunnell, a friend and a former actor) "with others" who owed Alleyn £50, and "The kinges Ma*ie*stie in the Exchequer" (i.e., the king's treasury) which owed Alleyn the staggering sum of £800.

In the preamble to his Memorandum for Dulwich College Alleyn noted specifically that most of his "evidences" were kept in "a chest at the bedsfeete in the yellow chamber[,] the keye whereof is in the till of my deske." Although this chest has disappeared over time, the Henslowe-Alleyn papers remain some of the most significant manuscripts that scholars use in reconstructing the history of the Shakespearean theater. As a collection they offer an unparalleled, unique window into the artistic, social, and financial practices of the Renaissance playhouses.

S. P. Cerasano
Colgate University

Progress to Parnassus

Ingenioso:	William Shakespeare.
Judicio:	Who loves not Adons love, or Lucrece rape?
	His sweeter verse conteynes hart throbbing line
	Could but a grauer subiect him content
	Without loves foolish lazie languishment[1]

The progresse to Parnassus (copy of the second part of *The Return from Parnassus*) ca. 1606

24 fols.; 200 x 150 mm.

J. Symond of Gray's Inn, 1795 - John Towneley - J. O. Halliwell-Phillipps manuscript

V.a.355

CONTEMPORARY REFERENCES to Shakespeare are few and far between. This manuscript comedy of unknown authorship, the last part of a dramatic trilogy performed at St. John's College, Cambridge, between 1598 and 1601, satirizes the social pretensions of professional actors and playwrights.[2] Not only is Shakespeare referred to, but so are his fellow actors, the tragedian Richard Burbage and the comedian William Kemp.

Performed in 1601 and published twice in 1606 under the title *The returne from Pernassus: or The scourge of simony. Publiquely acted by the students in Saint Iohns Colledge in Cambridge* (London, 1606), the play concerns the miseries of two recent university graduates, cousins Philomusis and Studioso, who are searching for careers and purpose after being cast out into the "real" world. They reject acting as a career ("And must the basest trade yeeld vs reliefe?") after an encounter with "Burbage" and "Kemp," who are caricatured as vain and foolish professional actors. After a short stint as fiddlers, they decide that the pastoral life is the one for them and become shepherds.

Judicio's estimation of Shakespeare in the quotation at the top of the page mocks a phrase in Shakespeare's dedication to Henry Wriothesley, earl of Southampton, in *Venus and Adonis* (1593), in which he vows to make good use of his idle time "till I haue honored you with some graver labor." Shakespeare's "graver labor" resulted in the publication of *The Rape of Lucrece* (1594), also dedicated to Southampton, but Judicio undermines the seriousness of this second narrative poem in spite of Shakespeare's claims to the contrary. Southampton, imprisoned in the Tower at the time of this play, had received his M.A. from St. John's College, Cambridge, in 1589.

In Act 4, scene 3, "Kemp" shows his lack of respect for university plays and playwrights and refers to a well-known battle of wits involving Ben Jonson.[3]

Kempe:	few of *the* vniversitye men penne plaies well, they smell too much of *that* writer Ovid, & *that* writer Metamorphoses & talke too much of Proserpina & Iupeter: Why heeres o*ur* fellowe Shakspeare putts them all downe, I & Ben Johnson too:

1. Folger V.a.355, fol. 7, from Act 1, scene 2. The printed text reads "hart robbing" in contrast to "hart throbbing" in the manuscript.

2. The performances took place during the Christmas Revels of 1598, 1599, and 1601. J. B. Leishman, in his edition of all three plays, suggests that the second part of *Return from Parnassus* was performed again in 1602 (*The Three Parnassus Plays* (London, 1949), 24). The first two plays of the trilogy, *Pilgrimage to Parnassus* and the first part of *Return from Parnassus*, were not published in the seventeenth century. Manuscript copies of the first two plays are at the Bodleian Library (Rawlinson d.398). The title on the Folger manuscript, "The pro*gr*esse to Parnassus as it was acted in St Iohns Colledge in Cambridge An*no* 1601," is possibly a corruption of "Progress from Parnassus," since the prologue states, "Now wee pr*esen*t vnto each pittieing eye / The schollers pro*gr*esse in their miserye."

3. Jonson administered a word-emetic to Marston and Dekker in his play *The Poetaster*, and Dekker responded with his "purge," a play entitled *Satiro-mastix*.

4. Act 4, scene 3, V.a.355, fol. 21v.

5. Act 4, scene 4, V.a.355, fol. 22.

6. Act 5, scene 1, V.a.355, fol. 23.

7. Act 4, scene 4, V.a.355, fol. 21v.

O *tha*t Ben Johnson is a pestilent fellowe, hee brought vpp horace giving *the* poetts a pill; but o*u*r fellowe Shakespeare hath given him a purge *tha*t made him beray his credditt[4]

Shortly after this, "Burbage" invites Philomusus to audition for the role of Shakespeare's Richard III.

Burbage: I like yo*u*r face & p*r*oportion of yo*u*r body for Richard *the* 3. I pray you Mr Philo*musus*: lett mee see you act a little of it.

Philomusus: Now is *the* winter of o*u*r discontent Made glorious sum*m*er by *the* sonne of Yorke &c

Burbage: Very well I assure you: Well Mr Philo*musus*: & Mr Studioso, wee see of w*ha*t abilitye you are, I pray walke wi*t*h vs to our fellowes & wee will agree p*r*esentlye.[5]

Philomusus' rote reply of the first two lines of the play suggests that university audiences were not only familiar with the text of Shakespeare's play, but also would know that Richard III was one of Richard Burbage's most acclaimed roles.

The play also lampoons professional actors for thinking that they could buy respectability and gentility. Studioso refers to the acquisition of land and coats of arms by Shakespeare and other members of the Chamberlain's Men when he comments: "W*i*th mouthing woords *tha*t better wits have fram'de / They purchase lands & now esquiers are nam'de."[6] Believing that he ranks highly in society, "Kemp" proudly declares: "And for honour, who of more reporte then dicke Burbidge & will Kempe? hee's not counted a Gentleman *tha*t knowes not dicke Burbidge & will kempe."[7]

It is not known whether Shakespeare, Burbage, and Kemp were aware of the *Parnassus* plays. The fact that the second part of *The Return from Parnassus* was published in two editions in 1606 suggests that the topical literary references certainly did not go unnoticed by a wider audience. The relationship between the Folger manuscript and the printed text is not known, although it is thought that the scribe of Folger V.a.355 had access to a manuscript version of the play with revisions that were not in the printer's copy used for the 1606 edition.

H. W.

Sir Edward Dering, bart. (1598–1644)

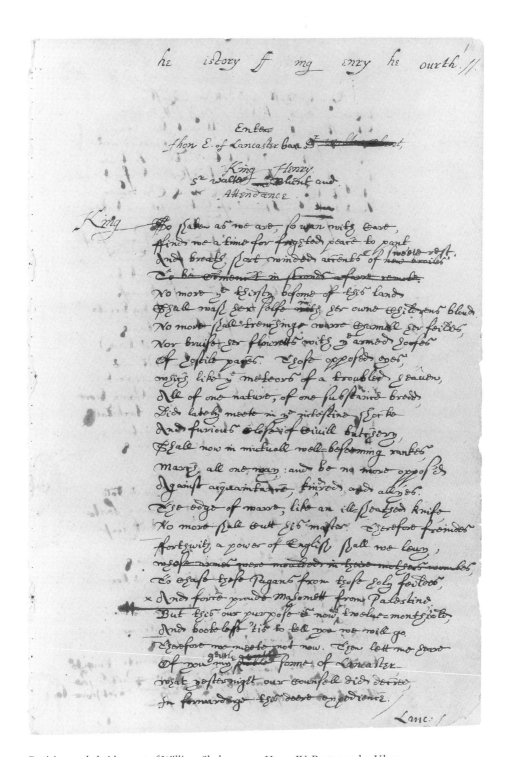

Revision and abridgment of William Shakespeare, *Henry IV*, Parts 1 and 2, V.b.34

87

Revision and abridg-
ment of William
Shakespeare, *Henry IV*,
parts 1 and 2
ca.1623

[1] 55 fols.; 295 x 200 mm.

J. O. Halliwell-Phillipps - Earl
of Warwick manuscript;
purchased as part of the
Warwick Castle collection
in 1897

V.b.34

1. For a facsimile of the
manuscript, see George
Walton Williams and Gwynne
Blakemore Evans, eds., *The history of King Henry the Fourth,
as revised by Sir Edward Dering,
bart.* (Charlottesville, VA, 1974).
Earlier contemporary extracts
from Shakespeare's plays exist,
but they are very rare. For
example, see Hilton Kelliher,
"Contemporary Manuscript
Extracts from Shakespeare's
Henry IV, Part 1," *English
Manuscript Studies 1100–1700*,
1 (1989): 144–81.

2. See Laetitia Yeandle's
transcription of V.b.297,
the manuscript catalogue of
Dering's books, in Robert J.
Fehrenbach and E. S.
Leedham-Green, *Private
Libraries in Renaissance
England* (Binghamton, NY,
1992), 1:137–269 (and the
supplement in 5:306–8). See
also T. N. S. Lennan, "Sir
Edward Dering's Collection
of Playbooks, 1619–1624,"
Shakespeare Quarterly, 16
(1965): 145–53. Dering's pocket
book is British Library Add.
MS 47787.

King:	So shaken as we are, so wan with Care,
	ffind we a time for frighted peace to pant,
	And breath short winded accents of ~~new broiles~~ ∧sweete rest.∧

THIS CONFLATED VERSION of *Henry IV*, parts 1 and 2, is the earliest known manuscript copy of any of Shakespeare's plays.[1] Most likely completed in the first two months of 1623, it belonged to Sir Edward Dering, first baronet, a Kent gentle-man with antiquarian, literary, and dramatic interests who later became a member of the Long Parliament. His account book, pocket book, and manuscript catalogue of books all testify to his interest in drama.[2]

The first page of the text and the scrap of paper now facing page 1 are in Dering's hand. The rest of the manuscript is in the hand of a scribe, one Mr. Carrington, to whom Dering paid four shillings for his efforts. Laetitia Yeandle discovered the name of the scribe in Dering's "Booke of expences," where Dering had written under the date February 27, 1623: "P*aid* mr Carington for writing oute *the* play of K*ing* Henry *the* fourth att 1ᵈ ob' p*er* sheete and given [him etc] 00 04 00."[3] Assisted by Peter Blayney in an examination of the watermarks and gatherings, she was able to identify six leaves from a different paper stock, which appear to contain revised text for the "transitional" scenes between the two parts of Shakespeare's *Henry IV*.

After Carrington finished his transcription, Dering then made numerous cor-rections and additions throughout the entire manuscript, primarily concerning staging. He also reworked scenes in order to condense them further, focusing the play on the defeat of the Northern Lords and King Henry's death. By eliminating eleven characters and reassigning various speeches, he was able to reduce the total number of lines from the original 6,148 lines of Shakespeare's two plays to a mere 3,401 lines. Eleven percent of the text of Part 1 and seventy-five percent of Part 2 do not appear in Dering's version.[4]

On a scrap of paper inlaid into the page facing the first page of the play are two crossed-out cast lists in Dering's hand for John Fletcher's play, *The Spanish Curate*.[5] The names on this list, including Dering himself, other family members, neighbors, and a servant from the buttery, suggest that both plays were intended for private performance at Dering's house in Surrenden, Kent. On the other side of this fragment are eight lines meant to be inserted into the king's speech on the first page of Dering's version of *Henry IV*.[6]

In their facsimile edition of the play, George Williams and Gwynne Evans have argued that *Henry IV*, part 1, was transcribed from the 1613 quarto edition and *Henry IV*, part 2, from the second issue of the 1600 quarto edition. Other scholars believe that the manuscript was based on a manuscript copy of a single five-act play by Shakespeare that predates the two distinct printed plays.

This manuscript was discovered in 1844 by the vicar of Ryarsh Parish as he was going through the charters and manuscripts of Sir Edward Dering, 8th baronet (1807–1896) at Surrenden Hall, in Kent. Shortly after, in early 1845, it was edited by James Orchard Halliwell, who then purchased the manuscript for himself before selling it to the fourth earl of Warwick. It received its nineteenth-century binding either by Halliwell or Warwick, at which time the first two flyleaves were removed. When the earl died, it was acquired by Henry Folger.

Through her work on the Dering family, Laetitia Yeandle was able to attribute another Folger manuscript to Sir Edward Dering, a scenario of a play set in Thrace and Macedon.[7] The Folger has numerous other manuscripts related to the Dering family as well, including a commonplace book, a notebook, a catalogue of books, a collection of notes for a family history, a book of pedigrees and arms, and an assortment of family records, all in Sir Edward Dering's hand.

H. W.

3. See Laetitia Yeandle, "The Dating of Sir Edward Dering's Copy of 'The History of King Henry the Fourth,'" *Shakespeare Quarterly*, 37 (1986): 224–26. That is, he was paid 1 1/2 pence per sheet for a total of 4 shillings. The words in brackets are conjectural. This manuscript is U350 E4 at the Centre for Kentish Studies, Maidstone.

4. Williams and Evans, eds., ix.

5. *The Spanish Curate* was not printed until 1647. It was licensed to be played in 1622.

6. According to Laetitia Yeandle's study of the stylistic changes in Dering's hand, the added lines were written closer to 1628, as Dering's hand was transitioning from a secretary hand to an italic hand.

7. Folger X.d.206.

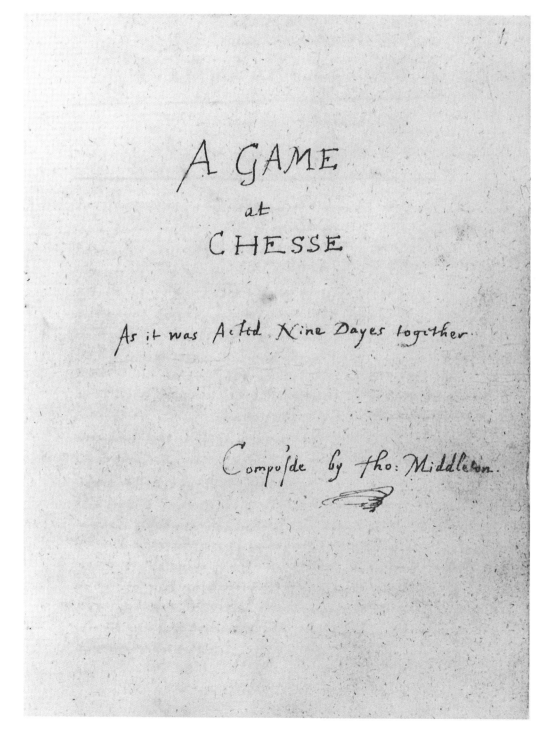

A Game at Chesse, The "Rosenbach" Manuscript, V.a.342

Thomas Middleton (1580–1627)

IN *A GAME AT CHESS*, the most scandalous play of the Jacobean age, Thomas Middleton satirized the Spanish monarchy and its representatives, including its previous ambassador to London, the Jesuit priest Count Gondomar. Middleton used a giant chessboard for his stage and presented King James I and his noble Protestant courtiers as white chess pieces being played against their corrupt and sexually licentious Spanish-Catholic counterparts in black. In an unprecedented nine-day run of consecutive performances (exempting Sunday) in early August 1624, the play attracted to each performance at the second Globe theater an audience of three thousand, many of them London's most influential citizens. The current Spanish ambassador angrily complained to James, and his Privy Council stopped the play's run and banned its circulation in print or in any other form.

An accomplished author of plays, masques, pageants and prose works, and a collaborator or colleague of all the major Elizabethan and Jacobean dramatists, including Shakespeare and Jonson, Middleton most certainly knew how politically provocative his play would become. As the official City Chronologer of London from 1620, he moved in the most important government circles. He may have received protection from the Master of the Revels, Sir Henry Herbert, the official government censor who approved the play for performance, or he may even have written the play at the urging of Prince Charles, a recent suitor of the Spanish Infanta. Although summoned to appear before the Privy Council, Middleton sent his son Edward instead. The actors of the King's Men company did appear with their licensed manuscript of the play (now lost), but they "confidently protested that, they added or varied from the same, nothing at all." The furor soon died down, and Herbert, the actors, and their dramatist apparently suffered no serious repercussions for Middleton's recklessness and disobedience.

Although *A Game at Chess* was banned after its notorious performances in August 1624, Middleton participated in the production of at least six manuscript copies of the play, each variant from the other. He was also probably involved in the printing of three quarto editions of the play between 1624 and 1625. Of the six extant manuscripts, two are now at the Folger, the "Rosenbach" and "Archdall" manuscripts. Middleton wrote the "Trinity College, Cambridge" manuscript by himself, co-wrote the "Bridgewater-Huntington Library" manuscript with two scribes, and oversaw the production of the other four wholly scribal copies, including the "Rosenbach" manuscript. Three of these, the "Archdall," "Malone," and "Lansdowne" manuscripts, are in the hand of Ralph Crane, a professional scribe and sometime employee of the King's Men acting company who had already produced printer's copy for at least the first four plays printed in the 1623 First Folio of Shakespeare's works.

A Game at Chesse

The "Rosenbach" Manuscript
ca.1624

Autograph title page, signed

77 pp.; 187 x 143 mm.

Purchased from A. S. W. Rosenbach in September 1941

V.a.342

The "Archdall" Manuscript
August 13, 1624

Scribal copy in the hand of Ralph Crane (fl. 1622–1625)

93 pp.; 165 x 127 mm.

Mervyn Archdall manuscript; purchased from A. S. W. Rosenbach in January 1941

V.a. 231

'tune they were burnd indeed. whole bundles on 'em
Letters from his daughter Blanch, and daughter Bridget
from their safe-Sanctuary in the white-Friers,
this from two tender Sisters of Compassion
in the bowells of Bloomesbury,
three from the Nunnerie neere at Temple-Bar in Drury Lane
a fire: a fire: good Jesuitesse, a fire ---- † what haue you here

Bl. B. A note Sir, of State-Pollicie
and our proceeding safe - one

Bl. Kt. I pray, let's see't, Sir,
To steale away all the Powder in a Kingdom,
to prevent blowing - up: that's safe. I'de able it.
Here's a facetious Observation now
this suites my Genius better: He writes here
some widows in England will commit Adultery
and then send to Rome for a Bull for their Husbands.

Bl. Bp. Came these this List.

Bl. Kt. oh there's no Aemall breathing
sweeter, and subtler: Here (During) take this Paper
softly 'em - one bundle: burne 'em to Asheing dust
and put 'em in aight.

Bl. B. why, what's your Mistrie?

Bl. Kt. oh Sir, 'twill worke the Adversarie strangely
if ere the house be search'd. 'twas don in Venice
vpon the Jesuiticall - Expulse there

what

The title page of V.a.342, written in Middleton's italic hand, promises a text of the play "as it was Acted Nine Dayes together," a boast that does not appear in the other two known manuscript title pages that he wrote. The text that follows, written in the hand of two unknown scribes (neither of which appears in the other surviving manuscripts), presents the longest and most complete version of the play, so perhaps this manuscript is a literary composite of the other texts or indeed the final version "as it was Acted" by the end of its run. In his title page, Middleton has embellished his role as author with his wording of "Compos'de by" (instead of his usual "by"), suggesting to the readers of this manuscript that they have been gifted with a creative composition, a theatrical marvel, and a work of art.

Folger V.a.231 (the "Archdall" manuscript) carries the date of August 13, 1624, and was thus probably completed before the play's final performance on August 14. What kind of text, whether authorial 'foul papers,' a fair copy of it, the company 'book' (or promptbook), or another manuscript that Crane copied from is unclear, as V.a. 231 lacks portions of the text that appear in other manuscripts, including V.a.342, and print versions. This manuscript may represent the earliest version of the play, which was revised or enhanced as performances continued. Or perhaps its brevity reflects a hasty attempt to produce a commissioned or presentation copy of the play for a purchaser or patron. Page 32 (Act 2, Scene 1) shows Crane's usual, meticulous devotion to neatness, clarity, presentation, and aesthetics in a mixed secretary-italic hand marked by his characteristic flourishes. He has ruled off the top, bottom, left, and right margins, punctuated clearly and consistently, and produced virtually error-free lines of script. Most importantly, he has taken a playscript intended for performance and transformed it into a manuscript book designed specifically for a reader. He has turned theater into literature.

Middleton probably worked closely with Crane throughout the manuscript's transcription, finally proofreading the scribe's copy, adding here in his mixed secretary-italic hand the line "what haue you ther" to the Black Knight's speech, a line found in other versions of the text. A later hand has altered "without Temple-Bar" to "in Drury Lane," and the manuscript contains similar non-authorial additions, probably made by later owners to regularize it against other texts of the play. However, this manuscript's unique variants, and its direct and indirect signs of collaboration between author and scribe, offer us truly exciting, firsthand evidence about the stages of a Jacobean play's transmission and its evolving shape in the playhouse and beyond.

Grace Ioppolo
The University of Reading

The Trevelyon Miscellany, V.b.232, fols.158r–158v

Musicke teacheth men to sing and to make difference of tynes, as well by voice as instrument, therefore he y doth not make musicke by art, according to art, is not a musition but a crowder

Geometry teacheth men to measure the length, breadth, higth, or depth, of grounds, towers, valyes, or such like, and it is very necessarye to them y will professe the skill of architecture or of building

Musicke

Geometry

Astronomia

Astronomy teacheth men the course of the starrs and the motion of the planets, the Eclipse of the Sune and Moone, the opposition of the houses, order of the zodiace, the Ecliptiche lynes, the tropices of Cancer, and capricorne, the Colners and the whole course of heauen: ʃʃʃʃʃʃʃʃʃʃʃʃʃʃʃʃʃʃʃʃʃʃʃʃ

Miscellany
1608

297 fols. (leaves are foliated
to fol. 327, with 31 leaves now
missing); 420 x 264 mm.

Bookplate of the Winnall
family - Bookplate of Richard
Henry Alexander Bennet, of
Beckenham, Kent, late 19th
century; sold at Sotheby's on
December 10, 1923, no. 170,
to Maggs; sold at Pierpont
Morgan sale at Parke Bernet,
March 21, 1944 to Lessing J.
Rosenwald

Gift of Lessing
J. Rosenwald, 1962

V.b.232

1. Owned by Sir Paul Getty,
KBE, this miscellany has
nearly twice as many pages
as the Folger one. See the
facsimile edition, Nicolas
Barker, ed. *The great book
of Thomas Trevilian*, 2 vols.
(London, The Roxburghe
Club, 2000).

Rhetorice teacheth men to debate. and of a small matter to make a longe
talk. and as the old proverb is to make a longe harvest of a littell corne,
or to set manye colours vpon a littell peice of woode:

THIS MAGNIFICENT, elaborately-illustrated miscellany was completed in 1608
by Thomas Trevelyon. Essentially a history of England and the world since the
beginning of time, Trevelyon's miscellany covers an astonishing range of subjects.
Contents include a picture calendar with occupations of each month; a gazetteer;
Old Testament history; proverbs and epigrams; portraits of the kings and queens of
England and Scotland from 1108; illustrations of various professions and occupations; well-known historical figures (including the Gunpowder Plot conspirators,
pagan, Jewish, and Christian heroes, and the nine worthies of the world); allegorical
figures (the nine muses, the seven deadly sins, the seven virtues, the seven liberal
sciences, four forms of cards, seven things that trouble a city, and seven kinds of
fools); Ptolemy's descriptions of the sizes of the planets; descriptions of the
Universities; parish churches and parishes of London; a list of the mayors and
sheriffs of London from 1190, and portraits and lives of the Lord Mayors from
1558; alphabets in different styles of handwriting; and patterns and designs for the
applied arts.

Little is known about Trevelyon aside from what can be gleaned from this manuscript and a similar one compiled eight years later, now in the Wormsley library in
England.[1] Trevelyon, whose family originated in Cornwall, states that he was sixty
years old in 1608, but does not mention a wife or children in either miscellany. The
text and imagery in both volumes evince a resolutely Protestant sensibility. Judging
from his source material and the quality of his drawings and lettering, it would
seem that Trevelyon was most likely involved in the London textile trade, possibly as
a draftsman for professional embroiderers. He had access to a wide range of popular images and texts of his time, which were sold both in book form and as single
sheets. His drawings are as crude as the English and Flemish woodcuts and prints
from which he copied and adapted them, and the texts are largely taken from printed sources—broadsides, scriveners' alphabets, and copy-book texts. Trevelyon
copied "The seaven liberall sciences," reproduced on the previous page, from a set of
engravings by Hans Sebald Behan. Other illustrations in Trevelyon's miscellany can
be traced to prints by Maerten de Vos (1532–1603), many in later versions or English
adaptations. While some of the illustrations have no obvious printed sources, it
is highly possible that Trevelyon copied them from woodcuts and prints that are no
longer extant. The sources for the embroidery patterns can be surmised by comparison to patterns found in contemporary portraits and surviving clothing from

the period.[2] Trevelyon provides a list of "The Names of the Authours In this Booke Alledged" on fol. 23v of the miscellany, which includes Bede, Tacitus, Geoffrey of Monmouth, Leyland, Lydgate, Bale, Rastall, Gower, Merlin, Matthew Paris, William Caxton, and the Domesday Book. This list illuminates how one compiler incorporated his wide reading into a personalized collection.

Why would Trevelyon have engaged in such a large and time-consuming project? In "the author's apostrophe to the reader," he writes:

> Here may you see, what as the world might be: the rich, the poore, Earle, cesar duke and kyng death spareth not . . . While then we liue let vs endeu-our still: that all works agree with gods good will. . . .[3]

Trevelyon's prologue to the 1616 miscellany offers further clues. In it, he describes the three subject areas covered by the manuscript: historical, prophetical, and evangelical. He then compares the manuscript to a statue, "whose matter allureth, forme teachethe," and urges readers to withhold judgment until the end: "A figure colored slightly over is not rightly discerned untill it be finished, so this booke is not discerned till the end be viewed, it is a miscelane and noe otherwise to be respected, not learned and therefore the easyer to be pardoned. All I hope that see it are my frynds and accept it frendlye . . . So willing your frendlye favour, I leave it to your viewing."[4] Trevelyon hoped that his extraordinary manuscript would be forgiven for its shortcomings, since its primary purpose was simply the enjoyment and edification of himself and his friends. In collecting images and text for his over-sized miscellanies, Trevelyon (in the words of Nicolas Baker), transmuted the ephemera of his age "into his own vision, a picture of the Elizabethan age not less vivid and immediate because it is the work of one man."[5] His two miscellanies are the only known source for an unknown number of ephemeral images, greatly augmenting our knowledge and understanding of Protestant popular verse and imagery.

H. W.

2. In his introduction to the facsimile edition of *The great book*, Barker discusses and illustrates Trevelyon's source material at length, which includes woodcuts and engravings by De Passe, Sadeler, Godet, Galle, Golzius, Wierix, and Anthonisz. J. L. Nevinson also lists sources in "The Embroidery Patterns of Thomas Trevelyon," *The Walpole Society*, 41 (1966–68): 1–9.

3. Folger V.b.232, fol. 135v.

4. *The great book*, p. 1 of facsimile.

5. *The great book*, introduction, p. 133.

A booke of diverse devices, V.a.311, fols. 47v–48r

Thomas Fella (d. ca.1639)

Now pleasannt may spreds forth swete smelling flowers
Fresh sprouting buds green fieldes & springing trees
And all delights enforst by Aprill showers
She forceth therwith to glade man as he sees

A booke of diverse devices and sorts of pictures with the alphabets of letters ca.1585–1622

81 fols.; 200 x 150 mm.

Jane Parron, 1714 - Philip Simpson - William May of Gower's Farm, Stisted, Essex, 1860 - Frederick May, 1873; Sotheby's, London, sale December 17, 1928, no. 587; purchased from Maggs Bros. in 1930

V.a.311

THOMAS FELLA COMMENCED this extensively-illustrated book of emblems, proverbs, poems, "ditties," and other items in 1585, took it up again in 1593 and 1594, and finally completed the book in July 1622. On the title page, Fella encouraged his readers both to enjoy his work and to benefit from its moral instruction: "first view, then read. last, iudge *with* regarde geve. the auctor. goode wordes. he claimes. no reward." That is, look at the pictures and then read the text before passing judgment. All the author asks for is kind words in return.

Fella personalized his collection in many ways: he integrated his initials into some of the drawings, he included a self-portrait, and he incorporated local scenery, such as the windmill in his home town of Halesworth, and a drawing of "sea worte" made during a trip to the coastal town of Dunwich in July 1622. A furtive-looking man in a hat and coat, possibly Fella himself, lurks on the borders of some of the illustrations, eyeing the reader. Occasionally, a topical reference appears. One page is devoted to Queen Elizabeth, and another, surprisingly, to the murder of the French Catholic king, Henri III: "A discripcion of the cursed frutes that comethe by falce Religion and of the cruell treason donne to Henrye de valoys late the frenche king which was murdered the first of august. 1589."

Each of the twelve months has a two-page opening with idyllic representations of the particular labors associated with that month. For some of the month "scenes," Fella inserted dialogue. In January, one man pulling fruit from a tree says to his assistant, "hould right," to which the assistant replies, "so I doe," while a third picker exhorts, "gather vp." In February, a woman exclaims, "gitt woode to the fyer quickly." In December, a woman who has completed her task of mixing and kneading dough says to the baker and another woman arranging the bread, "I can not gitt the dirte & past of my hands."

Some of the illustrations resemble woodcuts found in contemporary almanacs, while many of the mottos, verses, and allegorical pictures are related to items in George Whitney's *A Choice of Emblems* (Leiden, 1586). Fella's elaborate drawings include butterflies, elephants, chickens, monkeys, "two hopping toads," two men being hung, a skeleton, beans, pear trees, melon trees, the second-century physician and anatomist Galen, and various patterns, mazes, and borders.

Not much is known about Fella. The inclusion of a scrivener's alphabet of large capital letters and his use of a variety of hands and styles—gothic, secretary, and

1. The will is now located in the Suffolk Record Office, (IC/AA1/76/54 (original) and IC/AA2/65/71 (registered copy)). See J. L. Nevinson, "Lively Drawings of a Suffolk Scrivener," *Country Life Annual* (1964): 156–58.

2. Suffolk Record Office, Rev. 124/L2/1. The account book is for rentals at Bushy Close, which was purchased by the parish of Halesworth so that the revenue could benefit the poor of Halesworth. The purchase money came from Robert Launce when he died.

italic, among others—suggest that Fella might have been a professional scribe. The mention in his will of "my written bookes of precidents" suggests that he was trained to prepare legal documents.[1] In a 1611 account book in his hand, he has mysteriously drawn a "tree of divers frutes" with monkeys, birds, a butterfly, and the initials "T.F." lurking in the branches.[2] Thomas Fella identifies himself in this account book by his full name (he is identified only by his initials in the Folger manuscript), states that he is from Halesworth, and signs with a merchant's mark. In his will, written in 1637 and proved in 1639, Fella leaves all of his books, including his "englishe bookes and written bookes," to his grandson, Francis Wullnowgh.

H. W.

Esther Inglis (1571–1624)

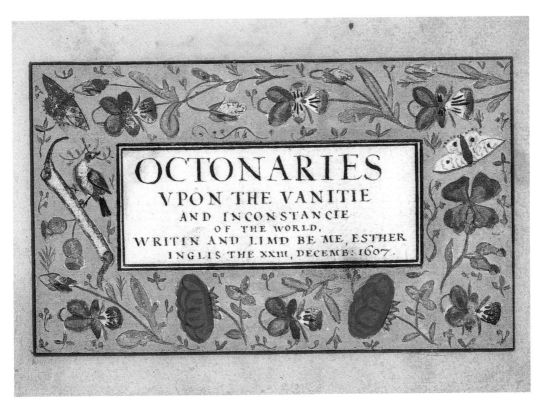

Octonaries, December 23, 1607, V.a.92

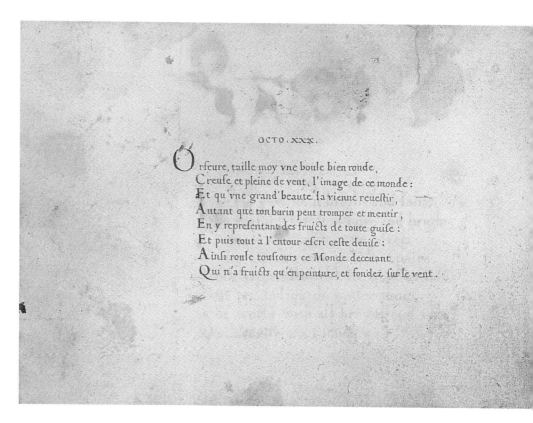

OCTO. XXX.

O rfeure, taille moy vne boule bien ronde,
  Creufe et pleine de vent, l'image de ce monde :
  Et qu'vne grand'beaute la vienne reueftir,
  Autant que ton burin peut tromper et mentir,
  En y reprefentant des fruiƈts de toute guife :
  Et puis tout à l'entour efcri cefte deuife :
  Ainfi roule toufiours ce Monde deceuant,
  Qui n'a fruiƈts qu'en peinture, et fondez fur le vent.

Octonaries, January 1, 1601, V.a.91, fols. 30v–31r

O CTO · XXX ·

Goldsmiths beat me out a hedge round hollow ball
Wires full of wind, wee map the world his image call
And left it as much rare and dainties beauties fame
As all thy cunning can with curious hand engrave.
Expressing there-vpon fruicts of all sortes and kynd.
And then with this deeply deck me the refiler Boule;
But doth the world still about her center rowle.
Sole fruicts but painted are, and founded on the wind.

Octonaries upon the vanitie and inconstancie of the world, by A. de la Roche Chandieu January 1, 1601

[1] 51 [1] fols.; 113 x 163 mm.

John L. Clawson manuscript

Gift of Lessing J. Rosenwald, 1946

V.a.91

Octonaries December 23, 1607

[4] 52 [4] fols.; 113 x 158 mm.

Gift of Lessing J. Rosenwald, 1959

V.a.92

1. For biographical information, see A. H. Scott-Elliot and Elspeth Yeo, "Calligraphic Manuscripts of Esther Inglis (1571–1624): A Catalogue," *The Papers of the Bibliographical Society of America*, 84 (1990): 11–14; and on her Protestant connections, Georgianna Ziegler, "'More than Feminine Boldness': the Gift Books of Esther Inglis," in Mary E. Burke, et al., ed., *Women, Writing, and the Reproduction of Culture in Tudor and Stuart Britain* (Syracuse, NY, 2000), 19–27.

2. See Anneke Tjan-Bakker, "Dame Flora's Blossoms: Esther Inglis's Flower-Illustrated Manuscripts," in Peter Beal and Margaret J. M. Ezell, eds., *Writings by Early Modern Women: English Manuscript Studies*, 9 (London, 2000): 49–72.

ESTHER INGLIS, or Langlois, was the daughter of French Huguenots who fled to London around 1569, then relocated a few years later in Scotland. Her father, Nicholas Langlois, eventually became Master of the French School, with a stipend from James VI. Inglis herself was born about 1571 and was evidently trained in the fine art of calligraphy by her mother, Marie Presot. As her talent flourished, she used it to further the Protestant cause, which was so close to the heart of her family.[1] Around 1586 Inglis started making the small decorative books for which she is known. Miraculously, over fifty-five of her manuscripts survive, and four of these are in the Folger Library, given by Lessing J. Rosenwald from 1946 to 1959.

The two manuscripts on display here represent one type of Inglis manuscript: those that contain the text of the *Octonaires*, religious moralistic verse by the French Protestant theologian, Antoine de la Roche Chandieu (1534–1591). With the exception of her dedications to various persons, the texts used by Inglis are not original but draw on popular Protestant religious works: the Psalms in various versions, portions of Proverbs and Ecclesiastes, the *Quatrains* of Guy du Faur de Pybrac, and the *Octonaires*. Her dedications—often to Protestant sympathizers at James I's court or to French and Dutch Protestant leaders—indicate that Inglis made her little books to be carried around for private devotion: "while the variety of handwriting delights the sight the spirit may similarly be raised towards the great Creator, by the diversity of prayers," she wrote to Prince Maurice of Nassau. In addition to their calligraphic styles, the books are often decorated with a variety of colored flowers, birds, moths, and even frogs, and a number of them have title pages with flowered borders on gold backgrounds in the Flemish style.[2] The flower on fol. 13 of Folger V.a.92 has been "pricked" with a pin, suggesting that Inglis used this design as a transfer pattern; she was certainly not immune to self-repetition.

Inglis usually dated her books on the title page, but evidence suggests that she made books ahead to which she could later add a dedication and/or date. Folger V.a.91 is dated January 1, 1600, but it was evidently never given away as it contains no dedication.[3] It also seems to represent an earlier format for the *Octonaries*, as Inglis copied the French version on the left page, facing an English translation on the right. In V.a.92, dated December 23, 1607, only the English version appears. All the French poems in V.a.91 are in the same clear Roman hand, while for the English translations Inglis used about forty different styles that showcase her skill as a calligrapher. The opening for Octonary 31 reproduced here is an example of mirror-writing (*lettera mancina*), decorated above with a rose and violets delicately outlined in gold. Watermarks in both volumes show that the paper she used came from the region of Montbéliard, not far from Berne and Strasbourg, in an area of

France controlled at the time by Protestant Germans. Such paper has also been found in The Netherlands, another distinctly Protestant region.[4]

Inglis presented V.a.92 to "the vertuous and my loving freinde and landlord" William Jeffrai in 1607, at the request of her husband. She was married to a clergyman of Presbyterian background, Bernard Kello, and appears to have helped in his somewhat mysterious political dealings with Robert Cecil for the Protestant cause. In this case, however, the gift book seems to have no subtext other than an expression of friendship.

On the verso of the title page of V.a.91, Inglis later pasted a pen-and-ink self-portrait dated 1624. It follows the style of three other self-portraits and is based on the portrait of French poet Georgette de Montenay.[5] Wearing a ruff and large black hat, Inglis sits at a table with a book, paper, and writing instruments spread before her. On the paper is the inscription, "De dieu le bien / de moy le rien" ("From the Lord goodness, from myself nothing"), a sentiment that Inglis frequently repeated. She saw herself as God's handmaid and her work as part of His service.

Georgianna Ziegler
Folger Shakespeare Library

3. See Scott-Elliott and Yeo, 42.

4. See E. Heawood, "Papers Used in England 1470–1750," *Library*, series 4, 10 (1929–30): 269.

5. Twenty-two self-portraits of Inglis survive. Scott-Elliott and Yeo have divided them into four types, of which V.a.91 represents type four (Scott-Elliott and Yeo, 18). For more on the portraits, see Ziegler, 35–36.

256

257

A Newyeares guift sent to the kings Ma:tie of
Scotland . Anno . 1602 .

A darke lanterne composed of four mettalls, gold, silver, brasse
and Iron .
1. The top of it was a Crowne of pure gold which also did
cover a Perfume Pan of silver.
2. In the inside was a plate of silver, like a Shield to giue
a reflexion to the light, grav'd on both sides .
Next to the light was graved and ymbost, the sunne,
the Moone and seaven Starrs .
On the other side, the storie of the birth and passion of Christ,
like y which is in Nottingham Castle, graved as is reported
by a king of Scotts, that was Prisoner in a Vault there cald
to this day, the king of Scotts Prison . The word was that of
the good thiefe . D.M.M.C.V.I.R. of the other side
Post Crucem lucem .

3. The waxe candle to be removed at pleasure with a loose
socket of silver to be sett in the top, and make a Candle-
sticke or a lanterne which you please : the bottom or
foote brass .
4. The snuffers of steele and all the outside of the Lanterne
of Iron and steele Plate .
5. The Perfume had a silver globe in yt fild with Muske
and Amber, of all which and their Applications
theise insewing Yearses, were written .

Epigrams, V.a.249, pp. 256–57

Sir John Harington (1561–1612)

SIR JOHN HARINGTON, educated at Eton and Cambridge, was the most prolific writer of verse and prose at the court of Queen Elizabeth I. In addition to his four books of epigrams, of which Folger V.a.249 is the latest complete manuscript copy, Sir John also translated into English verse a late medieval medical treatise, the *Schoole of Salern*, and all forty-five cantos of Ariosto's *Orlando Furioso*. He published the latter work in 1591 in an elaborately illustrated folio that also included his "Apologie of Poetrie," among the earliest formal defenses of creative writing in the language. Harington should also be remembered for his *Metamorphosis of Ajax* (1596), a Rabelasian prose satire intermingled with poetry, having as its overt purpose instructions for building a practical, working flush toilet.

Harington finished work on his collection of some 416 epigrams in 1602, then prepared a professionally transcribed copy for presentation to King James VI of Scotland as a New Year's gift. Along with the epigrams, Sir John presented the king with a lantern decorated (as he explains on p. 257 of the Folger manuscript), with "the storie of the birth and passion of Christ" as "graved" (inscribed) on the walls of Nottingham Castle by an earlier King of Scots. With the lantern Harington sent James verses in Latin and English professing his loyalty to "our Apollo rysing," in anticipation of James's ascent to the English throne. Sir John included these presentation verses along with the drawing of the lantern and explanation of its significance when he commissioned the Folger copy as a present for Prince Henry in 1605. V.a.249 is not a flawless edition of the epigrams, however. Although it was prepared by a competent scribe in a very legible italic hand, it includes more than a score of corrections and revisions, many in the hand of Harington himself. It seems likely that this text was intended as copy for the transcription of a final version of the epigrams fit to present to royalty. If so, that manuscript has not survived, and no record has come to light proving that Henry did in fact receive a copy of Sir John's poetry. The Epigrams did not reach print until 1615, with later editions in 1618, 1625, and 1632, although the individual poems continued to circulate widely in manuscript anthologies for decades afterward.

The epigrams in the Folger manuscript attracted a wide audience in part because they deal openly, often satirically, with identifiable persons and events of the reign of Elizabeth I. Yet many epigrams likewise conceal their satiric targets behind generic pseudonyms: Marcus, Paulus, Lesbia, Don Pedro, and the rest. Part of the fun for contemporary audiences must have involved trying to guess whom Harington had in mind as he exposed the vanity, hypocrisy, and ethical shortcomings of his fellow courtiers.

Sir John was by no means the first English poet to write epigrams. He was preceded by Sir Thomas More, Timothy Kendall, and the tremendously popular John

Epigrams
June 19, 1605

Autograph corrections

[4] 268 pp.; 200 x 155 mm.

Purchased from Dobell in 1935

V.a.249

Heywood, whose six books of epigrams saw nine editions between 1550 and 1598. The genre had classical roots, going back to the Greek Anthology and the Latin poet Martial, and it is not surprising that it became popular once again in Europe during the Renaissance. Yet for all the effort Harington lavished on these and his other verses, he affirmed in the "Apologie" that he was not a poet. Literary history has all but agreed with this verdict, giving Sir John very little credit for creativity or aptness of expression, yet he is probably at his best in the epigrams. They produce a wide range of effects, including sincere praise and congratulation, while the epigrams addressed to his wife have been termed some of the most genuine love poems of the Elizabethan age. At least one of the epigrams has retained its popularity to the present day, the well-known couplet from book three,

Treason doth never prosper. What's the reason?
If it do prosper, none dare call it treason.

Steven W. May
Georgetown College, Kentucky

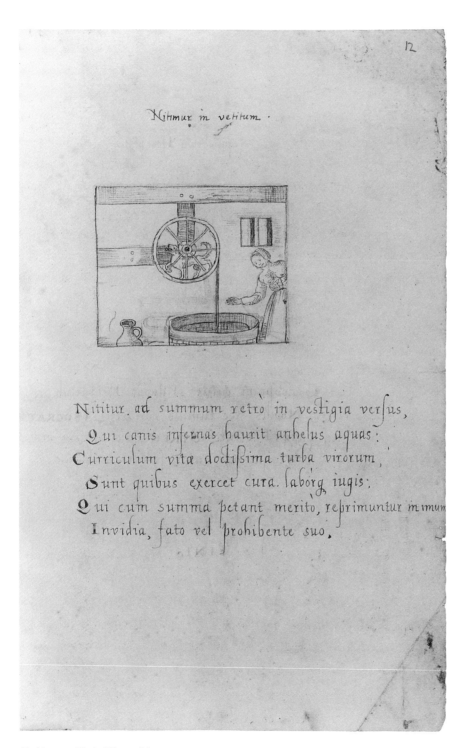

Nitimur in vetitum.

Nititur ad summum retrò in vestigia versus,
Qui canis infernas haurit anhelus aquas:
Curriculum vitæ doctissima turba virorum,
Sunt quibus exercet cura, laborq; iugis:
Qui cum summa petant merito, reprimuntur mimum
Invidia, fato vel prohibente suo.

Emblemata Varia, V.b.45, fol. 12r

*Emblemata varia
recens adinventa suis
iconibus unaque
carmine Latino donata*
ca.1621

Autograph manuscript, signed

12 fols.; 286 x 183 mm.

Thomas Brooke - W. T.
Smedley manuscript;
purchased with the Smedley
Collection in 1924

V.b.45

1. Although the manuscript is
undated, Peacham noted in the
dedication that it was written
seventeen years after he had
presented a manuscript collection of emblems to James I,
which places the current manuscript around 1621/22. For dating, see Alan R. Young's intro-
ductory note to the facsimile
edition of this manuscript,
Henry Peacham, *Emblemata
Varia*, English Emblem Books,
32 (London, 1976).

2. *The Compleat Gentleman*
(London, 1622), 162.

3. *The Truth of Our Times*
(London, 1638), 39.

4. Bodleian Rawlinson Poetry
146 and British Library MS
Royal 12A lxvi were dedicated
to Prince Henry; British
Library Harleian 6855 art. 13
was dedicated to James I.

HENRY PEACHAM DEDICATED THIS unpublished manuscript of twenty original pen and ink emblems to Sir Julius Caesar (1558–1636), Master of the Rolls, in 1621 or 1622. Each emblem consists of a motto, an illustration, and a Latin poem.[1] Peacham's dedication to Caesar was most likely a renewed bid for patronage, or financial support—an attempt by Peacham, then a schoolmaster, to display the transferable skills and learning necessary for a government post or royal service. In 1612, Peacham had dedicated to Caesar one of the emblems in his printed emblem book, *Minerva Britanna*, and in the dedication of the manuscript shown here, he acknowledged Caesar's expression of admiration for the former work. That Peacham was successful in his bid is suggested by a statement in *The Compleat Gentleman*, a courtesy manual published by Peacham the following year, in which he confessed that he was in "many wayes obliged" to Caesar.[2] In a later work, how-ever, Peacham, a younger son, admitted that dedications were not a viable means of achieving financial support, let alone stability: "I never gained one halfe-penny by any Dedication that ever I made, save *splendida promissa*."[3]

Educated at Trinity College, Cambridge, Peacham had a great interest in music, drawing, and poetry. His first book, titled *The Art of Drawing* (1606) came out in numerous editions under variant titles. In *The Compleat Gentleman* (1622), he alluded to the fact that he studied music in Italy with Orazio Vecchi, and he was also known to be a friend of the renowned lutenist John Dowland. Between 1603 and 1610, he compiled at least three manuscript collections of emblems for James I and his son Henry, Prince of Wales.[4] Most of these emblems, which were based on James I's advice book to his son, *Basilikon Doron*, found their way into *Minerva Britanna* (London, 1612). He also published epigrams, elegies, essays, and pamphlets.

The emblem shown here, a well operated by a panting dog running in place on a wheel, is to be read against the motto "Nitimur in vetitum" from Ovid's *Amores* (III.iv.17), which translates to "We strive for the forbidden." The poem focuses on the ambitious and envious dog, who remains in the same place despite his contin-ual efforts to climb up the inside of the wheel. Even though his own intentions are thwarted, he usefully draws water from the well for his master.

H. W.

Hugh Alley (1556–1602)

I thought it most fittinge for this present tyme, to publish, this smale Booke, or plott, of fforwarninge of offences, against penall lawes: to the end, it might stirre vp, the mindes of some kinde, of people, to carrie better consciences, and not to Rack, and Sacke, all vnto their owne, greedie, couetous, purses, and paunches: to the enrichinge of themselues, and impouerishinge, of their poore Neighbours. But vpon lawfull Warninge, to take good head, in Breach of the same Lawes:[1]

THIS "SMALE BOOKE" of drawings was presented to the Lord Mayor and Aldermen of London by Hugh Alley, "Citizen and Plaisterer," and professional informer in the Court of Exchequer. In his dedicatory epistle to Sir Richard Saltonstall, the mayor, Alley explained that as a "dutifull citizen" he felt obligated to notify him of the abuse of existing market regulations and to urge him to make reforms. In a separate epistle, Alley addressed "the courteous Reader," piously justifying his reasons for writing the book and apologizing for its faults.

Although the mayor and aldermen were no doubt aware of the transgressions in the markets, Alley's pictorial representation of the situation certainly accentuated the fact that the markets needed closer supervision. In a possible bid for employment, Alley asked the mayor to accept "this smale worke of myne . . . and admitt both it, & the author thereof, into your patronage, and protection." Alley's efforts were not ignored. His schemes were discussed by the Court of Aldermen in February and July of 1599, and in September of that year they appointed him to be one of four overseers whose mandate was to prevent the resale of victuals by enterprising hucksters.[2] In this role, he was to attend market throughout the day, ring the bell at the end of trading, and keep a log of trading offenses.

Thirteen London food markets are depicted in pen and wash in this manuscript. On the facing page of each scene are watercolor depictions of the alderman and deputy for the ward in which that market was located. Following are drawings of four of the City's gates with vendors passing through with goods.[3] In the market illustrations, Alley curiously included pillars with words on them, which most likely were part of his proposal for reform. For the common markets (where non-citizens sold victuals produced outside of the city), the pillars were inscribed with the names of counties, and for the citizen markets, a single pillar was inscribed with one of the three major market offences, either "Regrators," "Engrocers," or "Forstallers," with a blank board hanging from the pillar. The purpose of these blank boards is not fully understood, and there is no evidence that such pillars were ever constructed.

H. W.

A Caveatt for the citty of London
1598

[1] 24 fols.; 170 x 230 mm.

Major H. E. Wilbraham (his sale, Sotheby's, London, March 19, 1928, no. 60) - to Maggs Bros.; purchased from Maggs Bros. in June 1928

V.a.318

1. Folger V.a. 318, fol. 5.

2. The act was formalized in February 1600. See the facsimile edition by Ian Archer, Caroline Barron, Vanessa Harding, eds., *Hugh Alley's Caveat: The Markets of London in 1598* (London Topographical Society, 1988), 15, 32.

3. It is not known if Alley was the artist. In his address to the reader, he apologizes for the simplicity of the sketches, suggests that a painter was employed to add color to the drawings, and confesses that the aldermen and deputies were "not soe neare to the lief of a man, yet to the countenance, and habite of a man."

A Caveatt for the Citty of London, V.a.318, fols. 10v–11r

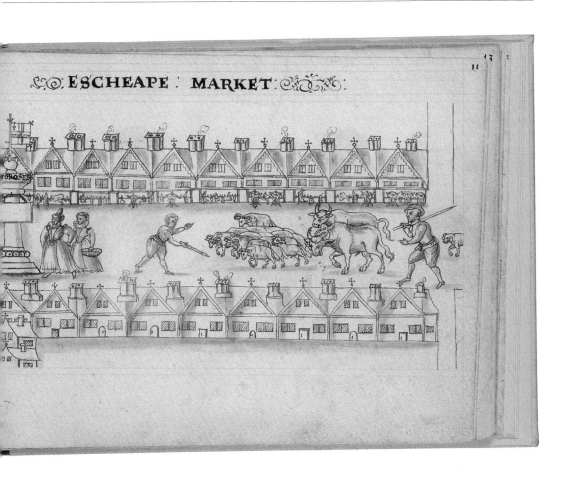

ESCHEAPE : MARKET

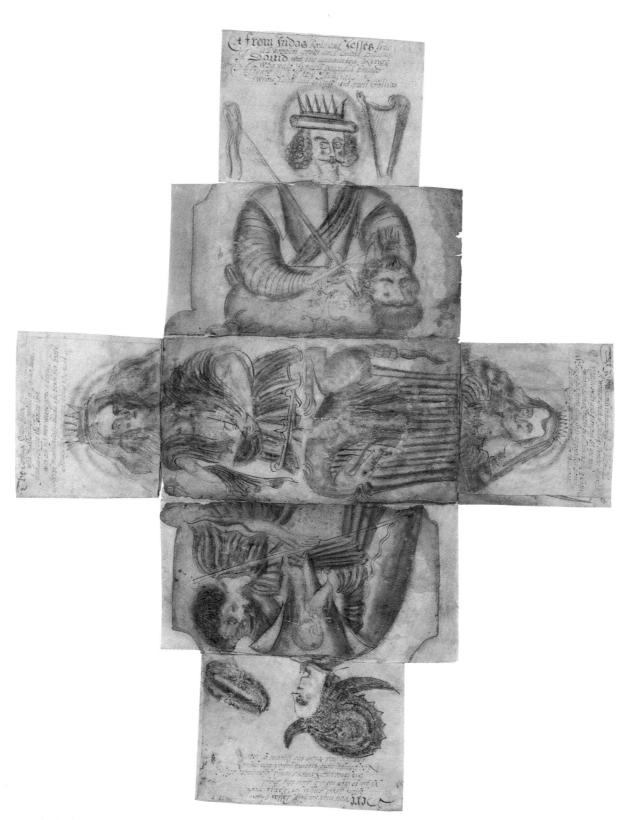

Elizabethan conceit, V.b.319

Elizabethan conceit

A RARE SURVIVAL from Elizabeth's reign dated only sixteen days before her death, this manuscript curiosity unfolds as a verbal and pictorial tribute to the queen. Its physical form resembles a modern novelty book, where a variety of figures can be created by combining partial bodies from each of several flaps. Unlike modern examples, though, the flaps here provide only the figures' heads. Lifting the first fold reveals the beginning of a poem:

> As Paris had a goulden Ball
>> for to present the Queene withall
> So I present vnto youre veiw
>> this small conceite invented new
> Yf you be pleased then I am blest
>> lifte vp this leafe and veiw the rest

The poem continues under the next fold, where Paris kneels before Juno, the "golden ball" in his hand. Lifting successive flaps changes Juno into Pallas Athena, and then into Venus, all the while continuing the poem. Next, a quarter-turn brings up a series of tragic lovers throwing themselves upon the sword: Dido "the Carthage Queen," Pyramus, and Thisbe. Then come three figures who "pleasure toake to Conquerr those that vnto God weere Mortal foes": David, Judith, and Joshua. The poem and imagery culminate in the fourth set, made up of "three Creatures sweet and all Diuine" triumphing over sin: the Woman Clothed with the Sun from Revelations, St. Michael the Archangel, and finally, Elizabeth herself.[1] The conceit was presumably given as a gift on Shrove Tuesday, the traditional day of feasting and rowdiness before Lent.

The ingenious folding design allows visual imagery to transcend a picture's customary limitations of time and space. Like poetry, the total portrait of Elizabeth is built up gradually, in a rhythmic pattern of four groups of three. Like a dance, it has to be physically enacted in three dimensions in order to have meaning. Nevertheless, the final product does not lose the intimacy of a miniature portrait on vellum. Reading the poetry aloud to others or describing the whole in words cannot possibly do it justice. It must be held in the hands, and experienced by one person at a time.

Erin Blake
Folger Shakespeare Library

Elizabethan conceit
March 8, 1603
(Shrove Tuesday)

1 piece of parchment, folded
into 15 rectangles; 504 x 420 mm.

Purchased from Hofmann
and Freeman in 1978

V.b.319

1. For the appropriation of religious symbolism to Elizabeth, see John N. King, "The Godly Woman in Elizabethan Iconography," *Renaissance Quarterly*, 38 (1985): 41–84.

Ein wahres Probiertes und Pracktisches geschriebenes Feuerbuch, V.b.311, fol. 129r

German military book

EARLY MODERN EUROPE witnessed revolutionary changes in the art and conduct of war. Most dramatic were those brought about by the introduction of gunpowder. Although gunpowder was known as early as the thirteenth century, a deeper understanding of its power, coupled with technological developments of the Renaissance, had a profound influence both on military campaign strategy and on operational tactics.

With the introduction of gunpowder and the cannon, the medieval castle could no longer be considered invulnerable, and the whole craft of war had to be re-examined. Increasingly, war became a series of long sieges interspersed with raids and skirmishes. Trench warfare replaced combat on the broad battlefields of the past while artillery, considered too cumbersome to be used against troops, was employed to attack fortifications. As the heavily armed horsemen of the Middle Ages virtually disappeared, the infantry became the most important part of the army. Those who looked after the maintenance of equipment and supplies supplemented the numbers of fighting men. War had become a specialized art in which the military engineer assumed a new and important role.

In the fifteenth century there was a flood of technical military treatises and instructional manuals concerned with the tools of "modern" siege warfare and with new and improved methods of fortification. At first they circulated almost exclusively in manuscript since the highly illustrated nature of the texts made their transition from manuscript to print (which was still in its infancy) somewhat problematic. Few of the authors of these texts are known, but those that have been identified were, for the most part, military or technical specialists. A popular progenitor of many of the later military treatises was the *Feuerwerkbuch*, a two-part instructional manual that dates from about 1420. The *Feuerwerkbuch* is sometimes attributed to Abraham von Memmingen, master gunner to Duke Friedrich IV of Austria, although the actual author is unknown.[1] Following a dialogue between a master gunner (Büchsenmeister) and a student on tactics and maneuvers is a descriptive text on making and using gunpowder, guns, and incendiary devices. The format and content of the *Feuerwerkbuch* were adapted, modified, and incorporated into military tracts over the next several centuries.

Ein wahres Probiertes und Pracktisches geschriebenes Feuerbuch (1607) is in the tradition of the *Feuerwerkbuch*. Acquired by the Folger Library in 1969, the manuscript, bound in vellum, contains 306 leaves in secretary hand and thirty magnificent color illustrations. It is dedicated to "all Christian Princes who wish to defend and protect their people," and the anonymous author assures his readers that all the weapons and methods described have been tested and proven.

Ein wahres Probiertes und Pracktisches geschriebenes Feuerbuch 1607

306 fols.; 308 x 198 mm.

Purchased from Beijers in 1969

V.b.311

1. J. R. Partington, *A History of Greek Fire and Gunpowder* (Cambridge, 1960), 152.

Like the *Feuerwerkbuch*, the Folger manuscript is divided into two parts. The first describes the various forms and contrivances used to alarm or attack the enemy, including cannons, rockets, and fire bombs, and illustrates the manner of their use. Also illustrated are fire-arrows and hand grenades, and even the use of animals to carry incendiary devices into otherwise impenetrable enemy camps and castles. The second part of the manuscript describes, by question and answer, all that a master gunner needs to know: the construction of protective trenches, the making of cannonballs, shot, and explosives, and the methods of projecting them. The author also considers the use of fireworks for purposes other than military ones. He advises the reader that fireworks are best viewed at night when it is dark, provided one is able to stay up that late. And, in an admonition that is often repeated today, the author cautions users of fireworks to stand well back from explosives and never to hold an incendiary device in one's hand while lighting its fuse.

Betsy Walsh
Folger Shakespeare Library

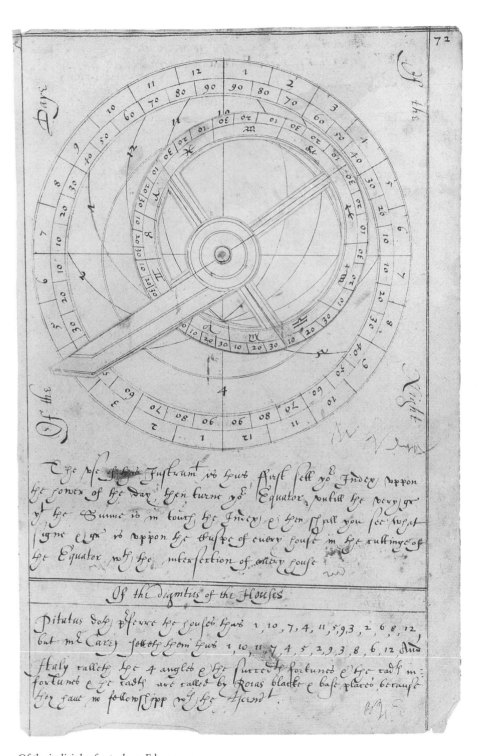

The vse of this Instrum is thus First sett yo Index vppon
the power of the day, then turne yo Equator vntill the verry gr
of the Sunne is in touch the Index & then shall you see what
signe & gr is vppon the cuspe of every house in the cuttinge of
the Equator wth the intersection of every house

Of the Dignities of the Houses

Pitatus doth deferre the houses thus 1, 10, 7, 4, 11, 5, 9, 3, 2, 6, 8, 12,
but mr Carey setteth them thus 1, 10, 11, 7, 4, 5, 2, 9, 3, 8, 6, 12. And
Italy calleth the 4 angles & the succeedt fortunes & the cad in=
fortunes & the cads are called by Roias blacke & base places, because
they haue no followshipp wth the Ascent.

Of the judicials of astrology, E.b.4, p. 72

*Of the Judicials
of Astrology*
ca.1620

177 pp.; 290 x 190 mm.

Purchased from Maggs Bros.
in 1954

E.b.4

1. Judicial astrology is to be distinguished from natural astrology, which was used for calculating natural phenomena such as time, tides, and eclipses, rather than the non-physical influences of the stars.

2. Keith Thomas describes these four branches in *Religion and the Decline of Magic* (London, 1971), 286–87.

3. The sources are listed on p. 84 and elsewhere.

4. This page is darker and dirtier than others and has scribbles that do not appear elsewhere. The gutter contains debris—hair and other particles.

5. See Thomas, 320–21, for consultation fees.

The vse of this Instrum*ent* is thus[:] ffirst sett y*our* Index vppon the hower of the day, then turne y*our* Equator vntill the very gr*ade tha*t the Sunne is in touch[es] the Index & then shall you see what signe & gr*ade* is vppon the Cuspe of euery house in the cuffinge of the Equator with the intersection of euery house.

JUDICIAL ASTROLOGY WAS WIDELY PRACTICED in sixteenth- and seventeenth-century England—maidservants and monarchs alike consulted with astrologers in an attempt to foresee and resolve a wide variety of situations.[1] The astrological manual shown here, written in an early-seventeenth-century secretary hand, includes instructions in the four branches of judicial astrology: general predictions (relating to weather, politics, war), nativities (maps of the sky at the moment of birth), elections (choosing the right moment for the right action), and hororary questions (the resolution of specific questions by considering the state of the heavens at the moment that the question was asked).[2] Much of the material in the five "books" of this manual has been translated or adapted from works by Abas Haly (Ahmad ibn Yusuf), Guido Bonatus, Claude Dariot, Cyprianus von Leowitz, Johann Schoner, Joannes Ganivetus, Thomas Bretnor, Robert Fludd, and others.[3]

The large circular diagram in the illustration is known as a volvelle. Volvelles, used to determine the rising and setting of the sun, the moon, and the tides, consisted of one or more movable circles surrounded by other larger circles. This one has a pointer, or index, which was to be set to the hour of the day. The second circle, or "equator," was then aligned so that the sun's location lined up with the pointer. The subsequent determination of which signs were upon which "houses" assisted the astrologer in making a prognostication. Although there are charts and diagrams throughout the manual, this page shows more signs of use than any other in the volume.[4]

On the two front endleaves of the manuscript, someone (in a different hand from the hand that wrote the main text) has listed the payments of over 120 clients, including men, women, children, apprentices, and servants. In keeping with other astrologers who catered to the middling classes, the owner of this manual charged his or her clients between two and six shillings per consultation.[5] Another page of the manuscript shows direct evidence of a consultation. Under a question concerning whether or not one's missing beasts have been impounded is a brief note concerning "Robert Hyron," who apparently asked the astrologer about the whereabouts of his beasts on "May 8 10 AM 1638." "Thomas Hartley his booke ejus liber" is written on the second leaf, as are details concerning the rental of rooms and land belonging to one George Wheeler, but it is not known if either of these men was the original owner.

The hororary questions reflect an anxiety over the overwhelming number of unpredictable events that could permanently alter one's life. Thus, there are separate chapters for determining "Whether one that is absent be dead or aliue," "whether a man shall obtayn riches," "Whether there be treasure in a suspected place or not," "Whether a man shall buy the Land he hopeth for," "Whether a woeman may haue children or nott," "Whether the child be borne in Adulterie," "Whether a damsell be a mayd or not," "Whether the disease be curable or not," "The time of deathe," "To knowe what thinge it is that is loste," "Whether it weare stollen by day or night," "The sex of the theife," "That the theife will escape," "Whether a mariadge wilbe effected or not," "Of the loue between them if they marry," "Whether one shall haue his wifes dowerie or not," "To knowe what a man dreamed of or saw in his dreame," "How many wifes a man shall haue," "Whether the husband or wife shall dye first," and "Whether letters sent, be true or false."

In addition to this manuscript, the Folger has other astrological manuscripts including the *Book of Magic*, ca.1580, a horoscope for James II's daughter, Isabella, ca.1676, and "The Nativity of a Gentleman," 1681, by John Gadbury.[6]

H. W.

6. Folger V.b.26, X.d.28, and MS Add 634.

The first Booke or Acte of the
Countess of PEMBROOKES
ARCADIA.

ARCADIA amonge all the Provinces of Grece was
ever had in singuler reputation, partly for the sweetnes of y[e] ayre
and other naturall benefitts: But, principally, for the moderate & well tempered
myndes of the people, who, fyndyng howe true a Contentation ys gotten by following the Workes of Nature, And howe the skyming title of glory so mutche affected by other Nations, dothe in deede help litle to the happines of lyfe) were the
onely people, w[hi]ch as by theire Justice and providence gave neyther cause nor
hope to theyre Neighbours to annoy them, so were they not stirred with false
prayse to trouble others quyett. Thinckyng yt a smalle rewarde for y[e] wasting
of theire owne lyves in ravenyng, that theire posterity shoulde longe after saye,
they had done so: Even the Muses seemed to approve theire good determination, by thosyng that Contrie as theire cheefist repayring place, and by
bestowing theire perfections so largely there, that the verr Shepeardes themselves had theire fancyes opened to so highe Conceipts (as the moste learned
of other nations have bene longe tyme sins content) bothe to borrow theire names
and imitate theire Conning. In this place some tyme there dwelte a mighty
Duke named Basilius, a prince of suffiaent skill, to governe so quyett a
Contrie, where the good myndes of the former Prints had sett downe good
Lawes, and the well bringing up of the people did serve as a moste sure Bonde
to keepe them: Hee marryed Gynecia, the Daughter of the Kinge of
Cyprus, a Lady worthy enoughe to have had her Name in continuall Re-
membrance, yf her latte tyme had not blotted her well obteyned youthe:
Allthoughe the womde fell more to her owne Consyence, then to the knowledg
of the worlde, extme some thinge supplying her wante of vertue. Of her
the Duke had twoo faire Daughters, the elder Pamela, the yongier
Philoclea, bothe so excellent in all those giftes w[hi]ch are allotted to reasonable
Creatures, as they seemed to bee borne for a suffiaent proof that Nature ys
Steppmother to that Sexe: How muche soever the ragged disposition of
some men sharp witted onely in evill speaking, have sought to disgrace
them. And thus greive they on, in the good intourse, till Pamela a
yeare older then Philoclea came to the poynte of Seaventeene yeares of
age: At w[hi]ch tyme, the Duke Basilius, not so muche stirred w[ith] the
care

The Countess of Pembroke's Arcadia, H.b.1

Sir Philip Sidney (1554–1586)

WHEN THE BOOKSELLER BERTRAM DOBELL bought the copy of Philip Sidney's long romance the Old *Arcadia* now in the Folger Shakespeare Library, one of the great literary mysteries of the English Renaissance was on the way to being solved. A much-admired writer, courtier, soldier, and politician, Sidney had been killed when he was only thirty-two at the battle of Zutphen in The Netherlands, leaving all his works in manuscript. In addition to his celebrated sonnet sequence *Astrophel and Stella* and his important piece of literary criticism, *A Defence of Poesie*, he had written a long prose romance, interspersed with poems, about the adventures of two princes in the Greek kingdom of Arcadia. He began the first version of the work, known as the Old *Arcadia*, in the autumn of 1579, when "in these my not old years and idlest times," he "slipped into the title of a poet," and completed it by the end of 1580 or the spring of 1581. A few years later in 1583–84 he entirely recast the work, transforming his pastoral, erotic romance, which has distinctly comic overtones, into a much gloomier and darker work aspiring to epic proportions: the five books of the Old *Arcadia* became the New *Arcadia*, a work almost twice as long, but which, even so, ended in mid-sentence in the middle of the third book.[1]

It was this incomplete masterpiece that was printed in 1590; but when a second edition was published in 1593, the incomplete New *Arcadia* had the ending from the Old *Arcadia* imposed on it. Early readers noticed that "this end wee see of it" was "not answerable to the precedents," yet it was the hybrid *Arcadia*, a work its author never envisaged, that in its many new editions became the standard version for the next three centuries. This *Arcadia* was the one known to generations of readers. From it Shakespeare took the Gloucester sub-plot in *King Lear*; King Charles I was accused of using Pamela's prayer from it when he was imprisoned; and Samuel Richardson took the name of the heroine of his novel *Pamela* (1740–41) from one of the princesses in the romance. Although Sidney's reputation began to decline in the eighteenth century, and his work was unfavorably criticized by Horace Walpole, William Hazlitt, and later T. S. Eliot, he was defended by Charles Lamb and Virginia Woolf.

The Old *Arcadia* simply disappeared from sight and remained unread in manuscript until Dobell bought three copies in quick succession in 1906–07. The first of these, the Folger manuscript, passed from Dobell to the New York dealers Dodd, Mead, & Company, from them to the collector W. A. White, and from him to the Folger, which acquired it in 1940. It was from this manuscript that the Old *Arcadia* was first printed in 1926, nearly 350 years after it was written. Some ten more or less complete manuscripts of the Old *Arcadia* survive, but the Folger copy is one of the most interesting because its scribe (they are usually anonymous and unidentified)

The Countess of Pembroke's Arcadia (The "Old" *Arcadia*) ca.1581–82

Scribal copy in the hand of Richard Robinson (ca.1545–ca.1603)

228 fols.; 290 x 205 mm.

Alexander Clifford, John Lloyd, Arthur Throckmorton, and other names on endleaves, ca. 1600 - Hodgson sale of December 13, 1906, to Dobell - Dodd, Mead, & Co. to W. A. White; purchased from A. S. W. Rosenbach in 1940

H.b.1

1. Philip Sidney, *The Countess of Pembroke's Arcadia* (The Old Arcadia), ed. Jean Robertson (Oxford, 1973).

2. George McGill Vogt, "Richard Robinson's Eupolemia (1603)," *Studies in Philology*, 21 (1924): 629–48.

3. H. R. Woudhuysen, *Sir Philip Sidney and the Circulation of Manuscripts, 1558–1640* (Oxford, 1996), 326–32.

can be identified by name. Richard Robinson (ca.1545–ca.1603) earned a precarious living in London as a hack writer and translator; he supplemented his modest income by compiling works, which he then sold individually in handwritten copies, and by working as a professional copyist. A large number of his manuscripts survive, allowing a picture to be built up of his distinctive italic and secretary hands, how he liked to lay works out and decorate them, even of the types of paper he used. Among the manuscripts is one in the British Library (Royal MS 18 A. LXVI), which supplies some valuable autobiographical material about his publications and earnings, including the fact that in 1579 Sidney gave him four angels for dedicating his English translation of Latin prayers by the German reformer Philipp Melancthon to him, and that he and his father were "many tymes benevolent unto my pore study."[2] It seems most likely that Sidney commissioned Robinson to make a copy of the Old *Arcadia* sometime during 1581 or 1582; in addition to the romance, Robinson copied all but the first two poems in Sidney's collection known as *Certain Sonnets*. The manuscript's immediate history after it was written is by no means certain: the different names on its endpapers suggest it may have belonged either to Sidney's sister, Mary Herbert, the countess of Pembroke (1561–1621), at her home in Wilton, Wiltshire, or to the naval commander and enthusiast for courtly entertainments, George Clifford, third earl of Cumberland (1558–1605), for whom Robinson is also known to have worked.[3]

Despite the bold confidence and handsome appearance of his script, Robinson's was not a happy life. On August 7, 1593, a few days after he had unsuccessfully tried to sell a manuscript to Robert Griffith, a local scrivener and dealer in such items, Griffith's apprentice Richard Veale started up a cry of "Hold him, Holde him!," alleging that Robinson was on his way to steal a cloak. The cry, "sounding in my eares every hower of the day," was taken up by apprentices, servants, and children and followed Robinson around the city everywhere he went for the next few years: he suffered, as he put it, "all howers of the day, all dayes in the weeke, all weekes in the moneth, all monethts in the yeare." He approached every figure of authority he could, right up to Elizabeth I, to try to get them to stop the slanderous abuse, but with no success. Robinson's evident paranoia might have received some relief from the subsequent career of his persecutor. Veale was sacked for stealing five pounds from his master, took to "gamyng, ryoting, myspending of money," became ill, fled his debts in London for Bath, returned for a while to the capital "lurcking here and there," and with a warrant for arrest against him may have fled to Brill in The Netherlands.

H. R. Woudhuysen
University College London

Lady Mary (Sidney) Wroth (ca.1586–ca.1640)

§ Pamphilia to Amphilanthus §

.I.

When nights black mantle could most darknes proue,
  and sleepe deaths Image did my senceses hiere
  from knowledg of my self then thoughts did moue
  swifter then those most swiftnes need require:

In sleepe, a Chariot drawne by wing'd desire
  I sawe: wher sate bright Venus Queene of loue,
  and att her feete her sonne, still adding fire
  to burning hearts w[ch] she did hold aboue,

Butt one hart flaming more then all the rest
  the goddess held, and putt itt to my brest
  deare sonne, now shute sayd she: thus must wee win,

Hee her obay'd, and martir'd my poore hart,
  I, waking hop'd as dreames itt would depart
  yett since: O mee: a louer haue I bin §

Deare =

Phillipps MS
9283

Pamphilia to Amphilanthus, V.a.104

*Pamphilia to
Amphilanthus*
ca.1615–1620

Autograph manuscript

[2] 65 [2] fols.; 192 x 143 mm.

Isaac Reed sale (London, 1807,
no. 8684) to Richard Heber;
his sale (London, 1836, XI,
no. 1110) to Thorpe (Cat. 1836,
no. 1026), who sold it to Sir
T. Phillipps (no. 9283); his
sale (London, 1899, no. 991)
to Sotheran for H. C. Folger

V.a.104

1. Folger V.a.104 has twice
been edited: *Pamphilia to
Amphilanthus*, ed. G. F. Waller
(Salzburg, 1977); *The Poems
of Lady Mary Wroth*, ed.
Josephine A. Roberts (Baton
Rouge, LA, 1983).

THIS VOLUME IS ONE OF THE MOST IMPORTANT of Lady Mary Wroth's literary manuscripts. A small quarto of sixty-six leaves, it contains 115 poems, including the earliest known version of *Pamphilia to Amphilanthus*, the first sonnet sequence written by an English woman, and nine poems that later were interspersed throughout Wroth's prose romance, *The Countess of Montgomery's Urania* (1621). Six poems appear nowhere else in Wroth's manuscripts or published works. All are written here in the author's own italic hand.[1]

In *Pamphilia to Amphilanthus*, Wroth reversed the traditional gender roles of the Petrarchan sonnet sequence, with its tortured male lover and unattainable, silent female beloved. The narrator, Pamphilia (or "all-loving"), speaks of a woman's experience of love. She is a woman, a poet, and a constant lover, who loves an inconstant man, Amphilanthus (or "lover of two"). Through the sonnets, the narrator explores the nature of love, with all of its tumult, conflicts, and struggles. The sonnet shown here is the first in the sequence. Pamphilia dreams of Venus and Cupid, who set her heart on fire, and upon waking she cannot escape the pain: "I, waking hop'd as dreames itt would depart / yett since: O mee: a lover have I bin."

Because this manuscript contains Wroth's own corrections and revisions, it allows us to watch an exciting writer at work on individual poems. We also can compare this version of *Pamphilia to Amphilanthus* with its later published version, noting which poems Wroth selected and how she reordered and revised them, a comparison that provides us a window on her larger creative process.

Pamphilia to Amphilanthus has received substantial praise. One of the finest tributes comes from poet and dramatist Ben Jonson, who wrote that Wroth's sonnets had made him "A better lover, and much better Poet."

Sara Jayne Steen
Montana State University

John Barclay (1582–1621)

JOHN BARCLAY DIED IN ROME only nineteen days before the publication of *Argenis* (Paris, 1621), his extremely popular neo-Latin prose romance. The Folger manuscript of *Argenis* in Barclay's hand is full of his extensive alterations and deletions in the margins, between the lines, and on tipped-in leaves. The manuscript is nearly identical to the first printed edition, suggesting either that this draft was used by the printer, or that the printer used a very reliable transcription of it. Barclay finished writing *Argenis* on fol. 310 of the manuscript, and the remaining leaves consist of drafts of his Latin poetry.

While Barclay's name is virtually unknown to us today, in the seventeenth century *Argenis*'s historical allegories and political observations were so intriguing that both James I and his son Charles I requested translations.[1] While Henrietta Maria's confessor advised that neither she nor her priests should read it,[2] the work appears among Lady Anne Clifford's books in "The Great Picture" (1646) by Jan van Belcamp at Appleby Castle.[3] In the first ten years after it was published, *Argenis* appeared in over twenty-four Latin editions. There were three continuations and two stage adaptations in the seventeenth century, and besides English, it was translated into French, Spanish, German, Italian, Dutch, Greek, Hungarian, Polish, Icelandic, and Swedish.[4] *Argenis* has been admired and praised by the likes of Coleridge, Leibniz, Goethe, Grotius, Pope, Cowper, Rousseau, and Richelieu.

Barclay, a Scottish-French Catholic who settled in Rome in 1617, dedicated *Argenis* to Louis XIII. He was careful to explain in his dedication that the story was meant to entertain and teach, and that no person or event was portrayed exactly. The romantic strain of the story concerns the attempts of three suitors to win the hand of Argenis, daughter of Meleander, king of Sicily. Within this romance are a number of political conflicts—one of Meleander's vassals, Lycogenes, rebels against him, and Radirobanes, who tries to kidnap Argenis, is killed by Poliarchus after returning to Africa to continue a raid against Mauretania. *Argenis* also contains chapters on such topical subjects as taxes, church corruption, and the effectiveness of different kinds of governments. Barclay's foil in the story, the court poet Nicopompus, explains that the romantic format was meant to draw in readers, at which point, "bringing them in love with the potion, I will after put in wholsome hearbes."[5] Soon after the first edition, a key was added linking anagrams and veiled names to historical figures and places (Hippophilus was the king of Spain, Meleander was Henry III, Sicily was France, Mergania was Germany, etc.). In his translation, Robert Le Grys was equivocal about the identity of many of the characters, however, reminding the reader that Barclay intended some to have no historical equivalent.[6]

H. W.

Argenis
ca.1620

Autograph manuscript

[3] 336 [1] fols.; 272 x 205 mm.

Purchased with the Smedley Collection in 1924

V.b.46

1. Ben Jonson's translation was entered in the Stationers' Register, October 2, 1623, but it was never published and apparently burned in the fire that destroyed his library. See Ben Jonson, *Works*, ed. E. H. Herford and Percy Simpson (Oxford, 1925), 1:75; 11:78. Kingsmill Long, trans., *Barclay his Argenis: or, The loues of Poliarchus and Argenis* (London, 1625); Sir Robert Le Grys, trans., *Iohn Barclay his Argenis* [verses trans. by Thomas May] (London, 1628).

2. In the Public Record Office, Kew, SP 16/7/85, from Danielle Clarke, *The Politics of Early Modern Women's Writing* (Harlow, England, and New York, 2001), 236.

3. The book is on the upper shelf in the right panel of the triptych. For a full list of books included in "The Great Picture," see George C. Williamson, *Lady Anne Clifford . . . Her Life, Letters, and Work* (Kendal, 1922), 341–45.

4. For a useful overview of *Argenis*, see J. Ijsewijn, "John Barclay and his *Argenis*," *Humanistica Lovaniensia*, 32 (1983): 28–44.

5. Kingsmill Long, trans., 109.

6. Robert Le Grys, trans., 485. Some of the keys added in manuscript to volumes lacking the printed key provide cross-references that are at odds with the printed key.

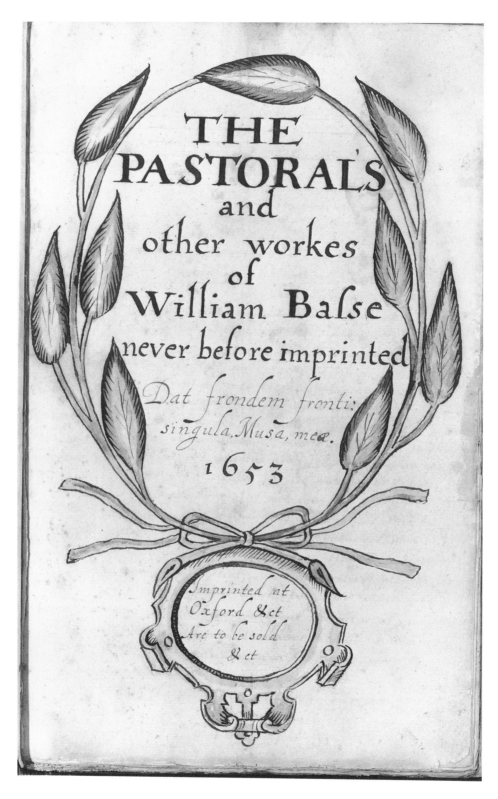

The Pastorals and other workes, V.b.235

William Basse (d. 1653?)

The Shepheard *Colliden*, who ere him know.
(Who know him, not that Shepheards liues doe fare.)
He that was wont, with siluer sheep-hooke goe.
and by his belt, the silken scrip to weare.
A iolly Shep-heard, to the outward showe.
Till sadly crazed, with loues youthfull care.
Low kept his flock, in humble vale where hye
Vpon a hill, kept *Laurinella* by.

IT IS NOT ENTIRELY CLEAR why William Basse's *Pastorals and other works* was never published, particularly since the title page is emblazoned with the year "1653" and states that it was "Imprinted at Oxford etc. Are to be sold etc." The dedicatory verses by Ralph Bathurst, "To Mr William Basse upon the now publishing of his Poems," also suggest imminent publication.[1] Basse dedicated the first work in the manuscript, "Clio, Nine Eclogues in honour of Nine Virtues," to his patron, Richard, Viscount Wenman, of Thame Park, Oxfordshire, with the caveat, "As it was in his dayes intended," since Wenman died in 1640. Appended to his dedication of the second work, "Urania: The Woman in the Moon" to Wenman's daughter, Lady Penelope Dynham, is an earlier dedication to Henry, Prince of Wales, who died in 1612. All of these details suggest not only that the poet's works had languished in manuscript for many years, but also that the time was finally ripe for their publication. However, the manuscript was not published for over two hundred years.[2] Basse's nineteenth-century editors assumed that Basse must have died in 1653, and that this was the reason publication was halted.

Basse is best remembered for his epitaph on William Shakespeare, which circulated widely in manuscript before being alluded to by Ben Jonson in his poem prefacing the First Folio edition of Shakespeare's plays in 1623.[3] It was subsequently published in the 1633 edition of Donne's poems (wrongly attributed to Donne), and later, in the 1640 edition of Shakespeare's poems, where it was attributed to "W. B."[4] Before that, Basse had published *Sword and Buckler* (London, 1602), *Three pastoral elegies* (London, 1602), and an elegy on Prince Henry, *Great Brittaines Sunnes-set, bewailed with a shower of teares* (Oxford, 1613), dedicated to Wenman. Aside from a few biographical details gleaned from his own works, in which he frequently mentioned his patrons, little is known of Basse's life. Three stanzas in the elegy to Muridella in *Three pastoral elegies* imply that Basse had a close friendship with Edmund Spenser, and he explicitly stated in the dedicatory verses of his "Nine Eclogues" that they were inspired by Spenser's *The Shepheard's Calendar*–"The famous Shepheard Collin, whom we looke / Never to match (though follow him we

The Pastorals and other workes of William Basse never before imprinted

ca.1612-53

Partially autograph manuscript, signed

99 fols.; 310 x 193 mm.

Cosens - Locker-Lampson - Bixby manuscript (*The State of Innocence*: the W. Lupton - T. J. Pettigrew manuscript); purchased from A. S. W. Rosenbach in 1942

V.b.235

1. Bathurst (1620–1704), an ordained minister and fellow at Trinity College, Oxford, went on to become a physician, Master of Trinity College, and Dean of Wells. Another copy of Bathurst's verses to Basse, published in Thomas Warton's *Life and Literary Remains of Ralph Bathurst, Dean of Wells* (1761), 288–89, is titled "To Mr. William Basse upon the intended publication of his poems, Jan. 13th 1651."

2. John Payne Collier, ed., *The pastorals, and other workes of William Basse: never before imprinted* (London, 1870); R. Warwick Bond, ed., *The poetical works of William Basse (1602-1653)* (London, 1893). Bond's edition contains a useful introduction and includes another unpublished work by Basse, *Polyhymnia*, which at one time existed in two manuscript copies, both now thought to have disappeared.

3. The Folger has at least eleven manuscript copies of the poem from the seventeenth century.

4. *Poems, by J. D.* (London, 1633); *Poems: written by Wil. Shake-speare. Gent.* (London, 1640).

5. An amusing poem about a raven who, finding that his favorite old walnut tree has died, invited all nut-bearing trees in the surrounding area to the funeral. Instead of a burial, however, it is decided that the wood from the walnut tree should be used to replace the wainscoting for Lady Dynham's pew at Borestall Church, which presumably had been destroyed during the civil wars.

may" (fol. 4). Basse's "Poemenarcha" in "Nine Eclogues" is the poet Mary Sidney, countess of Pembroke.

"Nine Eclogues" is thought to be in the hand of Basse himself, while the next two works, "Urania" and "The Metamorphosis of the Wallnut-tree of Borestall, In an Eglogue and 3 Cantos, betweene Jasper & Jefferye,"[5] are in a copper-plate hand. A crude pen and wash illustration of a pastoral scene (shepherds in the hills with their sheep) faces the first page of "Nine Eclogues." A copy of John Dryden's *The State of Innocence, and Fall of Man* (London, 1677), written in a secretary hand and titled "the fall of angells," is bound into the same nineteenth-century binding.

H. W.

Edmund Spenser (1552?–1599)

Copy of a letter in Spenser's hand, X.d.520

EDMUND SPENSER

Copy of a letter in
Spenser's hand from
Erhardus Stibarus to
Erasmus Neustetter and
two poems, "Joannes
de Sylva ad Lotichium"
and "Fr. Artifex Athensis"

Removed from Georgius
Sabinus, *Poëmata* (Leipzig, 1563)

2 pp. (1 fol.); 157 x 106 mm.

X.d.520

GEORGIUS SABINUS

Poëmata
(Leipzig, 1563)
"Immerito" inscribed
on title page

1 vol.; 157 x 99 mm.; previously
bound with Petrus Lotichius,
Poëmata (Leipzig, 1576)

J. Fazakerley of Eton, 1773 -
Coxe manuscript (sale by King,
July 1816); purchased from
Thomas Thorpe in 1927

V.a.341

1. Petrus Lotichius, *Poëmata*
(Leipzig, 1576) (PA8547 L7P7 1576
Cage). The two volumes were
separated in 1960. The manuscript leaf in Spenser's hand was
formerly sig. M8 of Sabinus's
Poëmata (the last leaf, which was
blank). Spenser copied the letter
and two poems from an earlier
work by Lotichius, *Elegiarum*
(Lyon, 1553).

"IMMERITÔ" ("the unworthy one"), the motto used by Edmund Spenser in his early poetry and in correspondence with his friend Gabriel Harvey, has been inscribed on the title page of the works of the German Neo-Latin writer Georgius Sabinus. It is perhaps in Spenser's hand but is more likely to be by a scribe or later owner. It has been confirmed, however, that on what was the last blank leaf of the volume, Spenser did transcribe three texts, a letter and two poems concerning another German Neo-Latin poet, Petrus Lotichius Secundus (1528–1560). They were in all likelihood copied to supplement information on Lotichius in a collection of his verse that was originally bound with this copy of Sabinus.[1]

One of the two poems is by Lotichius's friend Joannes de Silva (Jean du Bois) and, in terms that would have interested Spenser, praises the chasteness expressed in Lotichius's love poetry. The letter by Erhard Stibar, a pupil of Lotichius, sets forth an ideal of learned poetry that would also have appealed to Spenser and many poets of his age. The letter praises Lotichius's patron for his conspicuous care for literature and the liberal arts and in so doing portrays a humanist ideal of patronage that throughout his career Spenser struggled to adapt to the court of Queen Elizabeth.

Confirmation that Spenser owned copies of Sabinus's and Lotichius's works (made recently by Laetitia Yeandle and Lee Piepho) greatly broadens our understanding of the culture and literary options that lay open to Spenser. The Sabinus volume in particular is a record of the mainstream of humanist culture in continental Europe during the first half of the sixteenth century. In it are letters from the Dutch humanist Desiderius Erasmus and the German Protestant reformer Philipp Melanchthon, Luther's colleague and Sabinus's father-in-law. Italian humanism is likewise represented, most conspicuously by letters from Pietro Bembo and an important series of poems by Sabinus addressed to the famous Italian poet and literary theorist.

The introduction of the 1579 edition of Spenser's *Shepheardes Calender* would have us believe that in composing the poems Spenser attended solely to ancient models (Theocritus and especially Virgil) and their humanist successors in Italy and France. But the humanist movement popularized in Italy by Petrarch had also moved into northern Europe, and during the first half of the sixteenth century Georgius Sabinus and Petrus Lotichius were considered among the foremost humanist writers in Europe. The Lotichius volume was printed in 1576, and if Spenser acquired collections of the two poets around that time, it is probably because as a young poet still in his apprenticeship he was interested in what these two poets had written. Like Spenser, Sabinus and Lotichius composed pastoral poetry, and a comparison of their poems with the *Shepheardes Calender* confirms both Spenser's innovativeness (in adapting a wedding song to pastoral verse) and the conservatism of his collection (in retaining a strain of satire attacking ecclesiastical corruption that had disappeared from continental Latin pastoral). Further examination of the Sabinus and Lotichius collections will undoubtedly increase our understanding of the literary and cultural context within which Shakespeare's contemporary and Elizabethan England's most prominent non-dramatic poet developed.

Lee Piepho
Sweet Briar College

Gabriel Harvey's annotations, H.a.2, fols. 72v–73r

TTI, ET FATTI

ACEVOLI,

ET GRAVI;

IVERSI PRINCIPI,

ILOSOFI, ET

CORTIGIANI.

OLTI DAL GVICCIARDINI;

RIDOTTI A MORALITA'.

N VINEGIA,

esso Christoforo de' Zanetti

M D LXXI.

Annotations in
Lodovico Domenichi,
*Facetie, motti, et burle
di diversi signori et
persone private* (Venice,
1571), and Lodovico
Guicciardini, *Detti et
Fatti Piacevoli, et Gravi;
Di Diversi Principi,
Filosofi, Et Cortigiani*
(Venice, 1571)
ca.1580–1608?

211 fols.; 148 x 94 mm.

Purchased from Grafton & Co.
in 1928

H.a.2

It is not bookes, that makes the skillful man, but the knowledg of bookes: & the memorie of knowledg: & the practis of memorie, both in Words, & in deeds. He deserues to be esteemed the most cunning man, that can best negotiate his Lerning, viua voce, & vivo opere.[1]

THIS PROFUSELY ANNOTATED VOLUME formerly owned by the writer and scholar Gabriel Harvey is one of seven now held at the Folger.[2] Harvey's method of annotating—which consisted of cramming every available blank space with comments in Latin, English, and other languages, all written in a distinctive and elegant italic hand—was so well known among his Cambridge peers that he was lampooned in a Latin comedy, *Pedantius*, performed at Trinity College, Cambridge on February 6, 1581. In this play, the Pedantius/Harvey character decides that he could earn money by selling his books that were "enriched with marginal annotations like precious gems or stars."[3]

Of particular interest among the Folger's collection of Harvey-annotated books is the book shown here, which he began annotating in the year prior to *Pedantius*. It consists of two works bound together of Italian aphorisms, mottoes, anecdotes, and jests collected by Lodovico Domenichi, Thomaso Porcacchi, and Lodovico Guicciardini.[4] More so than most surviving examples of his annotated books (roughly two hundred survive), the annotations here reveal not only his professional reading skills, but also his personal reactions to his readings. Relying on the printed text as a trigger for his own ideas, Harvey used the margins to outline his strategies for self-improvement, to encourage himself in his studies, to make cross-references to other readings, and to comment on a variety of themes. At the end of the volume he appended a list of the books most necessary for civilized elocution, which included many of the authors already praised in the margins for their conciseness, elegance, wit, and jest.

Harvey was an ambitious and goal-oriented reader whose methodology can be summarized by two marginal annotations: "Enioy the souerain repetition of your most excellent notes. Quotidie lege, lege: sed quotidie repete, repete, repete" (Daily read, read; but also daily repeat, repeat, repeat) and "Make most of such Examples, as may serue for Mines of Inuention; Mirrours of Elocution, & fountains of pleasant deuises."[5] While many of his annotations bespeak his desire continually to improve the substance and style of his rhetoric (he had published two Latin works on rhetoric in 1577), other comments suggest that he trawled the book on more than one occasion for varying purposes, and that it was read both alone and in tandem with a wide range of other works.[6] Indeed, in one of his annotations he urged himself to read "Domenichi and Gandino; Gandino and Domenichi, often, more

1. Annotation by Gabriel Harvey in Folger H.a.2, fol. 97v.

2. Harvey became a fellow first at Pembroke Hall and then at Trinity Hall, Cambridge. He was Praelector of Rhetoric at Cambridge from 1573–75 and University Proctor in 1583. In 1585 he was made doctor of civil law at Oxford, and in the late 1580s he practiced at the Court of Arches.

3. Translated by Harold S. Wilson, "Gabriel Harvey's Method of Annotating His Books," *Harvard Library Bulletin,* 2 (1948): 346, from *Pedantius*, ed. G. C. Moore Smith (Louvain, 1905), 62.

4. Although the binding on this volume is not original, it seems likely that Harvey read these two books together, since the subject matter and his annotations are so interconnected. Only pp. 321–460 of Domenichi's *Facetie* are included in this volume.

often, and most often: together at one time, separately at another, sometimes in their entirety, sometimes in single parts."[7] Harvey made frequent cross-references to other works and classified his wide-ranging observations using a number of abbreviations and symbols to signify passages relating to such topics as kingship, natural history, astronomy, law, controversy, warfare, theology, and eloquence.

A few examples cannot do justice to the range and nature of the more than one thousand individual annotations in this volume. He commented on politics, referring to Lord Cromwell as "a ball of Fortune" and Lord Burghley as "a globe of Fortune," and on the monarchy: "No popularising, or optimating Lawes in a Monarchie" and "All impertinent, or vnproper Lawes must be repealed."[8] He included *Richard III* and *Hamlet* among a number of works exemplifying polished reasoning, oratorical skill, and "extemporall descants," and elsewhere referred to a play by Thomas Middleton: "Its a Madd world mie masters. The title of a new booke."[9] His annotation next to the printed aphorism, "Lo studio d'Amore impedire & tor via ogni altro studio" (The study of love impedes and turns away every other study) hints at his ironic resolve to remain focused on his work: "Bookewoormes: scriblers: pen & inkhorn men; paperbook men. men in their bookes, or papers: not in their heds, or harts." It can also be read in the context of another note to himself: "No love ought to be allowed in the decline of life. After fifty all coitus is pernicious."[10]

In addition to this volume, the Folger has Harvey's annotated copies of Lodovico Dolce, *Medea Tragedia* (Venice, 1566); George North, *The Description of Swedland, Gotland, and Finland* (London, 1561); Giovanni Francesco Straparola da Caravaggio, *Le notti . . . nelle quali si contengono le Favole, con i loro Enimmi da dieci donne, & da duo giovani raccontate* (Venice, 1560); Pindar, *Olympia, Pythia, Nemea, Isthmia* (Geneva, 1600); John Harvey, *A discoursive Probleme concerning Prophesies* (London, 1588), given to him by his brother; and Erasmus, *Parabolae, Sive Similia* (Basel, 1565), dated by Harvey January 1567, written around the time that he entered Christ's College, Cambridge.

H. W.

5. H.a.2, fols. 36r, 57r. Some of Harvey's annotations in H.a.2 are discussed in Virginia F. Stern, *Gabriel Harvey: His Life, Marginalia and Library* (Oxford, 1979), 178–90, and John Leon Lievsay, *Stefano Guazzo and the English Renaissance, 1575–1675* (Chapel Hill, NC, 1961), 92–96.

6. Lisa Jardine and Anthony Grafton have identified thirteen works, including this one, that Harvey read in 1580: "'Studied for Action': How Gabriel Harvey Read His Livy," *Past and Present*, 129 (1990): 50–51. They argue that some of Harvey's readings in 1580 related to his employment as the earl of Leicester's secretary, a position which he inherited from his friend, the poet Edmund Spenser. In this capacity, Harvey appears to have acted as a professional reader, reading, digesting, and synthesizing large quantities of books in order to "facilitate" the actions of his employer (48).

7. H.a.2, fol. 55v, "Domenicus, et Gandinus; Gandinus, et Dominicus, saepè, saepiùs, saepissimè: nunc coniunctim nunc diuism: modò toti modò singulares partes."

8. H.a.2, fols. 193v, 186r.

9. H.a.2, fols. 162r and 48r. For a discussion of the Shakespeare allusions, see F. D. Hoeniger, "New Harvey Marginalia on *Hamlet* and *Richard III*," *Shakespeare Quarterly*, 17 (1966): 151–55. The Middleton play is *A Mad World, My Masters* (London, 1608).

10. H.a.2, fols. 132r, 170r ("Nulla Venus permittenda declinanti aetati. Post quinquagesimum, omnis coitus perniciosus.")

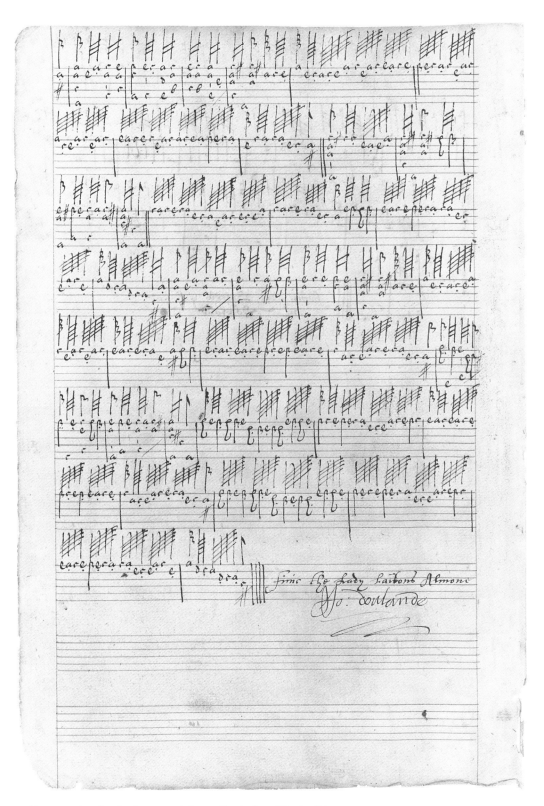

Commonplace book of songs and dances for the lute, V.b.280, fol. 11v

John Dowland (1563?–1626)

THE CARD CATALOGUE'S IDENTIFICATION of this worn manuscript volume as "A commonplace book of songs and dances for the lute [ca.1600]" obscures the fact that it is one of the most important and vexing pieces of lute tablature to survive from early modern England. Of the volume's roughly forty-four songs for solo, duet, and ensemble performance, six have been signed by the esteemed lutenist and composer, John Dowland. The tablature for the sixth of the signed pieces, "my Lady Hunsdons Allmande," is written out in his hand, as are parts of his "What if a day" and "Mrs. Clifton's Almain," and a few variant fragments of "What if a day" on two of the blank pages which follow the twenty-five folios of music. Three other songs are also attributed to Dowland and another is by him, but not identified as such.[1] Dowland, who practiced his art in England, France, Denmark, Italy, and Germany, received his bachelor of music from both Oxford and Cambidge and published five books of his compositions. The *First booke of songes or ayres of Foure Partes with Tableture for the Lute*, the *Second booke of songs or ayres*, and the *Third and last booke of songe or aires*, were published in 1597, 1600, and 1603, respectively; *Lachrymae* was dedicated to Anne of Denmark in 1605, and *A pilgrimes solace* was published in 1612, the year he was appointed a court musician to James I.

The manuscript also contains two pieces by the court lutenist and composer John Johnson (d. 1594), who signed one of them and whose distinctive signature is reproduced, in a cruder hand, after another piece. "Johnsons gallyard" is by John Johnson's son, Robert (ca.1583–1633), a musician to Prince Henry, James I, and Charles I, who composed music for plays by Shakespeare, Middleton, Jonson, and Beaumont and Fletcher.

Despite the fact that the signature "James Dowland Cuckney Notts" (b. 1751) appears on the back of the front endleaf, and that it was auctioned by the wife of James Dowland's grandson, Mrs. M. L. Dowland, the manuscript is not thought to have belonged originally to John Dowland, but to one of his students. The large quantity of playing directions and the number of hands (at least a dozen) that contributed to it, some supplying titles and others writing out the tablature, suggest that it was not the book of an accomplished musician, but a lesson book in which the teachers wrote out the pieces to be studied.[2] The manuscript's earliest known owner, who signed the volume "Anne Bayldon,"[3] seems to have supplied the titles, in an unskilled hand, for thirteen of the pieces. A note in drypoint in her hand, "and this leson made," visible only in raked, or angled, lighting, further supports the theory that this was indeed a lesson book.[4]

Anne Baildon was not the only person to leave her mark on the manuscript. A Thomas Bothby signed the last endleaf, and the endleaves also contain pious phrases in a different hand reminiscent of school writing exercises—"I lyft myne

Commonplace book of songs and dances for the lute by Dowland and others ca.1600

87 fols.; 290 x 200 mm.

Dowland family manuscript; purchased at M. L. Dowland sale, Sotheby's, London, November 15, 1926, no. 704

V.b.280

1. The six signed songs are "Lord Willoughby's Welcome Home" (untitled in manuscript), "the Lady Laitons Almane," "frog Galliard," "mr Smythes Allman," "Can she excuse," and "My Lady Hunsdons Allmande." "What if a day" and "Mrs. Clifton's Almain," untitled in the manuscript, are in his hand. "Winter gomps" (winter jumps) is by Dowland but not attributed to him in the manuscript. "Doulands rounde battell galyard" is by him, as are "the Battell gallyard" and "Lachrame," both attributed to "mr Dowland." For the contents of the manuscript, see John M. Ward, "The So-Called 'Dowland Lute Book' in the Folger Shakespeare Library," *Journal of the Lute Society of America*, 9 (1976): 5–29. Ward also suggests that eight measures of "Lady Laiton's Almain" are in Dowland's hand as well as performance directions for the pieces signed by him and possibly others (12).

2. John Ward makes a more technical argument for this manuscript as a lesson-book in "A Dowland Miscellany," *Journal of the Lute Society of America*, 10 (1977): 46–51, and Ward, 1976:7.

3. Diana Poulton, *John Dowland* (London, 1972), 103–4, discusses the possible identity of Anne Baildon.

4. The impression on fol. 21v could also have been made by writing "and this leson made" on a piece of paper placed on top of the page. Her first name, "Anne," appears in drypoint on fol. 25v as does a two-word indecipherable phrase. Other words in drypoint appear on fols. 21v, 22r, and 75v.

5. Fol. 76r. This manuscript will soon be published in facsimile by the Lute Society of England (edited by Christopher Goodwin).

hart to *the*," "the Lord of hostis"—and two couplets of Latin verse, one the beginning of Book 1 of Virgil's *Aeneid*, and the other a very loose paraphrase of Ephesians, chapter 5, verse 9: "Non vox sed votum no cordula . . . / non clamans sed amans clanget in aure dei." A phrase in cypher appears on the same page as "and this leson made," and a six-line verse in drypoint, for the most part indecipherable, appears on one of the blank pages.[5]

H. W.

John Donne (1572–1631)

Autograph letter, signed, to Sir George More, L.b.532

Autograph letter, signed,
to Sir George More
(1553–1632)
March 1, 1602

1 fol.; 295 x 202 mm.

Loseley Collection -
purchased via William H.
Robinson, Ltd. in 1940

L.b.532

WRITTEN IN DONNE'S CHARACTERISTICALLY NEAT, flowing, predominantly italic script, this letter was sent at the height of one of the great crises of his life. About three weeks before Christmas 1601, Donne secretly married Sir George More's daughter Ann. He only revealed the fact to More, with some trepidation, by means of a letter delivered by his intermediary Henry Percy, ninth Earl of Northumberland, on 2 February. As anticipated, and despite Donne's importunities that Ann should not feel "the terror of your sodaine anger," More reacted with fury. In a "passion of anger" (as Izaak Walton later wrote), he immediately had Donne arrested, as also his two accomplices at the clandestine wedding, Christopher and Samuel Brooke, and committed to prison on a charge of offending canon law. He also persuaded Donne's employer, Sir Thomas Egerton (later Lord Ellesmere), to dismiss him from his service. Donne's situation, aggravated by illness, distress, and separation from his wife, who had remained in her father's household, became for a time increasingly desperate, and the tone of his letters to More accordingly more penitent. Although Egerton relented sufficiently to have Donne released (albeit kept nominally under restraint), More initiated proceedings before the High Commission for the marriage to be annulled. His case was, however, dismissed; Donne's marriage was judged to be legally valid, and More had to begin to reconcile himself to the fact that Donne was his son-in-law, whether he liked it or not.

This was the situation on March 1, 1602, when Donne offered, in this letter, the most direct and most forthright importunities to More he had yet made, begging him "owt of an humble and repentant hart," for the sake of his daughter's well-being, to pardon the errant Donne and to intervene with Egerton for the recovery of his former employment.

> . . . I should wrong yow as much againe as I did, if I should think yow sought to destroy me, but though I be not hedlongly destroyd, I languish and rust dangerously . . . in these long and vncertain disgraces of myne. I therfore humbly beseech yow to haue so charitable a pitty, of what I haue, and do, and must suffer
>
> . . . In all the world ys not more true Sorrow then in my hart, nor more vnderstanding of true repentance than in yours . . .

The outcome of this appeal was More's surrendering of his daughter to Donne, but with sufficient reluctance and bad grace that he refused to contribute a penny to her support. Neither was it possible even for More to persuade Egerton to take Donne back as his secretary, for all Egerton's affection for the young poet, since, he claimed, it was firmly against official policy to readmit servants once they had been discharged.

This passionate and dramatic letter is one in a series of papers relating to Donne preserved in the Loseley Papers, which were acquired by the Folger in 1940 from the More family estate at Loseley Park, near Guildford, Surrey. Indeed, this series represents the single most substantial and most important body of original letters by Donne known to survive. They vividly illuminate aspects of Donne's personal life as relatively few other records do, as the present evocative witness to his state of mind in February 1602 amply demonstrates.

Peter Beal
Sotheby's, London

THE
CEREMONIAL LAW.

after ye vail.

The Introduction.

Two thousand years before my Savior came,
In Hieroglyphick Laws I see His Name.
My GOD prepar'd, before my self was born,
Great Joys wherwith I might my Life adorn.
He first ordain'd ye I a Life should liv
Of Swet Delights, wch His fair Hand did giv;
From whence since I by Sin revolted am,
He since ordain'd His son to be a Man.
Whom yt I might more certainly descrie,
With ancient figures He did Beautifie.
And made those Types by pleasant Posies be
Of His great Lov, & Kindness unto me.
Wherin I might wth Joy & Sacred pleasure,
His Goodness read, & see my Glorious Treasure.
Would it not Ravish one yt he should com
To such Delights even from a Beggars Womb!
That from a hous where nothing could be seen,
He should be rais'd to such a vast Esteem!
In Lands remote I see my self made High,
And wonder at ye State wch there I spie.
My Soveraign LORD, I in a long Design,
See ruling Kingdoms by His Might Divine
And Things Disposing, yt my Soul might be
So long before Enricht wth Majestie.
Being made by Ways yt Wisely do conspire,
Prevent, fulfill, Exceed my whole Desire;
A Prince-like Heir of glorious Works, yt pleas
My Soul, far more then Kingly Palaces.
I there behold a Tabernacle reard,
Wherin my GOD Himself for me appeard.
That He should com & in ye World be seen,
That He should Woo, & treat His Heavenly Queen

On

The Ceremonial Law, V.a.70

Thomas Traherne (1637–1674)

Two thousand yeers before my Savior came,
In Hieroglyphick Laws I see His Name.
My GOD prepard, before my self was born,
Great Joys wherwith I might my Life adorn.

FOR ALMOST FORTY YEARS, this 1800-line poem of heroic couplets based on the books of Genesis and Exodus was attributed to "Anonymous" in the Folger's card catalogue. Titled "The Ceremonial Law," the poem breaks off mid-line, leaving two-thirds of the volume blank. Laetitia Yeandle began investigating the manuscript in 1996 and was able to ascertain, through paleographical and internal evidence, that the hand belonged to Thomas Traherne. This discovery of an unknown original work by a seventeenth-century metaphysical poet was announced in *The Times Literary Supplement* the following year.[1] Each of the twenty-four sections of the poem expounds upon the devotional and typological significance of a story from Scripture, from the fall of Adam to Moses' descent from Mt. Sinai.

Traherne composed this poem in a tiny neat hand in a pocket-sized manuscript. Bound in contemporary calf with the remnants of metal clasps still visible, the manuscript contains many authorial revisions, some made after the lines were completed and others made during the process of composition. Traherne evidently needed encouragement to finish it—a note in a contemporary hand on the flyleaf states urgently: "I like this mightily, but I pray prosecute it, for which reason I haue sent this *tha*t you may know *the* bette[r] wher *y*ou Left & how to *p*roceed. I would you would goe thorow *the* whole Sacred Story. God direct & Inspire you." This same hand probably added a note that appears in the text: "heer wants a line," and in another location points out a missing word.[2]

The Traherne canon has expanded dramatically in the past 106 years. The only work to appear in print in Traherne's lifetime was *Roman Forgeries* (1673). A work in prose, *Christian Ethicks*, was sent to press just before he died and was published in 1675, while *A serious and patheticall Contemplation of the Mercies of God* was printed anonymously in 1699. Two autograph manuscripts of previously unknown poems were discovered by the bookseller Bertram Dobell in 1896–97, and a manuscript in the British Library, *Poems of Felicity*, was identified in 1910 as being the work of Traherne. *Commentaries of Heaven* was discovered in 1967. Laetitia Yeandle's discovery of *The Ceremonial Law* was followed closely by the late Jeremy Maule's discovery of yet another previously unknown Traherne poem at Lambeth Palace Library.[3]

H. W.

The Ceremonial Law
ca.1670

Autograph manuscript

[4] 170 pp. (pp. 53–163 and 165–168 blank); 142 x 83 mm.

Purchased from Hammelmann in 1958

V.a.70

1. Laetitia Yeandle and Julia Smith, "Felicity disguised in fiery Words: Genesis and Exodus in a newly discovered poem by Thomas Traherne," *The Times Literary Supplement* (November 7, 1997): 17.

2. A third hand makes a reference near the end of the volume to three works published by Nathaniel Crouch (alias Richard Burton) in 1681 and 1682. Perhaps a later owner planned to use the blank pages for extracts from other works.

3. Denise Inge and Calum Macfarlane, "Seeds of Eternity: A new Traherne manuscript," *The Times Literary Supplement* (June 2, 2000): 14.

Edward Howard (fl. 1669)

The Change of Crownes:
A Tragy-Comedy
1667

35 fols.; 300 x 190 mm.

R. A. Austen-Leigh manuscript;
purchased from Chaucer Head
Bookshop in 1989

Gift of The Arcana
Foundation

V.b.329

1. Folger V.b. 329, fol. 11r

2. Samuel Pepys, *The Diary*
of Samuel Pepys, ed. Robert
Latham and William Matthews
(Berkeley and Los Angeles, CA,
1974) 8:167–68.

Asinello:	*Sir*, I am Inform'd by some persons of Honour, that shall be namelesse, that you haue a power and favour with the Queene, and can doe a Curtesy to a Gentleman that has a mind to pay heartily for an office.
Malvecchio:	What Fellow's this?
Asinello:	He Calls me fellow already; I suppose you haue a neere Relation to her Majesty, Pray how does the Queene? shee's young and Handsome: I would very fayne see her.
Malvecchio:	Show him the Porters Lodge.
Asinello:	I humbly thanke you S*ir*, Is shee at *the* Porters Lodge? You are a Courteous Gentleman, tis the first Ciuillity, I had done me since I came to Court.[1]

THE CHANGE OF CROWNES was performed at the Theatre Royal by the King's Company for the first and only time on April 15, 1667. The actors played to a full house, including Charles II and his queen, Catherine of Braganza, the duke and duchess of York, and Samuel Pepys, who despite catching cold after being forced to stand close to the door for the performance, thought the play "the best that I ever saw at that House, being a great play and serious" and went to bed that night "mightily pleased with the new play."[2] However, Charles II took offense at the play, temporarily imprisoning one of the actors and suspending performances by the King's Company.

For 270 years the text of this play was thought to be lost, its existence known only through contemporary newsletters and Pepys's account of the ensuing controversy in his *Diary*. However, a prompt copy of the play was discovered in a private collection in 1938 and was purchased by the Folger in 1989. The last page of the manuscript contains the autograph license of Sir Henry Herbert, Master of the Revels, dated April 13, 1667, a mere two days before the ill-fated performance. The offensive passages are circled throughout, and two leaves have been removed from the manuscript, substituted with three, presumably more benign, ones. The play is written out in the hand of a professional scribe, with at least seven additional hands adding corrections, stage directions (many involving the sounding of a whistle), scene headings, and names of actors in the margins. A distinctive herring-bone mark appears at every stage-direction involving an entrance.

The Change of Crownes was written by Edward Howard, one of the three playwright sons of the first earl of Berkshire, and brother-in-law to John Dryden. The day after its first performance, Pepys took his wife to see it and was surprised to find that Ben Jonson's *The Silent Woman* was being performed in its place. The offending passages in *The Change of Crownes* were all part of a comic subplot involving a character named Asinello, played by the actor Thomas Lacy. Asinello, a newcomer to the Court who believed that he could gain preferment through bribery, is punished for his unethical attempts to rise at Court by being sent to the porter's lodge, where he narrowly escapes whipping by paying a fine. In one scene, he asks if he should petition the queen to be her favorite, to which a courtier replies, "there's a place voyd when her Majesty pleases, at a minuits warning" (fol. 22), and in another, he is brought onto the stage "tyed Neck and Heeles together" (fol. 29). Pepys learned from a friend that "the King was so angry at the liberty taken by Lacy's part to abuse him to his face, that he commanded they should act no more." Later in the day, after hearing his friends further discussing the scandal, Pepys decided that he "durst not own to my wife to have seen it."[3]

Michael Mohun, another actor in the King's Company and a favorite of the king, immediately convinced Charles II to allow the actors to resume performances (although not of *The Change of Crownes*), but Thomas Lacy received the same punishment as his character and was committed to the porter's lodge. Upon finding the Theatre Royal closed on April 20, Pepys learned that a fight between Lacy and Howard was the cause. Evidently, when Howard congratulated Lacy upon his release, Lacy blamed his imprisonment on Howard's "nonsensical play" rather than his inappropriate gags, and further added that Howard was "more a fool then a poet." Howard proceeded to "give him a blow on the face with his glove; on which Lacy, having a cane in his hand, did give him a blow over the pate [head]."[4] Howard complained to the king, and on the same day, a warrant was issued to arrest Lacy "for abusive words and actions" against Howard. On April 25, Lacy was ordered to appear before the Lord Chamberlain.[5] The dispute seems to have died down shortly afterwards, as Pepys noted a performance by Lacy on August 13. Howard did not have a play performed for more than three years, however—*The Woman's Conquest* was performed by the Duke of York's Company in November 1670.

H. W.

3. Pepys, 168–69.

4. Pepys, 173.

5. Some of this account is taken from Frederick S. Boas, ed., *The Change of Crownes, A Tragi-Comedy* (London, 1949), 9.

Sir Robert Howard (1626–1698)
George Villiers, 2nd duke of Buckingham (1628–1687)

The Country Gentleman
Written ca.1668; copied
ca.1695

50 fols.; 320 x 198 mm.

Purchased from Raphael King
in 1947

V.b.228

---

1. Folger V.b. 228, fols. 18r, 18v.

2. Howard, John Dryden's brother-in-law, was a prominent political and literary personage in 1669, a member of Parliament and loyal supporter of Charles II. He became Secretary to the Treasury in 1671. Buckingham, son of the favorite of James I and Charles I, was making a career out of orchestrating the removal from office of sympathizers of James, Duke of York, brother of Charles II and heir to the throne.

Cautious.	You must know Sir Gravity, that upon the modell of an Oyster table, I have plodded out a Table for buisnes.
Empty.	How Sir, a Table for buisnes? y gad that's very pretty.
Cautious.	Why Sir thus, to your hole in the middle, which you know is antient, I have added a modern passage into't.
Empty.	Very good y Gad: and what then?
Cautious.	This same passage I open and shut at pleasure, now Sir as soon as I am in, I fix my self upon a stool made for the nonce, which turns upon a swivell, and place my papers about me—See here, I have my Spanish papers, here my Dutch papers, here my Italian papers, here my French papers, and so round. Now Sir in a trice dispatch to what part of the world you please, I am ready for you.
Empty.	Admirable good y Gad, and this table may also serve for domestique affaires.
Cautious.	No, there shall be two, one for domestique, the other for forreigne; and in the forreigne there is somthing more considerable yet than all this.
Empty.	Very fine; what I pray?
Cautious.	Why the thing you know, that we men of buisnes ought to be most currant in, as to affaires abroad, is the position of the several interests of forreign Potentates, how they stand in amitie or animosity toward us, and with one another.
Empty.	Very good.
Cautious.	This cost a world of paines and expence by intelligence, and such like; wheras by the modell and directions of my forreigne Table, you have all that intrigue laid before you at one dash.
Empty.	Y gad thats very neat, what modell can this bee?
Cautious.	Why Sir the modell is not toedious neither, 'tis only thus: if enemies opposite, one here, t'other there, if friends—close touch—So I never trouble my self with reading newes books or Gazets, but go into my chamber, look upon my Table, and snap—presently Ile tell you how the whole world is dispos'd.[1]

SIR ROBERT HOWARD'S COMEDY *The Country Gentleman* was never publicly performed and never printed, and yet its interpolated scene by the duke of Buckingham still managed to land Buckingham's intended target in the Tower and ruin his political career.[2] The play was originally intended to be performed by the

King's Company on February 27, 1669. Sometime before this date, Buckingham slipped an extra scene into Howard's play in order to ridicule a political opponent, Sir William Coventry, one of the Treasury commissioners who had refused an offer of alliance with the non-Yorkist Buckingham faction. When Coventry discovered the plan, he informed the manager of the King's Company, Thomas Killigrew, that any actor impersonating him would "have his nose cut," which essentially halted rehearsals of the play.[3]

Buckingham's lampoon was based upon Coventry's innovative and well-known circular business desk. The preceding July 4, Pepys visited Coventry and reported: "he shewed me his closet, with his round Table, for him to sit in the middle, very convenient."[4] Despite its usefulness, the desk was an easy target for burlesque, and in the interpolated scene (Act 3, scene 1), Buckingham capitalized on the invention, turning it into two tables, one for foreign affairs and one for domestic affairs. In the scene, Sir Cautious Trouble-all (Sir William Coventry) proudly and self-importantly explains his invention to Sir Gravity Empty (Sir John Duncomb). Empty then bets a pair of embroidered gloves that he can be as fast as Cautious in swiveling to the relevant pile of documents (which were sorted by geographic region), and the section ends with several "towns" being scattered across the stage.

Charles II inspected a copy of the play in which the scene had been carefully excised, and therefore did not issue an injunction against it. As a result, Coventry took matters into his own hands and challenged Buckingham to a duel. Buckingham, however, had recently been pardoned for killing Lord Shrewsbury, his mistress' husband, in a duel, and he knew that another duel would ruin him politically. Hence, the challenge was conveniently leaked to the king, who sent Coventry to the Tower for the felony of conspiring the death of a privy councillor.

On March 3, John Nicholas wrote to his father, Sir Edward Nicholas, of the events,

> ... occasioned by a new Play made by Sir Robert Howard called the Country Gentleman in which the Duke of Bucks hath incerted a part to personate Sir William Coventry sitting in the midst of a Table with papers round him to which he can easily turne himself round on his chaire as he pleases, such an one it seems he hath, but there are other circumstances in the part likewise more abusive. .... It hath not yet been acted, & the King they say hath forbidden it.[5]

At his release from the Tower on March 20, Coventry was stripped of his government offices. Charles II admitted to his sister that the scandal caused by the play was well-timed: "I am not sorry that Sir William Coventry has given me this good

3. *The Country Gentleman*, eds. Arthur H. Scouten and Robert D. Hume (Philadelphia, 1976), 6, from Samuel Pepys's *Diary*.

4. Samuel Pepys, *The Diary of Samuel Pepys*, ed. Robert Latham and William Matthews (Berkeley and Los Angeles, CA, 1976), 9:255.

5. Scouten and Hume, 4, from British Library, Egerton MS 2539, fols. 327v–328.

6. Scouten and Hume, 14.

7. She married Sir Thomas Coventry, later earl of Coventry, in 1691.

8. The recovery of any lost play is extremely rare—the only other Restoration play recovered in the twentieth century is Edward Howard's *The Change of Crownes* (1667).

occasion, by sending my Lord of Buckingham a chalenge, to turne him out of the Councill. I do intend to turn him allso out of the Tresury. The truth of it is, he has been a troublesome man in both places, and I am well rid of him."⁶

The play was never printed, and was considered lost until this copy was identified at the Folger in 1973. The Folger copy is a complete scribal copy (ca.1695) in a single hand, with two corrections in another contemporary hand. It may have been made for Lady Anne Coventry, Sir William Coventry's grand-niece by marriage.⁷ Copied from foul papers, it has very few stage directions, and while each act opens with a scene 1, there are no further formal scene divisions.⁸

H. W.

Anne Finch, countess of Winchilsea (1661–1720)

Nor, shall the louder Rivers, in their fall,
Like unpaid Taylers, or hoarse, Pleaders Brawle,
But all shall form a concert, to delight,
And all to peace, and all to love envite.
  Come, then, my Dafnis, and the feilds survey,
  And throo' the Groves, with your Ardelia stray.

As Baucis, and Philemon spent their lives,
Of husbands he, the happyest he, of Wives,
When throo' the painted meads, their way they sought,
Harmlesse in act, and unperplext in thought,
Lett us my Dafnis, rural joys persue,
And Courts, or Camps, not ev'n in fancy view.
  So, lett us throo' the groves, my Dafnis stray,
  And so, the pleasures of the feilds, survey.

The Circuit   of Appollo

Appollo, as lately, a Circuit he made,
Throo' the lands of the Muses, when Kent he surveyd,
And saw there that Poets were not very common,
But most that pretended to Verse, were the Women,
Resolv'd, to encourage, the few that he found,
And she that writt best, with a wreath shou'd be crownd.
  A summons sent out, was obey'd but by four,
When Phebus, afflicted, to meet with no more;
And standing, where sadly, he now might descry,
* From the banks of the Stowre, th' desolate Wye,
He lamented for Behn, o're that place of her birth,
And said, amongst Women, was not on the earth,
Her superiour in fancy, in language, or witt,
Yett ownd that a little too loosely she writt:
Since the art of the Muse, is to stirr up soft thoughts,
Yett to make all hearts beat, without blushes, or faults.

*– Mrs Behn was Daughter to a Barber, who liud formerly in Wye
   a little market town (now much decay'd) in Kent — though the account of
   her life before her Works pretends otherwise; some Persons now alive
   do testify upon their knowledge that to be her Original.

Miscellany poems with two plays by Ardelia, N.b.3, p. 43

Miscellany poems with two plays by Ardelia ca.1685–1702

Autograph corrections

160 fols.; 365 x 230 mm.

Sir Edmund Gosse manuscript; purchased from Dobell in 1929

N.b. 3

NO RESOURCE CAN TEACH US as much about a writer's methods as manuscripts can, but the well of hard fact contained in them is still largely untapped. Until we develop the technological supports that will enable us securely to identify and classify and correlate bindings, papers, inks, and handwritings, much of what we do with manuscripts must remain guesswork, inspired guesswork maybe, informed guesswork certainly, but guesswork just the same. Take as an example N.b.3, which could answer many of the questions we have about the literary career of the poet born Anne Kingsmill in 1661 (the Honorable Mrs. Finch from 1684, and for the last seven years or so of her life, Countess of Winchilsea), who took in literature the name Ardelia. This, Ardelia's most important manuscript, was left by her husband to his chaplain, in whose family it remained until it was bought by Edmund Gosse in 1884; after his death in 1929 it was acquired by H. C. Folger.

This compilation of 108 poems and two plays began life as a handsomely bound folio of forty gatherings, in which the pages had already been signed A–Z4 and a–q4. It will one day be possible to determine when and where the book was originally made, and who originally intended to use it and for what purpose. It may have come to the impecunious Finches through any one of their grand connections, or they may have bought it from a London dealer when Heneage Finch formed the intention of making a second and more comprehensive copy of his wife's works for manuscript publication. Four leaves were left at the beginning for an index of contents that unfortunately was never written; there follow a title page, two commendatory poems, and an informative preface; pagination and the poems begin on the tenth leaf. The pagination continues without disruption to the sixty-seventh page, which is misnumbered fifty-nine, where the prefatory matter for the first play begins. This suggests that copying of the play began before the poems had filled the intervening pages. The copying of the two plays proceeds without a hitch, and then we encounter a new section entitled "Aditional Poems cheifly Vpon Subjects Devine and Moral." The devotional verses are followed by meditations on moral themes but, after fifty pages, occasional and more playful poems appear.

At what should have been page 229 in gathering f, further disruption occurs where leaf p4 has been substituted for f1 and leaves g2, g3, g4, h1, and h2 have been excised. The numbering of the succeeding pages is confused until m4, where the original numbering resumes. The last leaf, q4, is also missing, the endpaper being glued to the stub. It seems most likely that these leaves were removed while the compilation was being made rather than in the earlier life of the volume. We would know more if we could distinguish with certainty between pens and inks. If we could identify individual quills, for example, we could tell what was written before or after or at the same time as what. We could identify individual quills by electron microscopic examination and computer analysis of the scratches on the paper, but we have neither the software nor the hardware to do it. We might also be able to pick up the faint traces left on a succeeding page of what was written on a removed page. The right computer program would allow us to lift off apparently impenetrable scratchings out and cross-hatchings to find what was written underneath, as well as to read the faint impressions left on the paper after erasure.

Though fifty-two of the poems Heneage copied are to be found in the octavo manuscript[1] in virtually identical versions, the order of the octavo was not followed here, which might suggest that Heneage did not have it to hand and was copying once more from loose papers. To the poems from the octavo were added in no particular order fifty-six new poems, as well as the two plays. It would be helpful to be able to verify or discount the impression that Heneage was working rapidly, and may not have undertaken his task until both his wife's plays were finished ca.1699 when the Finches were living at Godmersham.

At some stage, Ardelia entered revisions and corrections in her own hand; that it is her hand is clear by comparison with her five surviving letters.[2] What ought also to be clear is that this hand appears nowhere else in Ardelia's surviving *carteggio*. Her hand is by no means illegible as some have alleged, but it is curious. Hands carry the marks of their breeding, of the family (the hands of parents and children and siblings are often very similar), and of the era and circumstances in which they were learned. Many women taught themselves to write by imitating print, but Ardelia was not one of these. If we had a database of hands to which scholars all over the world could contribute we might have an inkling how and why Ardelia developed her odd but attractive script. If we knew more about her ink and pens, we might know at what stage in the complex negotiations before the appearance of some of her work in print in 1713 she entered her revisions.

Another hand has scribbled suggestions for alterations to the preface, marked up both plays as if for printing, and selected poems which were later included in *Miscellany Poems on Several Occasions*, as the preface and one of the plays were not. Other scholars have assumed that these marks are all *post hoc*, but some of them seem to me contemporary, especially those in red pencil which include a straggling monogram that I read JB for John Barber, the publisher of *Miscellany Poems on Several Occasions*. If I am right, N.b.3 represents a unique example of a manuscript of its period that has been seen and marked by a publisher and subsequently returned to the author. It would be wonderful to be sure, one way or the other.

Germaine Greer
University of Warwick

1. Northamptonshire Record Office, MS Finch-Hatton 283.

2. Longleat House, Thynne Papers xvii, fols. 282–83, 313; Hampshire Record Office, 19M16/1406; Bodleian Library, Oxford, MSS Eng. Theol. 301 and Rawl. lett. 45, fols. 158–59.

Aphra Behn (1640–1689)
John Dryden (1631–1700)

APHRA BEHN

Autograph promissory
note, signed
August 1, 1685

1 fol.; 117 x 155 mm.

Jacob Tonson III - Bakers of
Bayfordbury manuscript;
purchased from Dobell in 1946

C.c.1 (4)

JOHN DRYDEN

Autograph receipt,
signed, for *Cleomenes*
October 6, 1691

1 fol.; 85 x 162 mm.

Jacob Tonson III   Bakers of
Bayfordbury manuscript;
purchased from Dobell in 1946

C.c.1 (13)

1. Folger C.c.1 (1–83).

2. Janet Todd, *The Secret Life
of Aphra Behn* (London, 1996),
353.

Where as I am indebted to Mr Bags *the* sum of Six pounds for *the* payment of which Mr Tonson has obligd him self—now I do here by impowre Mr Zachary Baggs incase the said debt is not fully dischargd before Michaelmas next, to stop what money he shall hereafter haue in his hands of mine, upon *the* playing my first play till this aforesaid debt of six pownd bedischargd: wittness my hand this 1ˢᵗ August 85

A: Behn

October *the* 6ᵗʰ – 1691.
Receiv'd the Sum of Thirty Guinneys for *which* I resigne to Mr Tonson all my Right in the Printing *the* Copy of Cleomenes a Trajady,

Witnesse my hand,

John Dryden

Witnesse

John Dryden Jun*ior*

THE FOLGER HAS A LARGE COLLECTION of receipts, letters, and papers belonging to the publisher Jacob Tonson (1655–1736) and his nephew, Jacob Tonson, Jr. (d. 1735).[1] In addition to the Dryden and Behn manuscripts shown in this exhibition, there are letters to Tonson from Congreve, Pope, Addison, Davenant, and Vanbrugh, among others. Known as the father of modern publishing, Tonson owned or shared the copyright to the works of many of the major writers of the day, including Shakespeare, Milton, Pope, and Dryden. He was chairman and secretary of the Kit-Kat Club, a literary and social society whose membership consisted of a select group of Whig MPs and writers.

Between 1678 and 1712, Tonson published the works of Aphra Behn, poet, playwright, fiction-writer, and former professional spy. Despite the success of her comedies on the stage, Behn was having financial difficulties in 1685. The Duke's Company, for whom she wrote, had merged with the King's Company, and the number of performances had been severely cut. The Behn manuscript shown here is a promissory note to Zachary Baggs, a moneylender who lived next to the royal theater at Dorset Garden.[2] In it, Behn promises that Tonson, who had published her *Poems Upon Several Occasions* with *A Voyage to the Island of Love* in 1684, will repay Baggs's six pound loan to her. If the debt was not repaid by the beginning of Michaelmas term (October), then she empowered Baggs to take the money from the proceeds of the performance of her next play. Behn was probably referring to her comedy of intrigue, *The Rover*, which was performed at court in October.

This note is one of only sixteen known letters in Behn's hand, and one of only three that are not at the Public Record Office in Kew.

In the 1670s and 1680s, only John Dryden was more prolific a writer than Aphra Behn. The intimate friendship between Dryden and Tonson began in 1679, and soon after, Tonson acquired the rights to most of Dryden's plays and became his exclusive publisher. The receipt shown here, signed by Dryden and witnessed by one of Dryden's sons, is for Tonson's payment of thirty guineas to Dryden on October 6, 1691, for the copyright of Dryden's tragedy *Cleomenes, the Spartan Heroe*, first printed in 1692.

The Folger has a number of other Dryden manuscripts of great interest. The warrant for Dryden's annual payment for 1675 of 200 pounds as "Poet Laureat & Historiographer to his M*aiesty*" is addressed to Dryden's brother-in-law, the playwright Sir Robert Howard, in his capacity as auditor of the exchequer.[3] Also at the Folger are a number of additional warrants and receipts for payments to Dryden,[4] papers concerning the publishing of the sumptuous folio edition of Dryden's translation of *The Works of Virgil*, published by subscription in 1697,[5] and two letters to Tonson in Dryden's hand.[6] There are also contemporary manuscript copies of two of his printed works, *The Satires of Juvenal* and *The State of Innocence, and Fall of Man*,[7] a contemporary copy of *Mr Purcells Sacrifice Musick in the Indian Queen*, ca.1695, with words by Dryden and Sir Robert Howard,[8] and two, possibly three, books formerly owned by Dryden.

H. W.

3. Folger X.d.14.

4. Folger X.d.9, 11, 15; C.c.1 (14).

5. Folger X.d.12 (1–4); C.c.1 (17).

6. Folger C.c.1 (15–16).

7. Folger V.a.224; V.b.235; V.b.225.

8. Folger V.b.279.

Mar. 31ˢᵗ 1722

Reverend and worthy Sˡ

In obedience to your Commands I here send you the
following short Essay towards the History of Poetry in England.

At first it was a Science we onely began to Chaw Sˡ,
a hundred years after, we ~~began~~ attempted to translate out of the
Psalms, but could not our Stern hold, In Q. Eliz. Reign
I think there was but one Dr — Spencer of good Verse, for his
Patron, though a great man, is hid nigh by the Length of Time.
Yet a little before her Death, we attempted to deal in Tragedy,
and began to Shake Spears; which was pursued under K. James
Iˢᵗ by three great Poets; In one of them you will find many
a Line so Strong, that you might make a Beam on't; the Second
indeed, gives us Sometimes but Flat cheer, and the third is Ben-
—ding a little to Stiffness

In the Reign of K. Char. Iˢᵗ there was a new Succession of
Poets; One of them though seldom reed, I ~~am very much~~ am
very fond of, He has so much Salt in his Compositions that you
would think he had been used to Suck Ling: As to his Friend the
Author of Gondibert, I'd'ave an Aunt write better. I say nothing
against your Favorite, though some censure him for writing too
Coolly, but he had a Rival whose happier Genius made him stand
like a Wall or a Pillar against Censure. During the Usurpation
we fell into Burlesque, and I think, whoever reads Hudibras
cannot but leer. I have Co't one more, who travestyed Virgil,
though not equall to the Former

After the Restoration, Poets became very numerous. The

A history of poetry, Y.c.1433

156

Jonathan Swift (1667–1745)

At first it was a Science we onely began to Chaw *Sir*, a hundred years after we ~~began~~ attempted to translate out of the Psalms, but could not our Stern hold, In Q. Eliz. Reign I think there was but one Di-Spencer of good Verses, for his Patron, though a great Man, is hid nigh by the Length of Time. Yet a little before her Death, we attempted to deal in Tragedy and began to Shake Spears; which was pursued under K. James 1st by three great Poets; In one of them you will find many a Line so strong, that you might make a Beam on't; the second indeed, gives us sometimes but Flat cheer, and the third is Bending a little to Stiffness. . .

SWIFT'S PUNNING HISTORY of poetry in England from Chaucer to Pope is written in his own hand in the form of a letter to an unnamed recipient, dated March 31, 1722. Despite being considered a "trifle" by his later editors, *A History of Poetry* was printed as a broadside in Dublin in 1726 (the same year that *Gulliver's Travels* was published in London) and was included by John Nichols in *A Supplement to Dr. Swift's Works* (London, 1779), 3:78.

The above passage plays on the names of Geoffrey Chaucer, Thomas Sternhold, Edmund Spenser, Sir Philip Sidney, Shakespeare, Francis Beaumont, John Fletcher, and Ben Jonson. Swift was a defender of punning and practiced it often, despite being satirized for it in Alexander Pope's broadside, *God's Revenge against punning; shewing the miserable fates of persons addicted to this crying sin in court and town* (London, 1716).

H. W.

[*A history of poetry*]
March 31, 1722

Autograph manuscript

2¼ pp. (bifolium);
238 x 185 mm.

Purchased at Anderson Auction Co. sale of the library of Adrian H. Joline, March 24, 1915, no. 515

Y.c.1433

James Boswell (1740–1795)

Commonplace book
ca.1755

Autograph manuscript

[162] fols.; 200 x 160 mm.

Purchased from Pearson in
November 1900

M.a.6

1. Folger M.a.6, fol. [1v].

2. Three years after his father's
death, the poet-antiquary Sir
Alexander Boswell (1775–1822),
Boswell's eldest son, wrote
on the front pastedown of this
volume, "Alexander Boswell
1798 This was my fathers
Common place Book at a
very early period of his Life."
Another hand adds, in pencil,
"(circa 1750)." Sir Alexander
helped collect his father's
papers for his executors, Sir
William Forbes, Edmund
Malone, and the Rev. William
Johnson Temple, who were
instructed to review Boswell's
manuscripts to decide which
should be published for the
financial benefit of Boswell's
younger children. For the
story of the dispersal of
Boswell's papers, see David
Buchanan, *The Treasure of
Auchinleck* (New York, 1974)
and Frederick A. Pottle, *Pride
and Negligence: The History
of the Boswell Papers* (New
York, 1982).

3. Recounted in his "Sketch
of the Early Life of James
Boswell," written by Boswell
for Jean Jacques Rousseau
on December 5, 1764 (Frederick
A. Pottle, *James Boswell,
The Earlier Years, 1740–1769*
(London, 1966), 2).

If I would put any thing in my common place book, I find out a head to which I may refer it. Each head ought to be some important and essential word to the matter in hand, and in that, regard is to be had to the first letter, and the vowel that follows it, for upon these two depend the whole use of the preceeding index. I omitt three letters K Y and W which are supply'd by C, J, and U, I put Q which is always followed by u, in the last space of Z, because it seldom happens that any head begins with Zu. When I would write a new head I look in the index for the characteristick of the word, and I see what page is assigned to that class. If there is no number, I look for the first back-side of a page if it is blank, I then set down the number in the index, and design that page with that of the right side of the following leaf to this new class. When the two pages designed for one class are full, I look forward for the next backside of a leaf that is blank, and if it be the one immediatly following I write at the foot of the page immediatly filled Vie Vente if the pages immediatly following are already full I write at the bottom of the page last filled V, with the number of the next empty backside of a leaf and at the top of this. I set down the number of the page last wrote upon this head. Every time I put a number at the foot of a page, I also put in the index, but when there is V I make no addition in the index. If the head is a mono-syllable, and begins with a Vowel, that is at the same time the first letter and the characteristick Vowel, When I borrow any thing from an Author, I first set down the Author's name, the name and size of the treatise, the page whence I take my observation, and the number of pages the whole contains. I put always my head at the top of the page Locke's: w: 2: v: 500/839.[1]

THIS UNFINISHED COMMONPLACE BOOK was most likely begun by James Boswell when he was just ten years old.[2] At the age of eight, he had left Mundell's School in Edinburgh and spent the next four years being tutored at home by two successive governors, Mr. John Dun, who encouraged him to read *The Spectator* and the Roman poets, and Joseph Fergusson.[3] It was probably under their tutelage that he began this manuscript, which predates all other known manuscripts in his hand by roughly four years.[4] Interspersed among the many blank pages are entries for only eight headings, written in a careful copybook hand, and forty pages of engraved Scottish coats of arms which appear to have been gathered from a heraldic book and glued to this one, four to a page.[5] Boswell's elaborate instructions for the compilation of the commonplace book, transcribed above, and the prefabricated alphabetical table of contents, which was never filled in, indicate his grand, but unrealized, intentions. The coats of arms and the entries reveal the interests and concerns of a precocious ten-year-old boy who would one day inherit his father's title, laird (lord) of Auchinleck.

Boswell's eight headings are "Death and Immortality," "Prodigies," "Travelling," "Persecution through Superstition," "Pastoral Life," "Grandeur, the great uncertainty of it," "Sleep," and "Sterling." Shakespeare figures largely in the entries—under "Prodigies," Boswell prefaces the quotation from *Julius Caesar*, act 2 ("Nor heav'n, nor earth, have been at peace tonight") with the observation, "Shakespeare in his Tragedy of Julius Caesar has given us a chain of the most astonishing prodigies, which, when cloathed with all the solemnity of language, and assembled together with such a nice taste and delicate judgment, cannot fail to strike the mind with the greatest horror." Under "Pastoral Life," he prefaces the quotation from the third part of *Henry VI*, act 2 ("Ah! what a life were this! how sweet, how lovely!") with the comment, "Shakespear introduces Henry the sixth oppress'd with cares, making a beautifull soliloquy on the innocent happiness of a shepherd. . . ." His quotation for "Sleep" comes from *Macbeth*, act 2, and his quotations for "Grandeur, the great uncertainty of it," come from Cardinal Wolsey's soliloquy from *Henry VIII*, act 3, and Ovid's *Metamorphoses* (I, iii, 135). Given the emphasis on Shakespeare in this volume, it is not surprising that Boswell's first published poem was a meditation on the first three lines of the prologue to act 4 of *Henry V*, published in the August 1758 issue of *Scots Magazine*: "Now entertain conjecture of a time / When creeping murmer and the poring dark / Fills the wide vessel of the universe."

H. W.

4. The next earliest manuscript in Boswell's hand is a letter to his mother dated July 17, 1754. For a transcription, see Pottle, *James Boswell*, 25–26.

5. The coats of arms were engraved by Robert Mylne (1643?–1747), the antiquarian and writer of pasquils.

David Garrick (1717–1779) and George Colman (1732–1794)

The Clandestine Marriage
ca.1763–1765

Written in Garrick's and Colman's autographs, as well as that of William Hopkins and possibly a fourth hand

91 fols.; various sizes

Purchased from Dobell in 1912

Y.d.114

1. For these details on the history of its performance, see: E. R. Wood's "Introduction" to his edition of *Plays by David Garrick and George Colman the Elder* (New York, 1982), 30–34. For notes on the first performance, see the entry for "D. L. 1765–1766" in John Genest, *Some Account of the English Stage, From the Restoration in 1660 to 1830* (Bath, 1832), 5:92–93. Printing and publication history can be found in Gerald M. Berkowitz, *David Garrick: A Reference Guide* (Boston, MA, 1980). Cimarosa's opera received its first performance in the Vienna Burgtheater on Feb. 7, 1792; see Jennifer E. Johnson, "Cimarosa, Domenico," in Stanley Sadie, ed., *The New Grove Dictionary of Music and Musicians* (New York, 1980), 4:401. The significance of the scandalous (for the times) title is covered by George W. Stone and George M. Karhl in their *David Garrick, A Critical Biography* (Carbondale, IL, 1979), 242–46.

2. Folger Y.d.114.

THE CLANDESTINE MARRIAGE was written by George Colman in collaboration with his friend and sometime-rival David Garrick, the celebrated actor and stage-manager of Drury Lane Theatre. The dynamic friendship between Garrick and Colman endured for years in spite of personal and professional competitions and—as shall become clear—more than a hint of "irritability" on both sides.

Despite the stormy disputes between the authors during its composition, *The Clandestine Marriage* was an instant success on its debut at Drury Lane on February 20, 1766. It ran for nineteen nights in its first season and went through three printed editions in six weeks. Shortly thereafter it was translated into French and German. The play was also seen in New York on June 5, 1789, by George Washington, and it served as the basis for Domenico Cimarosa's 1792 opera *Il Matrimonio Segreto.*[1]

As evidenced by this manuscript, Garrick and Colman worked both together and separately on outlines of the plot, suggestions about characters, and the revision of each other's writings: all this accomplished through extensive marking up of drafts on numerous unbound scraps of paper.[2] This working copy is in several hands, chiefly Garrick's and Colman's but also that of William Hopkins (Garrick's prompter acting here as amanuensis), and that of at least one other unidentified copyist.[3] Note the small sheet, perhaps in Garrick's hand, headed by the words "G------ takes -----" and listing a number of scenes that he intended to write. The surviving draft of the cast list shows evidence of early decisions—some later changed—regarding names of characters, and of well-known actors for whom these roles were intended.[4]

Quarrels between Garrick and Colman occurred—among other things—over casting and the credit for the text. On his return from Paris in 1765, Garrick refused to take on any new roles, including the main comic role in *The Clandestine Marriage*, that of Lord Ogleby. Colman wrote to Garrick in December of 1765 urging him to reconsider: "I cannot help being hurt at your betraying so earnest a desire to winnow your wheat from my chaff."[5] Garrick refused to be dissuaded, and the role of the aging rake Ogleby was played by Thomas King to critical acclaim.[6]

Controversies persist among scholars over the division of labor between Colman and Garrick.[7] Garrick is now thought by many to have written the bulk of the play, although Colman believed before the first staging that Garrick was publicly claiming more than his share of the credit. After all, initial inspiration for the literary work came from Colman, who based his ideas on the satiric first plate of William Hogarth's *Marriage à la Mode*, "The Marriage Settlement."[8] These disputes led Garrick to refer to *The Clandestine Marriage* as "this unhappy comedy" in a letter to Colman dated December 5, 1765.[9]

The Clandestine Marriage is considered one of the best comedies of the eighteenth century. Despite—or perhaps because of—its rocky road to completion, Garrick described it this way in a letter to the duke of Nivernois on May 3, 1766:

> A comedy called the Clandestine Marriage is now acting upon our stage with great success. It was written by my friend Colman & me, as a commemoration of a friendship which is not every day to be found among the *genus irritabile vatum*. I have made bold to send your Grace a copy of the play, which I hope you will receive as a small tribute of my gratitude and not as a token of my vanity.[10]

Jim Kuhn
Folger Shakespeare Library

3. Harry W. Pedicord and Frederick L. Bergmann attribute certain sections to each author based on their identification of the hands, in the "Commentary and Notes" section of their edited compilation, *Garrick's Own Plays, 1740–1766* (Carbondale, IL, 1980), 1:413–25.

4. Y.d.114, fol. 14: "G---- takes ----." Y.d.114, fol. 1: Cast list. Kalmin Burnim believes the casting, "in which even the most minor roles were taken by players who usually commanded leading parts was mainly responsible for that play's success." See his *David Garrick, Director* (Pittsburgh, PA, 1961), 28. See also Ian McIntyre, *Garrick* (London, 1999), 376.

5. Colman's and Garrick's letters during December of 1765 reveal many details about the dispute. See James Boaden, ed., *The Private Correspondence of David Garrick, With the Most Celebrated Persons of his Time* (London, 1831–1832), 1:209ff.

6. Ian McIntyre notes that, some years after his retirement, Garrick identified Ogleby as "the only character in which I should now wish to appear." See his *Garrick*, 376. For more on the question of casting, along with a reproduction of a portrait by Samuel DeWilde of Thomas King as Lord Ogleby, see Elizabeth P. Stein, *David Garrick, Dramatist* (New York, 1938), 205ff.

7. Boaden, 209ff. Both Pedicord & Bergmann and Stein identify Garrick as responsible for the majority of the play. Contrary opinions can be found in the 1820 defense of his father's authorship claims by George Colman the younger: "Papers Tending to Elucidate the Question Relative to the Proportional Shares of Authorship to be Attributed to the Elder Colman and Garrick, in the Comedy of *The Clandestine* Marriage," in his *Posthumous Letters, from Various Celebrated Men Addressed to Francis Colman and George Colman the Elder* (London, 1820), 327–47. For a concurring opinion see also Mrs. Inchbald's "Remarks" on her edition of the play in her edited compilation, *The British Theatre; or, a Collection of Plays*, 16 (London, [1808]), and see also Eugene R. Page, *George Colman The Elder* (New York, 1935), esp. 120ff.

8. This claim of Colman's is outlined in his letter to Garrick of Dec. 4, 1765. See Boaden, 210. For descriptions and reproductions of Hogarth's series, see Judy Egerton, *Hogarth's "Marriage à-la-mode"* (London, 1997).

9. David M. Little and George M. Kahrl, eds., *The Letters of David Garrick* (Cambridge, MA, 1963), 2, no. 378.

10. Folger Y.c.2600 (100). Little & Kahrl, 2, no. 401: these editors note that the Latin is from Horace, *Epistles*, II, ii, 102, translated by H. R. Fairclough as "the fretful tribe of bards." See his translation of Horace, *Satires, Epistles and Ars Poetica* (Cambridge, MA, 1939), 433.

1

Hampton July 31 1775

Dear Bate

If you pass by Cheltenham in
your way to worcester, I wish you
would see an actress there, a _Mrs._
Siddons, she has a desire I hear
to try her Fortune with us; if she seems
in your Eyes worthy of being transplanted,
pray desire to know upon what con:
:ditions she would make of Tryal, &
Ireceive write to her the post after
Ireceive your Letter — pray our
Complements to your Lady, & accept
of our warmest wishes for an
agreeable

Autograph letter, signed, to the Rev. Mr. Bate, Y.c.2600 (194)

David Garrick (1717–1779)
Sarah (Kemble) Siddons (1755–1831)

IN THE SUMMER OF 1775, David Garrick was anticipating his final acting season. After an illustrious career of thirty-four years performing in London, twenty-nine of them managing Drury Lane, he was planning for the 1775–76 season to be a glorious finale. The company numbered over one hundred players that season, and they would stage 189 performances from September to June, including sixty-seven plays and thirty-two afterpieces. Only weeks before the season was to begin, Garrick wrote his friend Henry Bate on July 31, 1775, with the request: "If you pass by Cheltenham on your way to Worcester, I wish you would see an actress there, a <u>Mrs. Siddon's</u>." Henry Bate (later Sir Henry Bate Dudley), a sometime pastor and editor of *The Morning Post*, had gained the nickname the "Fighting Parson" two years earlier when accompanying the actress Elizabeth Hartley to Vauxhall Gardens. Angrily confronting a group of men who had made rude comments concerning Mrs. Hartley, he thoroughly thrashed the guilty parties in the boxing match that ensued. (In 1780 Bate married Mrs. Hartley's sister, Mary White.)

The twenty-year-old Sarah Siddons had been born into a theatrical family, the first child of Roger and Sarah Kemble. She had grown up as a provincial strolling player alongside her brothers John, Charles, and Stephen, and her sisters Frances, Elizabeth, and Julia Ann. She met her husband, William Siddons, when he joined her father's acting troupe. William and Sarah had been married a year and a half, and Sarah was expecting their second child, when Henry Bate saw her performance as Rosalind in *As You Like It* in Cheltenham. On August 12, Bate wrote enthusiastically to Garrick: "I own she made so strong an impression upon me that I think she cannot fail to be a valuable acquisition to Drury Lane."[1] Sarah had a repertoire of twenty-three characters at that time. Garrick hired her but did not expect her to come to London until the birth of her baby. Daughter Sarah (called Sally) was born November 5, 1775. On December 29, Sarah Siddons made her debut at Drury Lane as Portia in *The Merchant of Venice*. It was a disaster. She suffered stage fright, and the press unanimously condemned her performance. It was a miserable start, and while she played numerous parts in the next six months, including Lady Anne to Garrick's Richard III, she did not greatly improve. In the summer of 1776 Sarah was informed that her services were no longer required at Drury Lane. She was devastated but did not give up. She worked the provincial circuit for six years before achieving great acclaim in Bath. Richard Brinsley Sheridan, now the manager of Drury Lane, saw her there in 1782 and invited her back to London. Mrs. Siddons made a triumphant return to Drury Lane in October of that year in one role after another. Her great success was celebrated by the theater's management giving her Garrick's dressing room. This was the beginning of an amazing thirty-year reign on Britain's stages.

DAVID GARRICK

Autograph letter, signed, to the Rev. Mr. Bate
July 31, 1775

2 pp. (1 fol.); 235 x 175 mm.

Purchased at Anderson sale of collection of Augustus Toedteberg, October 14, 1904, part IV, no. 277

Y.c.2600 (194)

SARAH (KEMBLE) SIDDONS

Agreement with Thomas Harris of Covent Garden Theatre for the 1809–10 season

1 fol.; 222 x 186 mm.

Most likely purchased as part of Christie's sale, June 18, 1902, no. 778

Y.d.450 (2b)

1. *A Biographical Dictionary of Actors, Actresses, Musicians, Dancers, Managers, and Other Stage Personnel in London, 1660–1800*, Philip H. Highfill, Jr., et al., eds. (Carbondale, IL, 1991), 14:4.

2. Robyn Asleson, ed., *A Passion for Performance: Sarah Siddons and Her Portraitists* (Los Angeles, CA, 1999), xvi.

Sarah Siddons specialized in tragedy and had a huge repertoire. Her signature roles included Belvidera in *Venice Preserv'd*, Elvira in *Pizarro*, Zara in *Mourning Bride*, Euphrasia in *Grecian Daughter*, Jane Shore, Lady Macbeth, and Queen Katherine in *Henry VIII*. She was painted by Sir Joshua Reynolds in 1784 as the embodiment of the Tragic Muse. Mrs. Siddons worked for Sheridan at Drury Lane throughout the 1780s and 90s but joined Covent Garden in September of 1803. Her brother, John Philip Kemble, had begun managing that theater.

Her contract agreement for the Season 1809–10 specified "Mrs. Siddons shall be announced as being her last Season of Acting." The year before had been a difficult one for Sarah. William Siddons had died in March, and on September 20 Covent Garden burned down, killing twenty-two people and destroying a career-long collection of costumes and jewelry. The theater was quickly rebuilt and was ready to reopen for the 1809–10 season. The New Covent Garden's premiere performance was *Macbeth* on September 18. Mrs. Siddons played Lady Macbeth opposite her brother, John Philip Kemble. The play was interrupted by riots protesting the increase in ticket prices to cover rebuilding expenses. Sarah Siddons wrote, "nothing shall induce me to place myself again in so painful and degrading a situation."[2] She did return to the stage, however, completing her contract, and postponed her retirement, officially giving her final performance on June 29, 1812. She was admired and remembered by many long after leaving the stage. When she died (May 31, 1831), 5000 people attended her funeral.

Susan Scola
Folger Shakespeare Library

Elizabeth Inchbald (1753–1821)

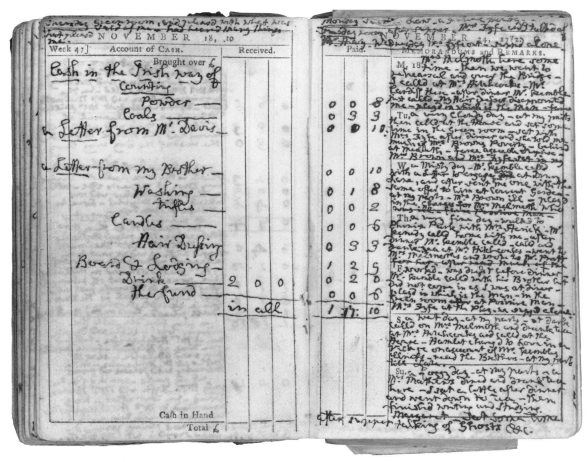

Diary, W.a.239

Diary
1782

Autograph manuscript

[88] fols.; 122 x 80 mm.

Purchased at the Philipps sale,
March 14, 1991, no. 96

W.a. 239

---

1. On a few occasions she used
other pocket-books, such as
*The Royal Engagement Pocket
Atlas for 1793* (Folger W.a.240).

2. Folger M.a.149–157 (purchased in 1924); W.a.239
(above) and W.a.240
(purchased in 1982).

3. Folger D.b.36.

[Monday, November 18]

Mrs Melmoth here some time—then we went to rehearsal and over the
Bridge—I calld at Mrs Hitchcocks—Mr Cardiff then—after dinner Mr
Kemble just calld—My Hair dresser disappointed me—playd in Which is
the Man . . .

[Wednesday]

a Misty day—Mr Kemble calld with a Letter to engage ~~me~~ ^him^ at Drury
Lane, and after sent me one with the same offer to him at Covent Garden—
at my parts—Mrs Brown ill—playd in the Chances for Mrs Melmoth who
was ill—farce Positive Man—Mrs Fyfe out—suppd alone.

[Friday]

Workd . . . Mr Kemble calld with his Brother but did not come in as I was at
dinner—playd in which is the Man—in the Green room ~~after~~ at Positive
Man—Mrs Fyfe at the Play. we suppd alone.

[Saturday]

a wet day—at my parts—at dark calld on Mrs Melmoth and drank tea at
Mrs Hitchcocks and calld at the House—Hamlet changd to Love in a Village
on account of Mr Kembles illness—read The Brothers—at my parts till Late.

[Sunday]

a foggy day—at my parts—a Mrs Mathers dined and drank tea here—I sat a
little after dinner and went down to tea—then finished writing and studying. Margaret—set some time after supper talking of Ghosts &c.

FOR OVER FIFTY YEARS, the actress, playwright, and novelist Elizabeth Inchbald
recorded her daily activities, expenses, thoughts, and feelings into annual editions
of "The Ladies' Own Memorandum-Book; or, Daily Pocket Journal."[1] The Folger
owns eleven of these diaries, for the years 1776, 1780–83, 1788, 1793, 1807–08, 1814,
and 1820.[2] In them, Inchbald writes in a compact hand, trying to fit the details of her
busy professional and personal life (performances, rehearsals, visits) into the tiny
space allotted for each day.

Inchbald moved to London in 1772 to seek her fortune as an actress, and within
months, married Joseph Inchbald, a portrait painter and actor seventeen years her
senior. While performing in Liverpool in 1776, the Inchbalds met actress Sarah

Siddons and her brother John Philip Kemble, for whom Elizabeth Inchbald had a tender affection for the rest of her life. Widowed in 1779, Inchbald made her London debut in October 1780. Although she retired from the stage in 1789, she continued to write plays, farces, and novels, and beginning in 1806, the prefaces to the twenty-five volume *British Theatre*.

In 1782, the year of the diary shown here, Inchbald performed under Thomas Harris's management at Covent Garden during the regular season and spent the summer season performing under George Colman the elder's management at the Little Theatre, Haymarket. On August 31, she received the Lord Chamberlain's license for a play which had been accepted by Thomas Harris (noted in her diary). In October Inchbald performed in Shrewsbury and from November until the end of May 1783, in Dublin. The diary is open to the week of November 18–24, 1782, during which time she was in Dublin, rehearsing her parts during the day and performing on most evenings, sitting in the "green room" and visiting with friends in her spare time. On most days, Kemble called on her; on Monday, she notes that "My Hair dresser disappointed me" and on Wednesday, she records that Kemble showed her letters from Drury Lane and Covent Garden seeking to engage him for the following season (he performed at Drury Lane from 1783 to 1802). On Sunday, "a foggy day," she "finished writing and studying" and sat for "some time after supper talking of Ghosts &c." On the opposite page, Inchbald records letters received and her expenses, including washing, trifles, powder, coals, candles, hair dressing, board and lodging, and drink. At the back of the diary are tucked a receipt and two short lists of "traveling expences." The receipt, dated June 26, 1782, is for more than two gallons of gin (Holland's Geneva). On the back of the receipt, she writes, "a present to Standingfield."

The Folger has a number of other Inchbald manuscripts as well, most importantly, an autograph copy of her play *A Case of Conscience*.[3] Inchbald wrote the play ca.1799 for Sarah Siddons and John Phillip Kemble, for performance at the Drury Lane Theater during the 1800–01 season, but it was never acted.

H. W.

consolation in the company of one who knew
who lov'd, who mourns and who will for ever
mourn the first of Men. — I write nonsense
I don't know not what I write. Be so very
good, as to ask my dear Mrs Garrick if
I shall come to her, and favour me with
your own opinion as to the propriety of
my taking this step, in case she forbids me.
From you I shall hope also to learn how
she is, for I know not to whom I cou'd so
well apply. May I venture to write to her

       Oh Sir! what trials are these mournful
offices of love for your benevolent heart!
    God Almighty comfort my dear Mrs Garrick
none else can. Forgive all this trouble

                in dear Sir

                  Your obliged

Bristol   but deeply afflicted Ser.t
Jan 23 - 1779   Han: More
      If my dear Mrs G. allows me
to come, I will be as near her as possible, and devote
all my time to her. — It was pear my time of coming
up if this calamity had not offered.

Hannah More (1745–1833)

. . . Oh Sir! What a friend have I lost! My heart is almost broken! I have neither eat[en] nor slept since my tears blind me as I write. But what is my loss, what is <u>my</u> sorrow? It is quite lost in the idea of what our beloued Mrs Garrick suffred or rather it is doubled in the reflection on <u>her</u> sorows. . . . Ask her, dear Sir, if she will allow me to come to her—I can not dry her tears, but I will weep with her.—I can be of no service perhaps, but there is a sort of mournful consolation in the company of one who knew who lov'd, who mourns and who will for ever mourn the first of men.—I write nonsense I don't know not what I write. . . . God Almighty comfort my dear Mrs Garrick. none else can. . . .

Autograph letter, signed, to Albany Wallis
January 23, 1779

2 pp. (1 fol.); 235 x 190 mm.

Purchased at Sotheby's, July 18, 1928, no. 580

Y.c.1651 (1)

HANNAH MORE, the bluestocking poet and writer of moral and religious treatises, wrote this letter to Albany Wallis, one of David Garrick's executors, three days after Garrick's death. More first met the Garricks after writing a letter to a friend in admiration of Garrick's *King Lear*. The friend proceeded to show the letter to Garrick, who asked to meet More. Soon after, More became intimate friends with David Garrick and his Austrian wife, Eva Maria Garrick. Garrick called More "Nine," in reference to the nine muses, and encouraged her to write plays. One of these, *Percy*, opened on December 10, 1777, and ran for twenty-one nights. Garrick's death affected More deeply, and during this period she wrote "Sensibility," a poem in heroic couplets which begins, "Ne'er shall my heart his loved remembrance lose, / Critic, guide, guardian, glory of my muse!" More lived with Mrs. Garrick off and on until Mrs. Garrick's death in 1822 at the age of ninety-eight. James Boswell, who noted that Mrs. Garrick referred to More as "her Chaplain," described one of the happiest days of his life as April 20, 1781, when Mrs. Garrick invited some of her closest friends to dine with her for the first time since Garrick's death. These included More, Samuel Johnson, Sir Joshua Reynolds, and Boswell.[1]

The Folger has over sixty letters written by Hannah More, most of them addressed to Mrs. Garrick, as well as letters to Mrs. Garrick from More's sisters, and poems and letters to More by both Mr. and Mrs. Garrick.

H. W.

1. George Birkbeck Hill, ed., *Boswell's Life of Johnson*, rev. and enlarged by L. F. Powell (Oxford, 1934), 4:96–99.

Autograph note to Eva Maria Garrick and Hannah More, Y.c.1650 (1)

Samuel Johnson (1709–1784)

Mr Johnson sends his respects to Mrs Garrick and Miss Moor. He has been confined to the house by diseases from Dec. 13. but is now much better, and hopes to wait on Mrs Garrick in a few weeks, and to tell Miss Moor all that <u>envy</u> will suffer him to say of her last poem, which Mrs Reynolds showed him.

March 15

Autograph note to
Eva Maria Garrick
and Hannah More
March 15, 1784

1 fol.; 80 x 121 mm.

Purchased from Rosenbach
Co., June 16, 1921

Y.c.1650 (1)

THIS NOTE WAS WRITTEN in the last year of Samuel Johnson's life, during a short reprieve in his final illness.[1] Johnson was very fond of Hannah More, whom he first met at the house of Sir Joshua Reynolds in June 1774. In this note he refers to *The Bas Bleu*, More's poem describing a bluestocking club, which he had been shown by Reynolds's sister. More acknowledged the note in a letter to her sister, writing, "I had a very civil note from Johnson about a week since. . . . He tells me he longs to see me, to praise the Bas Bleu as much as envy can praise."[2] After their meeting, she told her sister that Johnson told her "there was no name in poetry that might not be glad to own it," adding, "All this from Johnson, that parsimonious praiser."[3] On April 19, 1784, Johnson mentioned the poem again in a letter to Hester Thrale, calling it "a very great performance. It wanders about in manuscript, and surely will soon find its way to Bath" (it was published in 1786).[4] James Boswell described Johnson's May 14 dinner with Mrs. Garrick, Hannah More, Elizabeth Carter, and Fanny Burney, which was probably arranged as a result of this note to Hannah More and Mrs. Garrick, in his *Life of Johnson*.[5]

Hannah More mentioned Johnson in two letters to Mrs. Garrick that are now at the Folger. In one, dated July 21, 1783, she wrote: "I do love and honour him with all his faults, though I know it is not the fashion to do either."[6] David Garrick had been a pupil of Samuel Johnson in 1735–36, and they became life-long friends after traveling to London together in March 1737, sharing a single horse for the 120 mile journey.

Johnson's note was formerly tipped into an extra-illustrated copy of Francis Douce, *Illustrations of Shakespeare, and of ancient manners* (London, 1807).[7] This volume has another Johnson note to Hannah More as well, which simply states: "Mr Johnson will wait on Miss Moore to morrow, about Seven in the Evening Thursday."[8]

The Folger has other Johnson-related items, including letters from him, his copy of the second impression of Shakespeare's plays (1632), a letter from Samuel Richardson to him concerning Garrick's commitment to produce Johnson's *Irene*, and Garrick's epigram on Johnson's *Dictionary*.

H. W.

1. Published in Bruce Redford, ed., *The Letters of Samuel Johnson*, IV: 1782–1784 (Princeton, 1994), 296–97.

2. William Roberts, *Memoirs of the Life and Correspondence of Mrs. Hannah More* (London, 1834), 1:319.

3. Ibid, 1:320

4. Redford, 317.

5. George Birkbeck Hill, ed., *Boswell's Life of Johnson*, rev. and enlarged by L. F. Powell (Oxford, 1934), 4:275.

6. Folger W.b.487, no. 61.

7. This volume was from the Shakespearean library of Marsden J. Perry (Folger ART Vol. a9, facing p. 60). Johnson's note was attached to the opposite side of an engraving by Cosmo Armstrong (1821) of Sir Joshua Reynolds's painting of Samuel Johnson, which faced a page explicating act 2, scene 2, of *The Merry Wives of Windsor*. Douce records Johnson's observation that the liver "was anciently supposed to be the inspirer of amorous passions, and the seat of love."

8. Folger ART Vol. a9, facing p. 215.

Overture to *A Midsummer Night's Dream*, V.a.372

Felix Mendelssohn-Bartholdy (1809–1847)

FELIX MENDELSSOHN-BARTHOLDY COMPOSED HIS OVERTURE to *A Midsummer Night's Dream* when he was just seventeen years old and still living in Berlin at his parents' home. Long fascinated by the play, Mendelssohn wrote the overture to it as a piano duet, which he performed for the first time at home with his sister Fanny on November 26, 1826, for his former piano teacher Ignaz Moscheles. After being prepared for orchestral performance, the overture was publicly premiered in Stettin on February 20, 1827. Both the orchestral and piano versions were published in 1832, the piano version as *Ouverture zu Shakespeare's Sommernachtstraum* (Leipzig: Breitkopf and Härtel, [1832]). The manuscript shown here is Mendelssohn's copy of the piano arrangement in his own hand. It is thought that he made the copy during his first trip to England in 1829, based on the English watermark on the paper, "W King 1829," and on the English title page. Mendelssohn was one of the most popular composers in England in the nineteenth century, visiting the country ten times in his short lifetime.

Seventeen years after he wrote the overture, Mendelssohn was asked by King Friedrich Wilhelm IV of Russia to write incidental music for *A Midsummer Night's Dream* as part of a campaign to renew interest in the arts in Prussia.[1] Mendelssohn began writing the incidental music (which includes the well-known "Wedding March") in January 1843, and the play premiered with his overture and incidental music (*Ein Sommernachtstraum von Shakespeare*, opus 61) on October 14, 1843, at the New Palace in Potsdam, with the royal court in attendance.[2] The Shakespeare scholar and translator Johann Ludwig Tieck was responsible for the translation, staging, and direction of the production.

The Folger also has four letters written by Mendelssohn. One of them is a letter of instructions to the copyist of the incidental music for *A Midsummer Night's Dream*, Mr. Weissenborn, in which Mendelssohn asks to have a copy made as quickly as possible,

> But be careful with the manuscript, as I would like to have it back without alterations. And on no account let it out of your hands. Ask Schwarz to show you his copy and to explain to you how I would like the melodramatic passages written; write them in the same way, and also ask C. M. David to lend you the volume of his Tieck Shakespeare containing *A Midsummer Night's Dream*, from which you can copy the words of the dialogue (which in my manuscript are partly unclear, partly omitted) in the same way as Schwarz has done from my copy. . .[3]

H. W.

Overture to *A Midsummer Night's Dream*, arranged as a duet for two performers on piano (opus 21) July 10, [1829?]

Autograph manuscript, signed

8 fols.; 232 x 300 mm.

Purchased from English Books Co., Ltd. in 1937

V.a. 372

1. The king also commissioned Mendelssohn to write incidental music for *Antigone*, Sophocles' *Oedipus at Colonos*, and Racine's *Athalie*.

2. See Bryan N. S. Gooch and David Thatcher, eds., *A Shakespeare Music Catalogue* (Oxford, 1991), 2:1013–4.

3. Folger Y.c.1486 (2), translation by Werner Habicht (see his unpublished "Guide to Letters and Papers by German Authors at the Folger Shakespeare Library, 1777–1912").

Hexameters in an ~~such~~ imitation of Opian in the 5th No — For your
Dactyls I am sorry you are so sore about 'em — a very Sir Fretful —
In good troth the Dactyls are good Dactyls, but their measure is naught.
Be not yourself "half anger half agony" if I pronounce your darling
lines not to be the best you ever wrote in all your life, — you have written much.

for the alterations in those lines let 'em run thus.
    I may not come, a pilgrim, to the Banks
    of Avon, lucid stream, to taste the Wave   (inspiring wave) was too
    which Shakspere drank, our British Helicon;   common place
    or with mine eye &c &c
    To muse, in tears, on that mysterious youth &c .   (better than "drop a tear")

Then the last paragraph. alter thus
    Complaint begone; begone, unkind reproof: (letter refer to my own
    Take up, my song, take up a merrier strain,   "complaint" solely the
    For yet again, & lo! from Avon's vales,   half to that & half to
    another Minstrel cometh! youth endear'd,   Chatterton, as in your
    God & good angels &c . as before   copy, which creates a
                                                        confusion — "ominous fears &c.

Have a care, good master poet of the Statute de Contumelia, what as you
mean by calling Madame Mara harlots & naughty things? the goodness of ye town?
the verse would not save you in a court of Justice. But are you really coming to town?

Coleridge, a Gentleman called in London lately from Bristol, &
enquired whether there were any of the family of a Mr Chambers
living — this Mr Chambers, he said had been the making of his
~~fortune~~ friends fortune who wished to make some return for it. He went
away without ~~learning whether any of that family~~ seeing her
~~were living~~. Now a Mrs Reynolds — a very intimate friend of our
whom you have seen at our house, is the only daughter & that survives, of Mr Chambers — & a very little supply would
be of service to her, for she married very unfortunately &
has parted with her Husband. Pray, find out this Mr
Pember (for that was the Gentleman's friendly name) he is an attorney &
lives at Bristol. Find him out, & acquaint him with
the circumstances of the case, & offer to be the medium
of supply to Mrs ~~Reynps~~ Reynolds if he chuses to make her
a present. She is in very distrest circumstances. Mr Pember
attorney, Bristol. — Mr Chambers lived in the Temple.
Mrs Reynolds his daughter was my schoolmistress & is in the
room at this present writing. — This last circumstance

Autograph letter, signed, to Samuel Taylor Coleridge, Y.c.1460 (1), p. 3

Charles Lamb (1775–1834)

To the Poet Cowper
Cowper, I thank my God, that thou art heal'd.
Thine was the sorest malady of all;
and I am sad to think, that it should light
Upon the worthy head! But thou art heal'd,
and thou art yet, we trust, the destin'd Man,
Born to reanimate the Lyre, whose chords
Haue slumber'd & haue idle lain so long,
To the immortal sounding of whose strings
Did Milton frame the stately-paced verse;
Among whose wires with lighter finger playing,
Our elder Bard, Spenser, a gentle Name,
The Lady Muses dearest darling child,
Elicited the deftest tunes yet heard
In Hall or Bower, taking the delicate Ear
of Sidney, & his peerless maiden Queen.

Thou, then, take up the mighty Epic strain,
Cowper, of England's Bards the wisest & the Best. 1796[1]

Autograph letter, signed, to Samuel Taylor Coleridge
July 6, 1796

3 pp. (bifolium); 320 x 199 mm.

Purchased at Anderson sale, March 5, 1923

Y.c.1460 (1)

1. Folger Y.c. 1460 (1), p. 2.

2. The earliest letter, also to Coleridge, is dated May 27, 1796. It is at the Huntington Library, which has the largest collection of Lamb letters.

3. The latest edition of Lamb's correspondence to publish this letter is Edwin W. Marrs, Jr., ed., *The Letters of Charles and Mary Anne Lamb* (Ithaca, NY, 1975), 1:38–43. In it, Marrs includes the full text of "To Sara and Her Samuel," which an earlier editor, Edward Lucas, had copied from a facsimile of the poem post-marked July 5, 1796. The poem, as revised in this letter, appeared in the *Monthly Magazine*, 3 (January 1797): 54–55.

CHARLES LAMB WAS A WONDERFUL LETTER-WRITER. His conversational style, his inclusion of poetry, allusions to other writers, references to literary reviews, gossip, and inside references, make his letters both a pleasure and a challenge to read. The letter shown here, one of the earliest surviving letters by Lamb, is addressed to his life-long friend Samuel Taylor Coleridge, whom Lamb first met while they were students at Christ's Hospital.[2] Although Lamb worked as a clerk in the accountant general's department of the East India House, he was deeply immersed in the literary life of London, befriending and corresponding with some of England's greatest Romantic poets, in addition to publishing poetry, essays, and criticism. He first appeared in print in April 1796, having contributed four sonnets to Coleridge's *Poems on Various Subjects* (1796).

Three months later, he wrote this letter to Coleridge. Coleridge, who was lecturing in Bristol at the time, had married Sarah Fricker in October 1795, and Lamb's letter begins with a revised (and then cancelled) stanza to a poem he had written to them, "To Sara and Her Samuel," followed by two further revised stanzas on the third page of the letter.[3] Lamb then responds to Coleridge's appeal for London housing by describing various London neighborhoods: "Islington possibly you

4. Folger W.b.43 (1–4), Y.d.341 (100–101), Y.c.1460 (2–4).

would not like, to me 'tis Classical ground. Knights bridge is a desireable situation for the air of the Parks. St. George's fields is convenient for its contiguity to the Bench. Chuse." He discusses recent publications, magazine articles, poetry, reviews of Coleridge's *Poems*, and Coleridge's job offer of the co-editorship of the *Morning Chronicle*, and quotes from Coleridge's "Monody on the Death of Chatterton" and Robert Southey's "The Soldier's Wife." Having spent November–December 1795 in an insane asylum in Hoxton, Lamb shows his compassion for the poet William Cowper's recent recovery from insanity in his poem "To the Poet Cowper," which appears on the second page of the letter. He writes of the poem

> I fear you will not accord entirely with my sentiments of Cowper, as exprest above, (perhaps scarcely just) but the poor Gentleman has just recouer'd from his Lunacies, & that begets pity, & pity love, & love admiration, & then it goes hard with People but they lie!

Two months after this letter was written, Charles Lamb's sister Mary stabbed their mother to death in a fit of insanity. Lamb supported his sister, with whom he later collaborated on works such as *Tales From Shakespear* (1807) and *Poetry for Children* (1809). The Folger has ten holograph letters of Charles Lamb, including one to William Wordsworth and four to Lamb's intimate friend, Thomas Manning (one is written to Manning during Manning's trip to China).[4]

H. W.

Samuel Taylor Coleridge (1772–1834)

Autograph letter, signed, to Priscilla Maden Watts, Y.c.569 (7), p. 4

Autograph letter, signed, to Priscilla Maden (Wiffen) Watts [July 2, 1827]

4 pp. (bifolium); 185 x 110 mm.

Purchased from Maggs Bros. in 1905

Y.c.569 (7)

_____

1. Y.c. 569 (7), p. 1.

2. Folger Y.c.569 (8) is a ticket to one of his lectures written out in Coleridge's hand. His notes, essays, and lectures have been published in numerous editions.

3. Folger Y.c.569 (1–7); ART vol. b8, opp. p.221; Y.d.341 (26).

4. Folger W.a.143.

5. J. P. Collier's notes on Coleridge's lectures are Folger M.a.219–28.

6. Folger N.a.123–28; N.b.53–64. The marginalia in the Shakespeare edition appears in Samuel Taylor Coleridge, *Works*, vol. 12: *Marginalia* IV, ed. George Whalley (Princeton, NJ, 1992), 764–65.

O! dear Madam! the World is a stern and sour Goddess, that will not be conciliated without costly Sacrifices—and Life, and the Duties of Life, yea, even the very Affections, that give it zest and value, are pressed into the service, as her Whippers-on and Whippers-in.[1]

SAMUEL TAYLOR COLERIDGE ADDRESSED THIS LETTER to Priscilla Maden Watts, the wife of the poet Alaric Alexander Watts (1797–1864). Watts became acquainted with Coleridge when he took up the editorship of *Literary Souvenir*, to which Coleridge was a contributor. At the time of this letter, however, Watts was a frustrated sub-editor at a recently established evening newspaper, the *Standard*, and it is in this capacity that Coleridge commiserated with Watts's wife, since Watts himself was ill, on the "toils of Editorship." Coleridge also offered a "sheet-full" of epigrams for Watts to use in the *Standard*, "the far greater number of which have, I know, never been in print." All he asked is that he "would not have my name subscribed to things that if they afford amusement for the moment of their perusal have answered all, they were intended for."

The main purpose of Coleridge's letter, however, was to discuss the possibility of a new edition of Shakespeare's works, "with notes that should bona fide explain what for the general Reader needs explanation, as briefly as possible, and with the expulsion of all antiquarian Rubbish." Coleridge envisioned an edition with a textual apparatus that would allow readers "to distinguish and ascertain what Shakespear possessed in common with other great Men of his Age, or differing only in degree; and what was & is peculiar to himself." It is not clear if Coleridge had Watts in mind when he suggested that the work would best be done in collaboration, "could there be found a man of letters, who had confidence in me and in whom I could have confidence." Although Coleridge never published this projected edition of Shakespeare, and only mentions it in one other letter, he lectured and published widely on Shakespeare and other Renaissance writers.[2] At the time of this letter, the 1828 edition of his *Complete Poetical Works* was being prepared for publication.

The Folger has eight other holograph letters by Coleridge which concern his interest in Shakespeare,[3] as well as Coleridge's draft description of his proposed lectures on Shakespeare in 1818,[4] notes on Coleridge's lectures made by attendees,[5] Coleridge's own six-volume copy of Joseph Rann's *The Dramatic Works of Shakespeare* (1786), and twelve volumes from the thirteen-volume set of Anderson's *The British Poets*, which has annotations, some of them very dismissive, in the hands of Coleridge, Southey, Wordsworth, and Coleridge's son, Hartley Coleridge.[6]

H. W.

Autograph letter, signed, to Nicholas Lee Torre, Y.c.1455 (1), p. 2

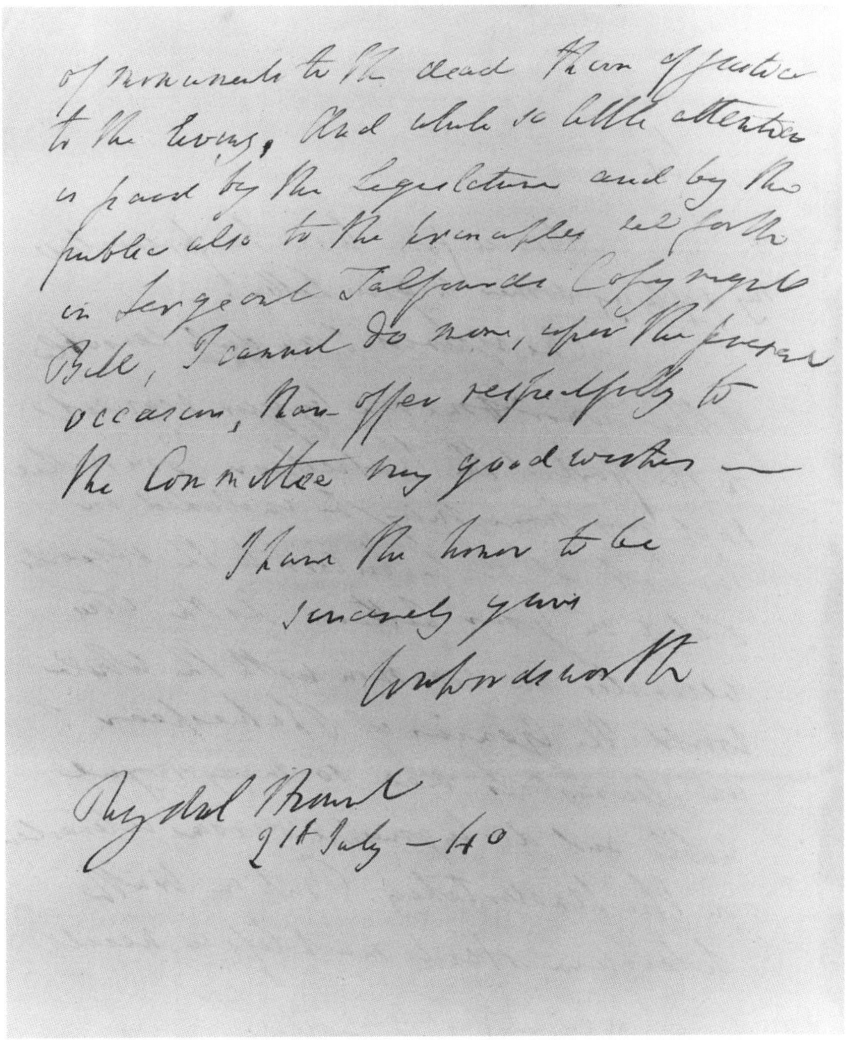

Autograph letter, signed,
to Nicholas Lee Torre
Rydal Mount,
July 21, 1840

2 pp. (bifolium); 229 x 186 mm.

Purchased from George D.
Smith in December 1909

Y.c.1455 (1)

1. This letter is printed in *The Letters of William and Dorothy Wordsworth*, ed. Alan G. Hill (Oxford, 1988), 7.4:93.

2. The Copyright Act of 1842 increased copyright protection from twenty-eight years or the author's life to the author's life plus seven years, not to exceed forty-two years total. For a detailed account of the bill, see Catherine Seville, *Literary Copyright Reform in Early Victorian England: The Framing of the 1842 Copyright Act* (Cambridge, 1999).

3. Seville, 6.

4. *Letters*, 7.4:17, 72.

5. *Letters of Charles Lamb, with a Sketch of his Life*, ed. Thomas Noon Talfourd (London, 1837).

Be assured I am duly sensible of the honor done me by your request on the part of the Shakespear Committee that my name may be included on the list of Contributors to the objects stated in your letter. As one who venerates in common with the whole world the Genius of Shakespear, I am pleased to see so many royal noble and distinguished Persons interested in the Undertaking. But in truth Literature stands much less in need of Monuments to the dead than of justice to the living, And while so little attention is paid by the Legislature and by the public also to the principles set forth in Sergeant Talfourds Copyright Bill, I cannot do more, upon the present occasion, than offer respectfully to the Committee my good wishes.

IN THIS LETTER, Wordsworth responds to a request by the Secretary of the newly-established Shakespeare Society, to support the society's project to encourage the publication of works relating to the plays of Shakespeare and his contemporaries.[1] Wordsworth's refusal to associate himself with the society's aims was in part a political boycott. Wordsworth was a key supporter of stronger copyright laws for living writers, as indicated by his reference in this letter to the copyright bill first proposed by his friend, the writer and serjeant-at-law Thomas Noon Talfourd, MP, in 1837. Reintroduced annually until a watered-down version was finally passed in 1842, the controversial bill, known as Talfourd's Act, was meant to reward authors instead of publishers.[2] Talfourd proposed that the copyright term be increased from twenty-eight years to the author's life plus sixty years, that international copyright protection be provided for writers, and that the various statutes for the protection of lectures, plays, engravings, and other creative genres and mediums be consolidated. His argument that copyright should be a recognition of "cultural worth" rather than a commodity[3] was strongly supported by Wordsworth and other writers, but not suprisingly, resisted by printers and publishers. Petitions and pamphlets were circulated by both sides of the debate. Wordsworth himself engaged in a letter-writing campaign to urge MPs to attend debates on the bill.

Wordsworth's letter to Torre was written just after the 1840 version of the bill was dropped. In February, Wordsworth had written to Talfourd about the temptation of authors to produce works to suit "transient" tastes rather than works of "lasting good" under current copyright law. In May, he provided further arguments for Talfourd to use in Parliament.[4] A playwright and poet himself, Talfourd was a friend not only to Wordsworth, but also to many other writers, including Charles Lamb, whose letters he published in 1837 as Lamb's executor.[5]

H. W.

Robert Southey (1774–1843)

THROUGHOUT HIS LIFE, the poet and author Robert Southey was an active and diligent gatherer of information, much of which he extracted from Renaissance literature, contemporary magazines, journals, and newspapers, or learned from friends. No fact, story, or quotation was too insignificant. In a letter dated July 11, 1822, Southey tries to explain his eclectic collecting habits:

> Like those persons who frequent sales, and fill their houses with useless purchases because they may want them some time or other; so am I for ever making collections and storing up materials which may not come into use till the Greek Calends. And this I have been doing for five and twenty years! It is true that I draw daily upon my hoards, and should be poor without them; but in prudence I ought now to be working up those materials rather than adding to so much dead stock.[1]

Both of Southey's commonplace books at the Folger are arranged loosely by subject. In addition to containing his own personal musings, they consist of literary extracts and interesting facts from a wide range of sources, written in English, Latin, Italian, Greek, Spanish, and other languages. Many of the subject headings appear multiple times in each volume—headings include Nonsense, the Soul, Medical Botany, Inoculation, Philosophy of Nonsense—Morosophy, Languages, Eternal Punishment, Beards, Bears, Food, Music, Hell, Witchcraft, Ireland, Oaths, Animals, Feeling toward inaminate object, Marriage, Physic, The Dead, Women, Theatre, Dreams, Leyden, Dancing, and Love.

One of the more amusing entries is headed, "To express the condition of an Honest Fellow . . . under the effects of good fellowship, it is said that he is." Southey proceeds to list eighty-seven synonyms for the word "drunk" and then adds a few more under "to these I add," followed by fifteen more from "Ray's collection." He frequently contextualized the entries. Under "19. Cup-sprung," he adds, "This is said to be the favourite state & expression of a great genius who is at present Porter to University Col. Oxford."[2] Another heading, "Horses," includes a quote by Horace Walpole, followed by a newspaper clipping about the stuffed head and skull of a sixty-two-year-old horse named Old Billy (who died on November 17, 1822), which could be seen at the museum of the Manchester Natural History Society.[3]

Southey's other commonplace book is signed by him on the front flyleaf and dated by him, June 27, 1799.[4] Southey's autograph essay, "Chapter Extraordinary," is a complaint about the bowdlerization of books, ca.1835.[5]

H. W.

Commonplace book
1799–ca.1838

Autograph manuscript
217 fols.; 160 x 100 mm.
Purchased from Maggs Bros. in 1928
M.a.159

1. *The Life and Correspondence of Robert Southey*, ed. C. C. Southey (London, 1849–50), 5:135.

2. Folger M.a. 159, fol. 93.

3. M.a. 159, fol. 105v.

4. Folger M.a.158. Neither of these commonplace books appears to have been included in the edition of Southey's commonplace books edited by J. W. Warter, *Southey's Commonplace Book*, 4 vols. (London, 1850).

5. Folger N.a.71.

Thomas de Quincey (1785–1859)

"Samuel Taylor
Coleridge"
ca. 1834

Autograph manuscript
fragment

14 pp.; 231 x 188 mm.

Purchased from Shana
Michelmore in 1928

Y.d.543 (1)

1. John E. Jordan, ed., *De
Quincey as Critic* (London,
1973), 13.

2. The magazine did not
include the last paragraph of
the essay from the manuscript.
It was subsequently printed in
*The collected works of Thomas
De Quincey*, ed. David Masson
(Edinburgh, 1896), 2:206–13,
and most recently in *The
Works of Thomas de Quincey*,
ed. Grevel Lindop (London,
forthcoming in 2002), vol. 10.

3. Thomas Carlyle,
Reminiscences, ed. C. E.
Norton (London, 1972), 347.
See also J. C. Hare, "Samuel
Taylor Coleridge and the
English Opium-Eater," *The
British Magazine*, 7 (1835):
15–27. De Quincey's assess-
ments of his other friends
can be seen in *Recollections
of the Lakes and the Lake
Poets*, ed. David Wright
(Harmondsworth, 1970).

4. Folger Y.d.543 (2–4).

Originally his sufferings and the death within him of all hope . . . came from opium. But two things I must add—one to explain, and other to justify Coleridge's case, and the other to bring it within the indulgent allowance of jus equitable judges. ∧First this,∧ Suffering from morbid derangements originally produced by opium had very possibly and to be such: that is, lost that ∧simple∧ character, and had prod themselves reacted in producing secondary states of disease and imitation not any longer dependant upon the opium so as to disappear with its disuse. Hence a more than mortal discour- agement to accomplish this dis use, when the pains of all-sacrifice were balanced by no glimmer of restorative feeling. Yet secondly C. did make prodigious efforts to deliver himself from the thraldom; and he went so far at one time in Bristol to my knowledge as to hire a man for the ∧express∧ purpose and armed with the power of resolutely standing ∧interposing∧ between him C. and the door of any druggist's shop. . . . Opium therefore, subject to the explanation I have made, was certainly the original source of C's morbid feelings, of his debility, and of his remorse.

THOMAS DE QUINCEY, author of "Confessions of an English Opium-Eater" (published in the September and October 1821 issues of *London Magazine*), first met Coleridge, Wordsworth, Southey, and Lamb in 1807–08. He began using opium in 1804 to relieve facial neuralgia, but by 1813 it had turned into an addiction which he was never able to overcome despite at least four major attempts.[1] His comments here on Coleridge's opium addiction are part of a longer work, "Samuel Taylor Coleridge," written shortly after the poet's death in 1834 and first published in *Tait's Edinburgh Magazine* (1834–35).[2] At the time, De Quincey's recollections created a small sensation because of his lightly-veiled suggestions that Coleridge was a plagiarist. Robert Southey recommended to Hartley Coleridge, the poet's son, that he "take a strong cudgel, proceed straight to Edinburgh, and give De Quincey, publicly on the streets there, a sound beating," and the accusation was discussed at length in contemporary periodicals.[3]

The Folger has three other De Quincey autograph writings. The essay "Shake- speare and Wordsworth" (ca.1843) was published posthumously, and the other two, a short piece on Shakespeare's birthday in 1853, and a very curious manuscript entitled "To make Oatmeal [or, as it is often called, Water] Porridge," which includes an illustration of a "Thible," or "Wooden Spatula used in stirring the P. whilst boiling," have never been published.[4]

H. W.

Mark Twain (Samuel L. Clemens) (1835–1910)

5

prominence while he lived, & none
until he had been dead two or three
generations. The Plays enjoyed high
fame from the beginning; & if he
wrote them it seems a pity ~~that~~ the
world did not find it out. He ought to
have explained that he was the author,
& not merely a _nom de plume_
for another man to hide behind. If he
had been less intemperately solicitous
about his bones, ~~and~~ & more solicitous about his Works, it would have been
better for his good name, & a kindness to us.
~~saved us fifty years of unrest &~~
~~discomfort.~~ The bones were not
important. They will moulder away,
they will turn to dust; but the Works
will endure until the last sun goes
down.

Mark Twain

Is Shakespeare dead?, S.a.107, fol. 124

183

MARK TWAIN

Is Shakespeare dead?
From my autobiography
February 13, 1909

Autograph manuscript, signed

124 fols.; 224 x 147 mm.

Purchased via A. S. W.
Rosenbach at Anderson
Auction Co. sale, January
24–26, 1923, no. 249

S.a.107

Is Shakespeare dead?
From my autobiography
New York and London:
Harper and brothers,
1909

Sir George Greenwood's copy
with his manuscript notes

Purchased with the Smedley
collection in 1924

PR2944 C7

Autograph letter, signed,
to M.B. Colcord
May 18, 1909

1 p.; 165 x 125 mm.

Purchased from Thomas F.
Madigan in 1928

Y.c.545 (1b)

You see, all I want is to convince sane people that Shakspeare did not write Shakspeare. Who did, is a question which does not greatly interest me.[1]

MARK TWAIN'S INTEREST IN THE SHAKESPEARE QUESTION, first sparked by his reading of Delia Bacon's book, *The philosophy of the plays of Shakspere unfolded* (Boston, 1857), was reignited in 1908 when he read *The Shakespeare Problem Restated* (London, 1908) by the British MP Sir George Greenwood.[2] Twain was particularly intrigued by Greenwood's argument that, while there is no evidence that Shakespeare the actor had any familiarity with the law, the author of the plays *must* have been a lawyer. In the book which resulted from his fascination with the authorship question, Twain describes his "pet argument" accordingly: "Shakespeare couldn't have written Shakespeare's works, for the reason that the man who wrote them was limitlessly familiar with the laws, and the law-courts, and law-proceedings, and lawyer-talk, and lawyer-ways."[3]

The Folger's manuscript copy of *Is Shakespeare Dead?* is dated February 13, 1909. The finished book, in a green cover, appeared in early April.[4] Harper and Brothers noted that "at the author's request this book was issued more hurriedly perhaps than any volume we have ever published. Only eighteen days elapsed between the time we received the manuscript and the appearance of the finished book." Twain's publisher also noted that "there is a rule in this office that none of Mark Twain's copy shall be changed—not even a comma. He is always very particular about that, and his wishes are respected."[5]

Twain immediately sent a copy of his new book to his friend Andrew Carnegie, who responded with a snappy note of gratitude despite his lack of agreement with Twain's premise:

My Dear Friend
Thanks for your latest.
Is Shakspeare dead? Guess not—never going to die.
Who was he—Don't care much so we've got him.
Bacon, or Johnson, [sic] or any other man what matter it—
A rose by any other name would smell as sweet.
That a man like Bacon, whose works were all so carefully preserved & pub-
lisht would let such gems as he must have known these were, to be scattered
in divers places & only rescued by two who acted therein—that would be a
greater surprise than that caused by an actor really writing them, an actor
known to many who testify that Will Shakspeare, when he started could
with difficulty be stopt, he astonished his hearers with his outpourings. . . .[6]

Sir George Greenwood received *his* copy of Twain's book shortly after its publication from an American friend, who inscribed it:

> Dear Greenwood:
>   This book is a fine boost for your book. Did Mark Twain get your permission to use your chapter "Was Shakespeare a Lawyer?" I assume that he did & that you have already got a copy. I send this for full measure. This book has created quite a Sensation. It is about the strongest dose that Sidney "Doubtless" Lee et als have received. It will have a wide circulation.[7]

Incensed, Greenwood inscribed in pencil at the beginning and end of the "lifted" chapter: "Lifted from my book without permission & without mentioning my name! See The Shakespeare Problem Restated p. 371" and "All this marked in pencil, from p. 79 to this p. 101 is taken from my book! See p. 4 of ~~Mark Twains~~ ^this^ book."[8] At the same time, he wrote to a Philadelphia friend:

> As to Mark Twain's book it will, no doubt, do me much good in the way of advertisement, but I find that literary men here think it inexcusable of him to lift 22 pages from my book without mentioning my name or that of my publisher. John Lane is up in arms about it, and is, I believe, going to enter a protest in some of your newspapers. As to the English edition we have requested that due acknowledgment may be made therein, & this, I understand, is to be done.[9]

In fact, while Twain neglected to include the names of the author and publisher in the footnote to the "pirated" chapter, he didn't completely fail to identify his source. The attribution on p. 79 of *Is Shakespeare Dead?* reads: "From Chapter XIII of 'The Shakespeare Problem Restated,'" and the extracted material appears in smaller type. This was not good enough for Greenwood's publishers, John Lane Company, however, who prevented Twain's book from being imported to England until the attribution problem was corrected and further demanded that future editions include a full-page advertisement supplied by them. By now, news of the controversy had reached *The New York Times*, who aired the opinions of both sides in a lengthy article on June 9, 1909. In their defense, Harper & Brothers showed that they had been granted permission by John Lane to publish the chapter, and argued that the absence of formal acknowledgment was a simple oversight in the rush to produce Twain's book. A day after this first article, *The Times* reported that Twain had concurred with his publisher in his reply to the charges by John Lane: "It was

ANDREW CARNEGIE

Autograph letter, signed, to Mark Twain
April 28, 1909

4 pp.; 168 x 135 mm.

Purchased from J. Wilson in 1988

Y.c.1470 (1)

SIR GEORGE GREENWOOD

Autograph letter, signed, to Dr. Isaac Hull Platt
May 30, 1909

7 pp.; 178 x 122 mm.

Purchased from A. S. W. Rosenbach in 1922

Y.c.1096 (15)

1. Folger Y.c.545 (1b).

2. Twain's annotated copy of Greenwood's book is in the Berg Collection at the New York Public Library. See S. Schoenbaum, *Shakespeare's Lives*, new ed. (Oxford, 1991), 410.

3. Folger S.a.107, fol. 14.

4. *Is Shakespeare Dead?* (New York, 1909). A modern edition was published by Oxford University Press in 1996, ed. Erica Jong.

5. "Can Mark Twain be a literary pirate?" *New York Times*, June 9, 1909.

6. Folger Y.c.1470 (1).

7. Folger PR2944 C7, front endleaf.

8. For a postmodern view of Greenwood's response to Twain's use of a chapter from his book, see Michael D. Bristol, "Sir George Greenwood's Marginalia in the Folger copy of Mark Twain's *Is Shakespeare Dead?" Shakespeare Quarterly* 49 (1998): 411–16.

9. Folger Y.c.1096 (15).

10. "Pays $1,900 for Rare Mark Twain Work: Dr. Rosenbach Buys Manuscript at Sale of Mrs. John B. Stanchfield Library," *New York Times*, January 25, 1923. According to the article, "This is a desirable manuscript because autograph manuscripts of this period of Mark Twain's life are uncommon. During the later years of Mark Twain's literary activity he generally resorted to stenographic dictation. This is one of his last in longhand."

merely an oversight in not giving the proper credit." On the following day, Twain, seemingly immune to unfavorable publicity, gave a lengthier response:

In writing my book I took the liberty of using large extracts from Mr Greenwood's book . . . because of the great admiration which I have for that book, and with the full permission of the publishers. I added a foot note in which I gave full credit to both author and publishers. The book was put through the press in great haste, and somewhere, nobody seems to know where, the foot note was lost, probably in the composing room. That is the sum and substance of the whole story.

But of course the John Lane Publishing Company of England, the publishers of Mr Greenwood's book, are good advertisers. Now, one of Mark Twain's books, so they tell me, is considered worth while reading. I know, at any rate, that my books have always sold well. But to have a man like Mark Twain steal portions from another man's book makes that book something extraordinary.

Messrs. Lane are well aware of this fact, and it is to be regretted that a mistake in the mechanical department of another publishing house should be made much of to accuse falsely one who has already won fame in the literary world and to put in a false light another who is the most modest and retiring of men.

The relationship between the Folger manuscript and the printed text is uncertain. Nearly all of the corrections to the manuscript are in the printed version, but the printed version includes a postscript not found here. *The Times* reported the sale of Twain's manuscript, "Is Shakespeare Dead?" at the Anderson Galleries on January 25, 1923. It was purchased by the Philadelphia bookseller Dr. A. S. W. Rosenbach for $1900, the highest price of the day. Henry Folger acquired the manuscript from Rosenbach a few weeks later.[10]

In addition to the manuscript work and letter, above, the Folger has fifteen letters and telegrams from Twain concerning Twain's forays into the theatrical world, as well as other letters relating to him and a book formerly owned by him. The Folger also owns Greenwood's annotated copies of his own work, *The Shakespeare Problem Restated* (London, 1908) and of Sidney Lee's *Life of Shakespeare* (London, 1915), twenty letters from Greenwood, and nine letters to him.

H.W.

Elizabeth Barrett Browning (1806–1861)

whose [...] yet [...] the [...] the lapse of ages
Ἀφρήτως, ἀθέμιςος, ἀνέςιος ἐςιν ἐκεῖνος — ?

Literature then is the food of the mind and instils into that blissful enjoyment of intellectual gra= =tification which at once renders it more en= =lightened more cultivated and more truly great. Reflection and enquiry, exalt, fire, and animate the soul, but reading renders it more [...] more intellectual more polished and more refined! Ovid says,

*Ingenuas didicisse fideliter artes
Emollit mores, nec sinit esse feros. —*

E. B. Barrett

"On Literature," Y.c.290 (4a), p. 6

"On Literature"
ca.1825?

Autograph manuscript, signed

5 ¾ pp.; 228 x 185 mm.

Purchased from Maggs Bros.
in 1924

Y.c.290 (4a)

1. Folger Y.c.290 (4a), p. 6.
Browning quotes from Ovid's
Ex Ponto, book 2, no. 9, lines
47–48, which translates to:
"Add the fact that to have con-
scientiously studied the liberal
arts refines behavior and does
not allow it to be savage."

2. Folger Y.c.290 (4a), p. 3.

3. A revised version of this
essay is in the Berg Collection
at New York Public Library.

4. Folger W.b.47. Published
in *The Letters of Elizabeth
Barrett Browning to Mary
Russell Mitford, 1836–1854*,
eds. Meredith B. Raymond
and Mary Rose Sullivan,
3 vols. (Waco, TX: Armstrong
Browning Library of Baylor
University, 1983).

5. Folger Y.c.290 (1-2).

Reflection and enquiry shall fire and annoint the soul, but reading renders
it more pure more intellectual more polished and more refined! Ovid says,
> Ingenuas didicisse fideliter artes
> Immolit mores, nec sinit esse feros![1]

IN THIS APPARENTLY UNPUBLISHED ESSAY, the poet Elizabeth Barrett
Browning passionately argues for the superiority of literature over all other activities, professions, and "savage pleasures." To bolster her theory that one could only
achieve true exaltation of the soul and enlargement of the mind by devoting oneself
to the pursuit of literary pre-eminence, Browning turns to Hamlet's soliloquy in Act
4, scene 4, shown here, writing,

As the eagle spurns the earth and binds his lofty flight to the regions of
eternal day so greatly does intellectual superiority triumph over corporal.
Shakespeare exclaims[,] inspired by his intimate knowledge of the
human heart-
> What is man
> If his chief good and market of his time
> Be but to sleep and feed? A beast, no more---![2]

Browning signs this essay "EB Barrett," for Elizabeth Barrett Barrett (her maiden
name). Its first page indicates that it was intended for the *Literary Gazette and
Journal of Belles Lettres*, to which she had contributed her first published work, "The
Rose and Zephyr," in 1825, followed by "Irregular Stanzas," in 1826. Most likely "On
Literature" was written in the same time period, when she was nineteen years old.[3]

The Folger also has a volume of thirty-seven incomplete letters written by
Elizabeth Barrett Browning to the author Mary Russell Mitford,[4] as well as a draft
and fair copy of a letter/essay to the editor of the *Literary Gazette* on the insincerity
of compliments.[5] Robert Browning, whom she married in 1846, is represented by
letters and a corrected proof of his poem on Shakespeare, "The Names." In one letter he confesses: "The very name of Shakespeare is made a terror to me by the people
who, just now, are pelting each other under my nose, and calling themselves his dis-
ciples all the while." A series of letters from Frederick Furnivall to Robert Browning
urges him to publish his wife's poetry in an inexpensive edition. The Folger owns
Elizabeth Barrett Browning's copy of the minor poems of Schiller (1844), and nine
books formerly owned by Robert Browning, many of them presentation copies.

H. W.

Washington Irving (1783–1859)

"The Bermudas: A Shakespearian research," S.b.107, fol. 8

"The Bermudas: A
Shakespearian research"
ca.1838

22 fols.; 200 x 123 mm.

Autograph manuscript,
with the exception of fols. 1
and 21, which were supplied
by the bookseller George S.
Hellman in his autograph

Purchased from Hellman
in November 1918

S.b. 107

1. Folger S.b.107, fol. 8.

2. Irving's account was based
on Silvester Jourdain's *A
Discovery of the Barmudas,
otherwise called the Ile of
Diuels: by Sir Thomas Gates,
Sir George Somners, and
Captayne Newport* (London,
1610) [STC 14816].

3. "The Bermudas,"
Knickerbocker, 15:1 (1840).

4. Information in this paragraph is taken from Stanley
Thomas Williams, *The Life of
Washington Irving* (New York,
1971 [1935]), 95, 100, 107.

5. They published the *History
of the Life and Voyages of
Christopher Columbus*
(Boston, 1839) in the following
year.

6. Folger D.a.2.

The storm subsided, but left her a mere foundering wreck. The crew stood in the hold to their waists in water, vainly endeavoring to bail her with kettles, buckets, and other vessels. The leaks rapidly gained on them, while their strength was as rapidly declining.[1]

IN "THE BERMUDAS," Washington Irving describes the 1609 English voyage to Virginia in which Admiral George Somer's vessel was ship-wrecked in the Bermudas.[2] He begins the essay by recounting his own return to America from England, when, after days of stormy weather, the sun broke through as they passed the Bermuda islands. Reminded of Oberon's description of music and moonlight on the ocean, Irving's interest in the islands was increased by his "fancying that I could trace in their early history, and in the superstitious notions connected with them, some of the elements of Shakespeare's wild and beautiful drama of the *Tempest*" (fol. 3). "The Bermudas" appeared in the *Knickerbocker* in 1840.[3] Like many other essays from this period, it was loosely based upon earlier writings—in this case, "The Voyage," from *The Sketch Book of Geoffrey Crayon, Gent.* (1820–1821), which recounts a stormy passage *to* England.

The late 1830s were difficult years for Irving. Devastated by the loss of his broth-er Peter, in June 1838, he frequently refers in letters to his "precarious resources" as he struggled to support his extended family. To make ends meet he began trawling his old notebooks, trying to convert words into ready cash despite his notorious aversion to writing for periodicals. His 1839 agreement with the *Knickerbocker* provided him with $500 quarterly for two and a half years. Securing the services of "Geoffrey Crayon" was a coup for the fashionable women's magazine, but his fellow writers felt that he had sold out. Longfellow observed that Irving "is writing away *like fury*, in the Knickerbocker;—*he had better not*; old remnants—odds and ends,—about Sleepy Hollow, and Granada. What a pity." Irving's financial situation improved when he was appointed Envoy Extraordinary and Minister Plenipotentiary to the Court of Spain on February 10, 1842, a position he held until 1846.[4]

This manuscript is in Irving's hand with the exception of leaves 1 and 21. On the verso of two leaves (fols. 7 and 8) are unfinished drafts of letters dated December 18 and 21, 1838. These letters are to the publisher (Marsh, Capen, Lyon, and Webb) of an abridged edition of *The Life and Voyages of Christopher Columbus*, which he was currently preparing.[5] The Folger also has one of Irving's commonplace books, ca.1810, which includes extracts from a number of non-Shakespearean Elizabethan plays. Some of the extracts later supplied chapter headings for the *Sketch Book.*[6]

H. W.

George Sand (Amandine Aurore Lucile Dupin) (1804–1876)

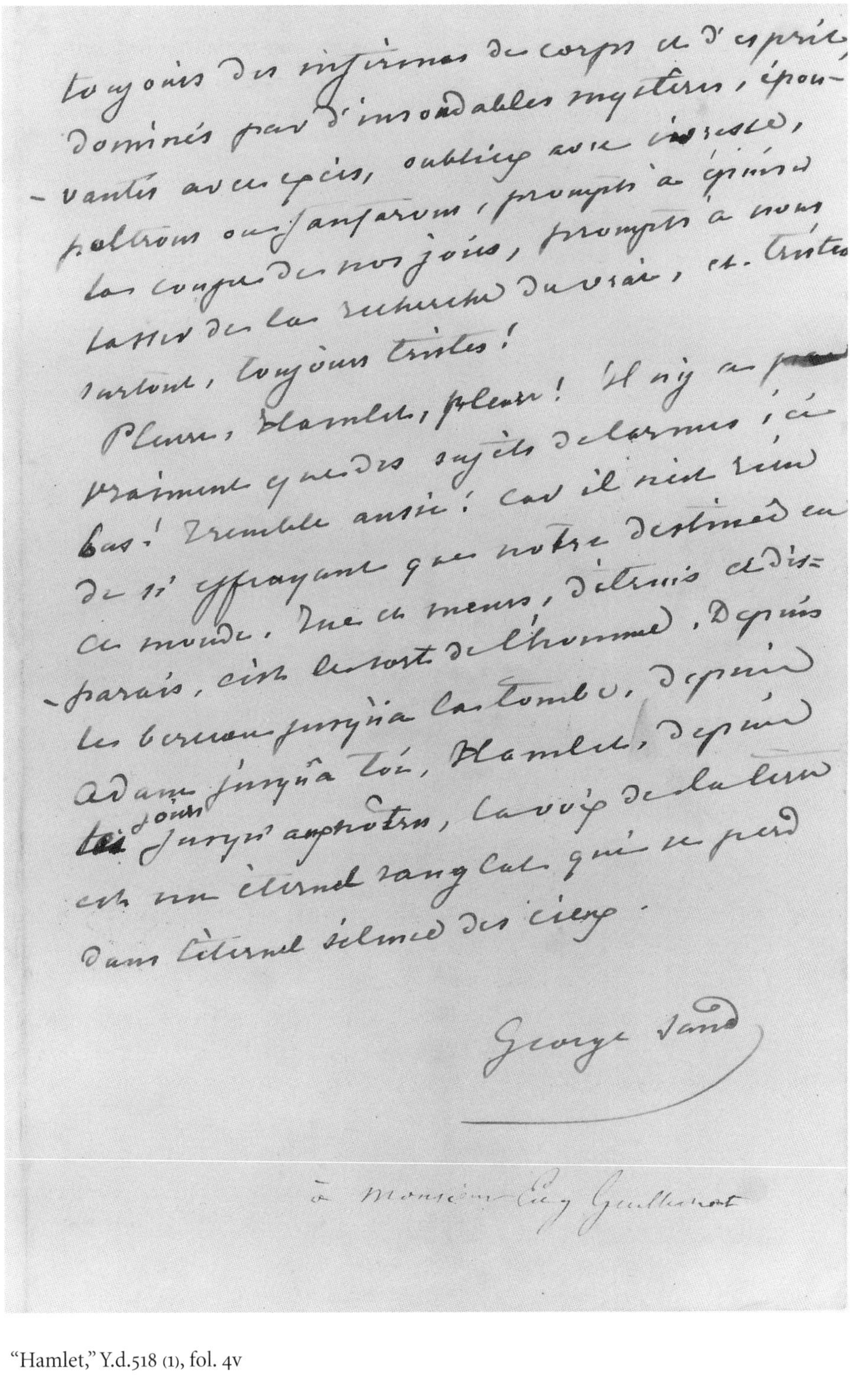

[handwritten letter in French, signed:]

George Sand

à Monsieur [...] Guillemot

"Hamlet," Y.d.518 (1), fol. 4v

"Hamlet"
[1845]

Autograph manuscript,
signed, in French

4 fols.; 205 x 134 mm.

Purchased from Anderson
Galleries in 1918

Y.d.518 (1)

1. Folger Y.d.578 (1), fol. 1.

2. For the 1844–1845 season in
Paris and the correspondence
between Macready and Sand,
see B. Juden and J. Richer, *W.
C. Macready et les comédiens
anglais à Paris* (*Revue des lettres modernes*, 74–75, 1962). A
modern edition of this essay
can be found in George Sand,
Questions d'art et de littérature,
eds. Henriette Bessis and Janis
Glasgow (Paris, 1991), first
published in 1878.

3. Folger Y.c.1652(1). Published
in *Correspondance de George
Sand*, ed. Georges Lubin
(Paris, 1964), VI:776–77.

4. *Correspondance*, VI:783.

5. Y.c.1652(2). *Correspondance*,
VI:797.

6. Y.c.1652(3). *Correspondance*,
VII:744–45.

7. Y.c.1652(4). *Correspondance*,
XIII:575.

O Hamlet, dis-nous le secret de ta douleur immense, et pourquoi nous
nous sentons vibrer autour de toi comme autant d'échos de ta plainte
mystérieuse?[1]

THE FRENCH NOVELIST and critic George Sand wrote this essay on *Hamlet*
shortly after seeing William Macready play the title role in Paris on January 13, 1845.[2]
First published in February 1845 in *L'Almanach du Mois*, it is in a sense an encomi-
um to Macready, who transformed her ideas about the play and the character.

On the same day that Sand witnessed Macready's performance, she wrote him a
"most eloquent and elegant" letter, now at the Folger.[3] In it, she thanks him from the
bottom of her heart for enabling her to feel and understand the character for the
first time. As a result, she writes, she had forgotten the Hamlet of her imagination
and now saw Hamlet as Shakespeare had intended him. Shortly after receiving this
letter, Macready paid her the first of many visits, and she excitedly reported the
meeting in a letter to her friend Pauline Viardot.[4] In early February, Macready wrote
to Sand's daughter, Solange, and the Folger has Sand's and her daughter's letters of
gratitude for this gesture.[5]

Sand's admiration for Macready was life-long. In a Folger letter of June 9, 1847,
which opens with the salutation "Mon cher Hamlet," Sand reports to Macready the
marriage of her daughter and her plans to dedicate her novel to him.[6] The novel,
Chateau des Desertes, was eventually published in 1851. In her letter dated April 10,
1856, Sand invites Macready to the dress rehearsal for her adaptation of *As You
Like It* ("Comme il vous plaira") so that she could benefit from "votre avis et votre
sentiment sur cette tentative!" ("your opinion and feeling on this endeavor!").[7]

H. W.

Algernon Charles Swinburne (1837–1909)

A Study of Shakespeare, S.b.96, p. 1 of part 3

A study of Shakespeare
ca.1875

Autograph manuscript

111 fols.; 335 x 212 mm.

Purchased from Maggs Bros. in 1918

S.b.96

---

1. John Milton, *Paradise Lost*, line 644.

2. Folger S.b.85.

3. Folger S.b.84.

The entrance to the third period of Shakespeare is like the entrance to that lost & lesser Paradise of old,

> With dreadful faces thronged, & fiery arms.[1]

Lear, Othello, ∧Macbeth,∧ Coriolanus, Antony, Timon, these are names indeed of ∧something more than∧ tragic purport. Only in the sunnier distance beyond, where the sunset of ~~his~~ ∧Shakespeare's∧ imagination seems to melt or flow back into the sunrise, do we discern Prospero beside Miranda, Florizel by Perdita, Palamon with Arcite, the same knightly & kindly Duke Theseus as of old; & above them all & all others of ~~all Shakespeare's~~ ∧his∧ divine & human children the crowning & final & ineffable figure of Imogen.

THE AUTOGRAPH MANUSCRIPT of Swinburne's *A Study of Shakespeare* (ca.1875) consists of a rough draft of portions of parts two and three of the three-part work, each part dealing with successive periods in Shakespeare's artistic development. It differs considerably from the text that was printed in 1880 and contains a number of unpublished passages. The page shown here, however, the first page of part three, is identical to that of the printed text.

Swinburne's dedication of *A Study of Shakespeare* (London, 1880) to the antiquarian scholar, James Orchard Halliwell-Phillipps, and his inclusion in the appendix of a satirical attack on Frederick Furnivall's New Shakespeare Society, titled "Report of the proceedings on the first Anniversary Session of the Newest Shakespeare Society" (the Folger owns Swinburne's ca.1879 autograph copy of this satire), led to what became known as the Pigsbrook controversy.[2] Furnivall (1825–1910), who had founded a number of societies in the late 1800s in his quest to publish accurate texts of medieval works, hoped that his newest society, founded in 1873, could determine "the succession of Shakespere's Work" through the use of metrical tests. Swinburne, no stranger to controversy, ridiculed this form of scholarship in a skit titled "The Newest Shakespere Society" in the April 1876 issue of the *Examiner*. He proceeded to denounce Furnivall's group, of which Robert Browning was president, as "sham Shakespeareans." The Folger has Swinburne's autograph copy of "Whence these tears?," another attack on Furnivall published in *The Athenaeum* on March 31, 1877, under the title "The Court of Love."[3] Furnivall saw Halliwell-Phillipps's acceptance of the dedication of *A Study of Shakespeare* as an act of betrayal, and in the foreword to a facsimile edition of the second quarto of *Hamlet* dubbed Swinburne "Pigsbrook" and Halliwell-Phillipps "H-ll-P." He responded in even stronger fashion with *The "co." of Pigsbrook & co.* (London, 1881), which was a reply to "A letter from Mr. J. O. Halliwell-Phillipps to the members of the New Shakspere society" (Brighton, 1881).

The Folger has a number of letters concerning the Pigsbrook controversy, as well as Swinburne's personal copy of the 1880 edition of *A study of Shakespeare* with his autograph corrections made in preparation for the third edition in 1895.[4] Other autograph Swinburne manuscripts, some of which were used as printer's copy, include his poem *Autumn Vision*, his parody upon Hamlet's "To be or not to be" soliloquy (satirizing the pedantry of William Carew Hazlitt), and essays on Christopher Marlowe, Beaumont and Fletcher, John Marston, Shakespeare's *Richard II* and *Pericles*, the historical play of *Edward III*, William Rowley, and Thomas Heywood.[5] Some of these essays appeared in periodicals such as *The North American Review*, *The Nineteenth Century*, *Harper's Monthly Magazine*, and *The Gentleman's Magazine*, and were later reprinted in Swinburne's *Age of Shakespeare* (London, 1908). Additionally, the Folger has a group of uncataloged essays, poems, prologues, letters, fragments, and corrected proofs as well as twenty-nine books formerly owned by Swinburne, some with presentation inscriptions to his close friend Theodore Watts-Dunton, with whom he lived from September 1879 until his death.

H. W.

4. Folger Y.d.329 (1–29), C.b.4, W.a.73 (1–43), W.a.153.

5. Folger N.b.26, S.b.83, D.b.29, D.b.28, D.b.27, S.b.86, S.b.89, S.b.99, S.b.98, D.b.30, D.b.31 (fragment only).

freer, completer than hitherto,
may discover in the plays named
only scientific (Baconian?)
the genuine inauguration of
modern democracy — furnishing realistic
and first=class artistic portraitures
of the medieval world, the feudal
personalities, institutes in their morbid
accumulations, deposits upon politics
and sociology, — may penetrate to
that hard=pan, far down and back of the
ostent of to=day, on which (and on
which only,) the progression of
the last two centuries has built
this democracy which now holds
The republicanism now holding
secure lodgment over the whole
civilized world.

¶ Whether such was the un-
conscious or (as I think likely)
more or less
the x conscious and foreperceiving
purpose of him who fashioned
those marvellous architectonics,
is a secondary question.

Walt Whitman

"What Lurks Behind Shakespeare's Historical Plays?", S.b.89, fol. 6

Walt Whitman (1819–1892)

I should specifically dwell on, ∧and make much of,∧ that inexplicable element of every highest poetic nature which ~~makes~~ ∧causes∧ it ~~delight~~ to cover up and involve ~~perhaps~~ its real purpose and meanings in folded removes and far recesses.[1]

IN THE SAME YEAR that Walt Whitman purchased his house on Mickle Street in Camden, New Jersey, he offered this short essay to Jeannette Gilder and her brother Joseph Gilder, co-editors of the literary journal, the *Critic*. In addition to requesting $15 and the right to review the essay in proof, he also stipulated that he receive twenty free copies and that he maintain the right to include the piece "in my future book."[2]

"What Lurks Behind Shakespeare's Historical Plays" appeared in print within two weeks of Whitman's letter to the Gilders, in the September 27, 1884, issue of the *Critic*. The manuscript copy shown here, in Whitman's hand, served as the printer's copy. It contains revisions by Whitman and by an editor (in red ink), who normalized punctuation and spelling despite Whitman's request on the first leaf to "follow copy—punctuation, capitalization &c." The essay was later reprinted in Whitman's collection of prose and poetry, *November Boughs* (1888).

In addition to raising the question of Shakespeare's identity, Whitman puts forth the view that Shakespeare's history plays, beginning with *Henry VI*, represent "the inauguration of modern democracy." He writes, "the distinctiveness and glory of ~~Shakspere~~ ∧the Poet∧ reside, not in ~~the~~ ∧his∧ vaulted ~~plays~~ ∧dramas∧ of the passions, but those founded on the contests of English dynasties, and the French wars." In the essay, he cites the comments of his friend William O'Conner, who had first inspired Whitman to think in this direction. Two days after it was published, Whitman sent a copy of the "little piece the whole idea of which I got from you, as you see," to O'Connor.[3]

The Folger has seven other Whitman-Shakespeare manuscripts in the collection: a set of marked-up printed pages from "Poetry To-day in America—Shakspere —The Future," a partial draft of his essay "George Fox (and Shakspere)," a partial draft of his essay "Shakspere for America" with a note to the editor of *Poet Lore*, a list of authors and works probably related to his essay "A Backward Glance O'er Travel'd Roads," a list of subjects for lectures titled "On Poems. . . ," a letter to Edward Dowden concerning, among other things, Dowden's book on Shakespeare, and an "At Home" calling card.[4] Whitman's copy of Shakespeare *Poems* (Philadelphia, 1847) is also at the Folger.[5]

H. W.

"What Lurks Behind Shakespeare's Historical Plays?" [1884]

Autograph manuscript, signed

6 fols.; 307 x 163 mm.

Purchased from A. S. W. Rosenbach in June 1921

S.b.89

1. Folger S.b.89, fol. 3

2. Prior to sending this essay to the *Critic*, he had already submitted it to *The Nineteenth Century* on August 8 and the *North American Review* on September 1, for the asking price of $50. See Walt Whitman, *The Correspondence, 1876–1885*, 1:3, ed. Edwin Haviland Miller (New York, 1964), 376–77.

3. *Correspondence*, 377.

4. For a brief overview of these items, see Arthur Golden, "Uncollected Whitman Material in the Folger Shakespeare Library," *Papers of the Bibliographical Society of America*, 79:4 (1985): 529–39.

5. Folger PR2841 1847a copy 1 Sh.Col.

Spirit of art, is merely an
intensified mode of over-emphasis.
"But life soon shattered the perfection
of the form. Even in Shakespeare
we can see the beginning of the end.
It shows itself by the gradual breaking
up of the blank-verse in the
later plays, by the predominance
given to prose & by the over-importance
assigned to characterization. The
passages in Shakespeare – & they
are many – where the language
is uncouth, vulgar exaggerated fantastic, obscene
even are entirely due to Life calling
for an echo of her own voice, and
rejecting the intervention of beautiful
style, through which alone should
life be suffered to find expression.
Shakespeare is not by any means a
flawless artist. He is too fond of
going directly to life, & borrowing
lifes natural utterance. He forgets
that when Art surrenders her
imaginative medium she surrenders

"The Decay of Lying," Y.d.520 (1), fol. 2

Oscar Wilde (1854–1900)

Shakespeare is not by any means a flawless artist. He is too fond of going directly to life & borrowing life's natural utterance. He forgets that when Art surrenders her imaginative medium she surrenders everything…

IN "THE DECAY OF LYING," one of Oscar Wilde's two major works of literary criticism, he expounds upon two central paradoxes of the aesthetic movement— that life and nature imitate art rather than the other way around, and that art is superior to both life and nature in terms of beauty and style. First published in the monthly periodical *The Nineteenth Century* in January 1889, "The Decay of Lying" is structured as a dialogue between two speakers, Vyvyan and Cyril (the names of his two sons, born in 1885 and 1886).[1] In *De Profundis*, Wilde notes that this essay, "the first and best of all my dialogues," was inspired by a dinner in a Soho cafe with his friend Robert Ross.[2] In a letter to Marie-Anne de Bovet, the French journalist, he takes pleasure in remarking that, "The admirable English are still much bewildered by 'The Decay of Lying,' but even here there are a few who can decipher its paradoxes."[3]

The Folger has in its collection four draft pages of the essay, written in pencil and corrected in purple ink in Wilde's own hand. The fragment consists of the section of the essay relating to Renaissance drama.[4] Vyvyan, sitting in the library of a country house in Nottinghamshire with Cyril, discourses on the tenuous balance between realism and imagination in English drama and bemoans the tendency of contemporary dramatists to imitate the vulgarities of life at the expense of artistic style and creativity. Reading from an article he plans to publish (called "The Decay of Lying: A Protest"), Vyvyan locates the beginning of this unfortunate trend in Renaissance drama. Even Shakespeare is not above reproach:

But Life soon shattered the perfection of the form. Even in Shakespeare we ~~discover~~ ∧can see∧ the beginning of the end. It shows itself by the ~~slow~~ ∧gradual∧ breaking up of the blank-verse in the later plays, by the predominance given to prose, & by the over-importance assigned to characterization. The passages in Shakespeare—& they are many—where the language is uncouth, vulgar, ∧exaggerated,∧ fantastic, obscene even, are entirely due to Life calling for an echo of her own voice, and rejecting the intervention of beautiful style, through which alone should life be suffered to find expression. . . . All that we desired to point out was that the magnificent work of the Elizabethan & Jacobean artists contained within itself the seeds of its own dissolution.

"The Decay of Lying"
ca.1888

Autograph fragment

4 fols.; 235 x 175 mm

Purchased from Maggs Bros. in February 1920

Y.d.520 (1)

1. *The Nineteenth Century*, 25 (Jan. 1889): 35-56. It received very favorable reviews when it was republished in revised form in 1891, shortly after the publication of *The Picture of Dorian Gray*, as one of four Wilde essays in *Intentions* (London, 1891).

2. Merlin Holland and Rupert Hart-Davis, eds., *The Complete Letters of Oscar Wilde* (London, 2000), 688.

3. Ibid., 393.

4. The New York Public Library has an apparently unrelated partial draft of "Decay," while another fragment is in the Donald F. Hyde Collection. The William Andrews Clark Memorial Library, Los Angeles, has a forgery of the essay made by Fabian Lloyd, the nephew of Wilde's wife. A fifty-four leaf version of the manuscript, given to Frank Richardson by Wilde, was sold at Sotheby's in 1910 and again in 1934.

Oscar Wilde

5. Folger Y.c. 1653 (2). Letter dated ca. September 8, 1894 (Holland and Hart-Davis, 608–9).

6. Y.c. 1653 (1). Letter dated June 15 or 16, 1877 (Holland and Hart-Davis, 53).

Wilde engaged with Shakespeare in other writings as well, favorably reviewing a number of plays in the 1880s for *Pall Mall* magazine, writing an essay on the importance of authenticity in staging Shakespearean plays, and writing a pseudobiography of the dedicatee of Shakespeare's Sonnets, titled "The Portrait of Mr. W. H." (*Blackwood's Magazine*, July 1889). The Folger has a letter concerning the republication of "The Portrait of Mr. W. H.," in which Wilde chastises the publishers Elkin Mathews and John Lane for defaulting upon their agreement and then suggests entering into a compromise:

> The delay in its publication has been very annoying to me, but I have always behaved towards your firm with perfect courtesy and kindness. Even now, when I am calmly told that one member of the firm refuses, after his stamped agreement nearly eighteen months old, to publish the book 'at any price': and the other calmly tells me that his publication of the book depends on his approval of it: I am not really angry: I am simply amused. However, I am quite ready to let you off your agreement, on condition that you send me a cheque for £25, by return. . . .[5]

Another holograph letter at the Folger, addressed to the editor of the *Irish Monthly*, concerns the printing of a particular phrase ("our English Law") in "O sweetest singer of our English land," a sonnet he had written upon seeing Keats's grave in Rome. Wilde writes, "I am sorry you object to the words 'our English Law'—its a noble privilege to count oneself of the same race as Keats or Shakespeare. However I have changed it. I would not shock the feelings of your readers for anything."[6] The sonnet appeared in the July 1877 issue of the *Irish Monthly* and in *Poems* (1881).

H. W.

Alberto Sangorski (1862–1932)

Songs and Sonnets, W.b.260

William Shakespeare
Songs and Sonnets, with Tributes of Three Centuries written to commemorate the tercentenary of his death, April 23, 1916, by Sir Sidney Lee
1926

Illuminated, illustrated, and bound by Alberto Sangorski

80 pp.; 193 x 145 mm.

Commissioned by Messrs. Robson & Co., Ltd., of London, 1924–1926; purchased from Robson in 1926

W.b.260

1. See Stanley Bray, Christie's (New York), catalogue 7156 (November 9, 1990): *The Chevalier Collection*, 67.

2. Ibid., 12.

3. Ibid., 67.

THE *TIMES LITERARY SUPPLEMENT* for December 23, 1926, reported that "For many years a Londoner of foreign descent, Mr. Alberto Sangorski, has been 'making' beautiful books . . . . He has just completed for Messrs. Robson and Co., of 7 Hanover Street, a richly illuminated manuscript of Shakespeare's *Songs and Sonnets* [which] has been in hand for five years, and every detail—designing, engrossing illumination, painting, and binding has been done by Mr. Sangorski." Alberto Sangorski created his calligraphic masterpiece using the finest vellum and employing twenty-three carat gold leaf in the illuminations. The illuminated initials are in stylized floral and foliate designs decorated in blue, shades of purple and violet, green, and brown, as well as gold leaf. Sangorski interleaved each page with moiré silk. The jeweled binding of reddish pink goatskin decorated in blind and gilt has sapphires mounted in eighteen carat gold in the corners and Shakespeare's coat of arms, inlaid with a ruby, in the center surrounded by an onlaid laurel wreath of dark green leather. Henry Clay Folger purchased this exquisite manuscript soon after it was completed.

Alberto Sangorski (1862–1932) was taught illuminating and bookbinding by his brother, Francis Sangorski. In 1901, Francis Sangorski and George Sutcliffe had founded the most celebrated bookbinding firm of the early twentieth century, Sangorski & Sutcliffe. Alberto Sangorski joined the firm but left it between 1910 and 1912 and joined its great rival, Riviere & Son. Stanley Bray, the nephew of George Sutcliffe, suggests that the death of Francis Sangorski in 1912 "may have had something to do with it."[1] On April 14, 1912, the famous jewelled Peacock binding, created by Francis Sangorski for *The Rubaiyat of Omar Khayyam*, was lost on the *Titanic*. Just a couple of months later Francis Sangorski drowned while on holiday in Sussex.[2] Alberto Sangorski, who must have followed with interest his brother's creation of the "Great Omar," had no contact with his brother's partner George Sutcliffe from the time of his brother's death until 1933.[3] It was during this period that he designed and created the manuscript acquired by Henry Clay Folger.

Frank Mowery
Folger Shakespeare Library

Giuseppe Verdi (1813–1901)

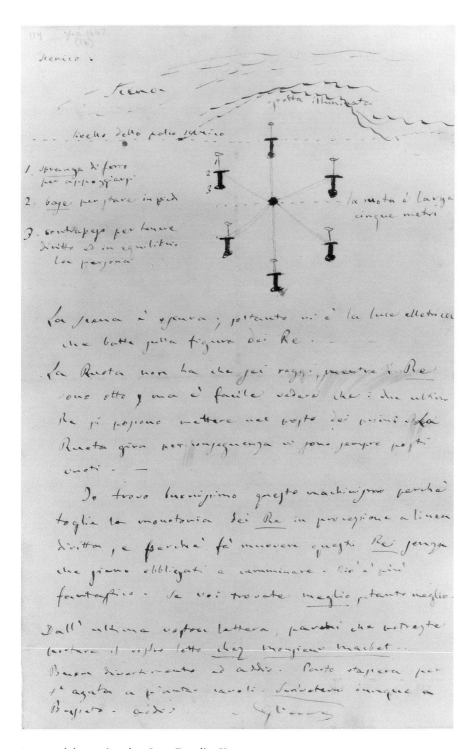

Autograph letter, signed, to Leon Escudier, Y.c.1447 (1), p. 5

Giuseppe Verdi

Autograph letter, signed,
to Leon Escudier,
in Italian
March 11, 1865

5 pp.; 210 x 133 mm.

Purchased at Sotheby sale,
December 11, 1902, no. 211

Y.c.1447 (1)

1. His other two Shakespeare-
inspired operas were products
of his later years. *Otello* was
completed in 1886, and the very
last opera he wrote, produced
in 1893, was *Falstaff*, based on
The Merry Wives of Windsor.

GIUSEPPE VERDI CAME CLOSE to giving up as a composer because of the personal and professional problems that beset him at the beginning of his career. He settled in Milan in 1839, where his *Oberto* was well received at La Scala, but the death of his young wife as he was composing his next work, *Un giorno di regno*, undoubtedly contributed to this work's failure. Verdi emerged from these setbacks, however, when he became inspired by the libretto of *Nabucco,* the opera which, when it was produced in 1842, established his reputation across Italy and Europe. *Nabucco*, like his next opera *I lombardi alla prima crociata,* had obvious political overtones. Verdi had found a combination of emotionally rousing music and tragic and heroic situations that hit home in an Italy on the eve of the Risorgimento and struggling for political freedom and unity, and in this political climate the two operas found great success.

Also belonging to this early period, which Verdi later called his "years in the galleys," is his first version of *Macbeth*, the first of the three plays by Shakespeare which, in the course of his career, Verdi set to music. *Macbeth* premiered in Florence on March 14, 1847; nearly two decades later, Verdi returned to the opera and revised it, and the new version premiered in Paris in April, 1865.[1]

The letter shown here, written in Italian to the French music publisher Leon Escudier, concerns Verdi's revision of *Macbeth*. It reveals the great care for details beyond the musical score that typified Verdi's interest in all aspects of the theatrical production of his works, and his vision of the way they all had to work together: the dramatic allusions in the orchestration, the appropriateness of dramatic gesture to action, the relationship between the action being imitated and the color of a singer's voice, the judicious use of "extras," his distaste for painted canvas backdrops, and his enthusiasm for stage machinery and the way it works. He crowns all this authoritative detail with the announcement to his friend that he is about to set off for Sant'Agata, his country house on the outskirts of Parma, in order to plant cabbages.

At the beginning of his letter, Verdi addresses three specifically orchestral questions (missing accidentals; instructions that the clarinets, bassoons, and violincellos should all play together; a correction for the trumpet at measure 70). He then moves on to the singers, with observations for the chorus, the tenor, and the soprano—most of his attention going to the latter's sleep-walking scene, which he considers the most dramatic moment of the opera. He is much struck by the dramatic interpretation of the actress Adelaide Ristori:

Anyone who has seen la Ristori knows that only the smallest gestures ought to be made; indeed, everything should be limited to a single gesture to wipe away a blood stain [Lady Macbeth] believes she has on her hand. Her movements must be slow. She should not take steps as such; rather, she should glide slowly across the ground as if she were a statue or a shadow that walks. Her eyes stare: staring cadaverous eyes. She is at the point of death. La Ristori gave a death rattle. In music, you cannot nor must not do this— just as the singer in the last act of *La Traviata* should not cough. Here the English horn has a lament that, more poetically, takes the place of the death rattle. It must be sung with the utmost simplicity, and with a dark color in the voice: she is dying. . . . There are points for the voice to come out with strength, but it has to be for the briefest second, a point I believe is indicated in the score. To sum up the effect, and for the terror this piece has to instil: a cadaverous figure, very few gestures, slow movements, a dark and expressive voice, etc. Notice here, as in the duet of the first act, that unless the singers sing *sotto voce*, the effect will be absolutely disgusting,

due to an imbalance between singers and a reduced orchestra (in which the violins, moreover, are playing with mutes). Verdi's suggestions for the scene of Birnham Wood indicate that

a magnificent effect can be obtained . . . with very few props and with simple velocity of movement. While Macbeth, in a short scene, sings his aria, 'pietà, rispetto, amore' you should prepare to occupy the entire stage, and not with a simple painted canvas backdrop. At the back of the stage there should be 3 or 4 rows of extras (MacDuff's soldiers), each one of these with a large tree branch that covers them. Some of these branches must be tall so that they will look like trees. When the scene opens this mass of men and fronds must be in movement, the further away the better. The movement must be slow and even.

At MacDuff's order, "Via le fronde," the army disappears "and all these surprise effects are theatrically impressive, so long as they are executed exactly and rapidly." At the time of this letter, the theater in Genoa was producing his old *Macbeth*, using a stage device for the appearance of the kings in Act 3, and Verdi wanted Escudier to know about it for possible use in the Paris production:[2]

2. Verdi's first version of the opera premiered in Florence (at the Teatro della Pergola) on March 14, 1847; the revised version premiered in Paris (at the Théâtre Lyrique) on April 21, 1865 (April 19 according to some sources).

It consists of a large wheel, that can't be seen, in which the kings are placed. And this moving circle rises and advances, lowers and then disappears. . . . The kings are above a small base, supported by a steel bar so that they can stand and remain in balance, with counterweights to keep the mechanism straight as the wheel is pushed. The wheel is completely below ground, and only its extremity is on a level with the stage. [See Verdi's sketch, illustrated on p. 203, of the curtain and illuminated grotto.]

1. Iron bar for support
2. Base to remain standing   The wheel is five meters in width
3. Counterweights to keep the
    person upright and in balance

The scene is dark; only the electric light illuminates the figure of the king.

The wheel has only six spaces, whereas there are eight kings, but it is easy to see that the last two kings can be put where the first ones were, since the wheel turns and there are therefore always empty spaces.

This mechanism appeals to me so much because it removes the monotony of the kings moving in procession in a straight line, and permits the kings to move without having to walk . . . which is fantastic. If you can find something better, so much the better.

Barbara Kreps
University of Pisa

George Eliot (Marian Evans) (1819–1880)

This declamation.

Nothing is here for tears, nothing to wail
Or knock the breast; no weakness, no contempt,
Dispraise, or blame; nothing but well & fair,
And what may quiet us in a death so noble.
                              Samson Agon.

But he, though blind of sight,
Despis'd & thought extinguish'd quite,
With inward eyes illuminated,
His fiery virtue rous'd
From under ashes into sudden flame,
And as an evening dragon came,
Assailant on the perched roosts
And nests in order rang'd
Of tame villatic fowl; but as an eagle
His cloudless thunder bolted on their heads.

Lear. (1.iv)   It may be so, my lord,—
Hear, nature, hear; dear goddess hear!
Suspend thy purpose, if thou didst intend
To make this creature fruitful!
Dry up in her the organs of increase;
And from her derogate body never spring
A babe to honour her!

Knight observes: "We print these four lines
according to the metrical arrangement
of the folio. In the quartos they are given
as prose. We cannot conceive of any
thing more destructive to the terrific
beauty of this passage than the regulation
by which it is distorted into the following

lines, the text of every modern editor:—
"It may be so, my lord,—Hear, nature, hear!
Dear goddess hear! Suspend thy purpose, if
Thou didst intend to make this creation fruitful."

Macbeth, III. 3   "Ere the bat hath flown
His cloister'd flight, ere to black Hecate's summons
The shard-borne beetle, with his drowsy hums
Hath rung night's yawning peal,
There shall be done a deed of dreadful note."
[knight's note. "We print these lines as in the
original. In modern editions they are inva-
riably regulated thus:—
Hath rung night's yawning peal, there shall be done
A deed of dreadful note.'
It is impossible, we think, not to feel that
there is a beauty in the original hemistich
of which such tampering has deprived us."]

ibid.   'Light thickens; & the crow
Makes wing to the rooky wood;
Good things of day begin to droop & drowse;
Whiles night's black agents to their prey do rouse.'

Act 5. 6.   This guest of summer,
The temple-haunting martlet, does approve,
By his lov'd mansionry, that the heaven's breath
Smells wooingly here: no jutty, frieze
Buttress, nor coigne of vantage, but this bird
Hath made his pendent bed & procreant cradle:
Where they most breed & haunt. I have observed
the air is delicate.'
[says knight   We request our readers to
repeat these celebrated lines, as we have
printed them. Our text is a literal copy

"Miscellaneous Quotations," M.a.13, pp. 142–143

"Miscellaneous
Quotations"
August 1868–ca. 1871

Autograph manuscript

174 pp.; 155 x 90 mm.

Purchased via Michelmore at
Sotheby's, June 27, 1923, no.
584 (by order of the executors
of the will of Gertrude, widow
of Charles Lee Lewes)

M.a.13

1. Folger M.a.13, pp. 142–43.
Quotation from John Milton,
Samson Agonistes,
lines 1721–4.

2. The other notebook at
the Folger, M.a.14, is dated
ca.1879. Two related
Middlemarch notebooks are
at the New York Public Library
and the Beinecke Library.

3. Eliot began the notebook
at both ends simultaneously—
one end for poetry, the other
for prose.

4. See John Clark Pratt and
Victor A. Neufeldt, eds.,
*George Eliot's Middlemarch
notebooks: a transcription*
(Berkeley, 1979), xxv.

Fine declamation.
Nothing is here for tears, nothing to wail
Or knock the breast; no weakness, no contempt,
Dispraise, or blame; nothing but well & fair
And what may quiet us in a death so noble.
Samson Agon.[1]

This "Partridge and Cooper's Patent Improved Metallic Book" contains 172 pages of quotations in the hand of George Eliot, compiled in preparation for her novel *Middlemarch*. One of two Eliot notebooks at the Folger, it includes extracts from the works of dozens of poets, dramatists, historians, literary critics, philosophers and mythologists, in English, German, French, Latin, Greek, Hebrew, Italian and Spanish.[2]

George Eliot began the notebook in August 1868 and finished it near the end of 1871, at the same time that the first of eight bi-monthly volumes of *Middlemarch* was published by John Blackwood in London.[3] The entries, some of which have direct counterparts in *Middlemarch*, record both her intellectual and physical journeys, and include extracts from works at the British Library and her personal collection as well as notes taken during trips to the Continent.[4]

The collected material represents her attempt to identify the "history of man," as she calls it in the first sentence of the novel. The opening shown here, headed "Fine declamation," includes quotations from Milton's *Samson Agonistes*, Shakespeare's *King Lear* and *Macbeth*, and extracts from Charles Knight's editorial comments in his second edition of the *Works of William Shakespeare* (1842–1844). In nearby pages she also quotes from *Henry VIII*, *Julius Caesar*, *Midsummer Night's Dream*, *Timon of Athens*, and Shakespeare's sonnets, as well as Tennyson, Horace, Swinburne and Byron.

Middlemarch was dedicated to Eliot's longterm companion, the literary scholar George Henry Lewes. The Folger has their annotated copy of *The Dramatic Works of William Shakespeare*, ed. Nicholas Rowe (London, 1832), as well as Eliot's copy of the Fourth Folio edition of Shakespeare's works (London, 1685).

H. W.

Dante Gabriel Rossetti (1828–1882)

This unpublished sonnet by Dante Gabriel Rossetti
(& in his handwriting) was given to Mr. Hall Caine
for his "Sonnets of Three Centuries", but was afterward
withdrawn, from its being out of harmony with the body of
the author's work

On certain Elizabethan Revivals.

O ruff-embastioned vast Elizabeth,
Bush to these bushel-bellied casks of wine,
Home-growth, 'tis true, but rank as turpentine
[what would we with] ouch skittle-plays at death?
Say, must we watch these brawlers' brandished teeth
Or to their reeking wit our ears incline,
Because all Castaly flowed crystalline
In gentle Shakespeare's modulated breath?

What! must our Drama with the rat-pit vie
Nor the scene close while one is left to kill?
[Shall this be poetry? And thou - thou man]
Of blood, thou cannibalic Caliban,
What shall be said to thee? - A poet? - Fie!
"An honorable murderer, if you will."

"On certain Elizabethan Revivals," Y.c.1457 (5)

"On certain
Elizabethan Revivals"
ca.1880

Autograph manuscript

1 fol.; 220 x 180 mm.

Purchased from G.
Michelmore & Co. in 1923

Y.c.1457 (5)

---

1. *Sonnets of Three Centuries*
(London, 1881), vii.

On certain Elizabethan Revivals.

O ruff-embastioned vast Elizabeth,
Bush to these bushed-bellied casks of wine,
Home-growth, 'tis true, but rank as turpentine,
What would we with such skittle-plays at death?
Say, must we watch these brawlers' brandished lathe,
Or to their reeking wit our ears incline,
Because all Castaly flowed crystalline
In gentle Shakspeare's modulated breath?

What! must our drama with the rat-pit vie,
Nor the scene close while one is left to kill?
Shall this be poetry? And thou—thou man
Of blood, thou cannibalic <u>Caliban</u>,
What shall be said to thee? – A poet? –Fie!
"An honorable murderer, if you will."

THIS AMUSING UNPUBLISHED SONNET by the great pre-Raphaelite poet and painter, Dante Gabriel Rossetti, was written for inclusion in Sir Thomas Henry Hall Caine's *Sonnets of Three Centuries: An Anthology* (London: Elliot Stock, 1881). It was afterwards withdrawn, according to the polite note at the top in Caines's hand, because it was "out of harmony with the body of the author's work." However, Caine did include six other sonnets by Rossetti in his collection: "Known in Vain," "Lost Days," "Mary Magdalene at the Door of Simon the Pharisee," "Raleigh's All in the Tower," "Stillborn Love," and "True Woman" (I. Herself; II. Her Love; III. Her Heaven), as well as sonnets by Rossetti's siblings Christina and William Michael.

The friendship between Caine (1853–1931) and Rossetti began as a correspondence devoted almost exclusively to the topic of sonnets. Rossetti encouraged the younger man to pursue his plan to compile a book that represented "within the limits of a quintessential selection the whole body of native sonnet literature down to our own time."[1] As a result, they engaged in long epistolary discussions on the sonnet-form, on sonnets written in the Renaissance and the Romantic period, on each other's sonnets, on the title of Caine's edition (Rossetti thought "The English Castaly"), on conditions for inclusion in Caine's volume, and on how to approach living poets for contributions.

On March 12, 1880, Rossetti wrote to Caine concerning his own possible entries for the collection: "The manuscript volume I proposed perhaps to send is merely an old set of (chiefly) trifles, about which I should like an opinion as to whether any should be included in the future."[2] None of these "trifles" apparently made it into the volume, for shortly afterwards Caine wrote to his mentor: "Doubtless you are right in what you say as to the difficulty which prevents your offering me a sonnet of your own . . . your kindness in giving me a sonnet would be observed even among the witnesses of so many other kindnesses."[3]

The letters led to a face-to-face meeting in September 1880, and Caine lived with Rossetti from November 1881 until Rossetti's death in April 1882. In that year, Caine published *Recollections of D. G. Rossetti* (London) and proceeded to become a writer of exceedingly popular sensational novels.

Like many other of Rossetti's surviving manuscripts, this single sheet was torn, probably by Rossetti himself, from one of the bound notebooks of lined paper that he consistently used from the 1840s until his death.[4] The Folger has five other Rossetti letters relating to Shakespeare as well.[5]

H. W.

2. Vivien Allen, ed., *Dear Mr Rossetti: The Letters of Dante Gabriel Rossetti and Hall Caine, 1878-1881* (Sheffield, 2000), 52.

3. Ibid., 168–70.

4. See Jerome McGann, ed. "The Rossetti Archive: The Manuscripts," in *The Complete Writings and Pictures of Dante Gabriel Rossetti: A Hypermedia Research Archive* (Charlottesville: Institute for Advanced Research in the Humanities, 2000) <http://jefferson.village.virginia.edu:2020/mss.html>. McGann writes, "The surviving manuscripts show that Rossetti plundered his notebooks when he set about the business of publishing his poetry. He would tear out the pages containing individual works and use them to arrange a printer's copy."

5. Folger Y.c.1457 (1–4), MS Add 1083.

An April Day.

or Autolycus in Service.

Prologue.

Autolycus appears before the curtain

Aut.: Some of you are perhaps acquainted with an obscure piece written by an old play actor, William Shakespeare. If so, I am charged to pass a word to you. Make no confusion between one Autolycus who figures there with some applause, but who was hanged long since, and your humble servant the Autolycus of our little comedy. It was thought convenient that I should borrow the old gentleman's name to put you in the key for my exploits; and indeed, as my own has been somewhat blown upon by the calumnious, I was for my part nothing loath. But except that I am likewise a "snapper up of unconsidered trifles", you must bear it in mind that our resemblance goes no further than the nine letters of the name and the native country where we dwell. (He, by his music, his gaiety and his most airy speech — I, by a kind of thinness of the blood — he by his engaging merits — I, alas! by my defects — betray our origin. For both were born in a far better land than any is inhabited by man, in that Sealand Bohemia of the mind, once discovered, now forever lost. ... the shadow of a shadow, the echo of the echo of sweet music; and for the sake of our origin, be tender to my frailties!

Aut

An April Day, or Autolycus in Service, N.b.32, fol. 2

212

Robert Louis Stevenson (1850–1894)

Aut: Some of you are perhaps acquainted with an obscure piece written by an old play actor, William Shakespeare. If ∧it be∧ so, I am charged to pass a word to you. Make no comparison between the Autolycus who figures there with some applause, but who was hanged long since, and your humble servant the Autolycus of our little comedy. It was thought convenient that I should borrow the old gentleman's name to put you in the key for my exploits; and indeed, as my own has been somewhat blown upon by the calumnious, I was for my part nothing loath. But except that I am likewise "a snapper-up of unconsidered trifles," you must bear it in mind that our resemblance goes no farther than the nine letters of the name and the native country where we dwell. ∧For both of us∧—He, by his music, his gaiety and his most ~~happy~~ ∧airy∧ speech—I, by a kind of thinness of the blood—he by his engaging merits—I, alas! by my defects—betray our origin. ~~Both of us were born in the clear air~~ For both were born in a far better land than any is inhabited by man, in that ~~once discovered~~ Seaboard Bohemia of the mind, once discovered, now forever lost. ~~Here he lived in honour till his end, but thence was I turned out For my land's sake, be tender to my frailties!~~ ∧Take me, then, for what I am—the shadow of a shadow, the echo of the echo of sweet music; and for the sake of mine original, be tender to my frailties!

IN THE YEARS BETWEEN 1878 and 1883, Robert Louis Stevenson, author of *Treasure Island* and *Dr. Jekyll and Mr. Hyde*, worked on a three-act romantic farce based on the Autolycus of Shakespeare's *A Winter's Tale*.[1] The Folger has the only three drafts of this unpublished play known to exist.[2] The manuscript shown here, a rewritten version of most of Act I, was probably composed in 1883. In February of that year, Stevenson informed his friend and sometime co-author William Ernest Henley that he would have a number of new pieces for Chatto, his publisher, including

an April Day: which . . . is 'Autolycus at Service' rewritten with a literary, not a dramatic, finish. I am indeed fattening up that starveling till I begin to love it. But I don't believe its a stage play, and I work upon it without much thought for the stage; only because I love the theme. I have practically finished the First Act, and, as I say, I love it. It seems to me lovely and of good report. It may be as well to take out what is necessary to secure dramatic right. . . . Perhaps some handling might make it fit for the stage; but I work merely for the pleasure of playing with my puppets.[3]

An April Day, or Autolycus in Service ca.1880

Autograph manuscript

32 fols.; 164 x 209 mm.

Sold by Isobel Strong, the author's step-daughter; no. 364 in the Stevenson sale, Anderson Galleries, November 24, 1914 (no. 365 was Folger N.b.31); purchased for H. C. Folger

N.b.32

1. For an edition and introduction to this play, see Nancy Blonder Schiffman, *A Critical Edition of Robert Louis Stevenson's Unpublished Play* Autolycus in Service (dissertation, University of South Carolina, 1973).

2. The 32-sheet version (Folger MS N.b.31) was displayed in a Stevenson exhibition at the Grolier Club in 1914. *First Editions of the Works of Robert Louis Stevenson, 1850–1914, with Other Stevensoniana Exhibited at the Grolier Club from November 5 to November 28, 1914* (New York, 1915). N.b.31 consists of a draft of a nearly complete version, with an earlier draft of the first six scenes of Act I on the verso of 11 leaves; N.b.32 is a later revision of Act I; N.b.33 (Walpole Galleries, February 21, 1919, no. 486) consists of 4 pages of revisions and additions to the first act, probably written after N.b.31 and before N.b.32.

3. Yale University, Beinecke Collection of Writings by and about Robert Louis Stevenson, no. 3164, dating conjectural, transcribed in Schiffman, 178–9. Henley collaborated with Stevenson on four plays, *Deacon Brodie*, *Admiral Guinea*, *Beau Austin*, and *Macaire*. The first two were privately printed in 1880 and the third in 1884; all three were published with the title *Three Plays* in 1892 (Charles Scribner's Sons, New York, and D. Nutt, London); the fourth was printed privately in 1885, published in the *New Review* in June 1895, and in book form in 1896 (Stone, Kimball of Chicago and W. Heinemann, London).

4. Beinecke Collection, nos. 4718–9, both conjecturally dated early 1879, transcribed in Schiffman, 183–5.

5. Schiffman, xiv.

6. Schiffman, xx. The original idea for an Autolycus play probably came from an unfinished short story by Stevenson called "Autolycus at Court" (*The Letters of Robert Louis Stevenson*, ed. Sidney Colvin (New York, 1911), 1:206).

Henley appears to have taken a strong interest in the writing of Autolycus, advising Stevenson on character development in a number of letters in 1879. In one he writes, "I reread Shakespeare's Autolycus the 'tother day; he's not so good as he ought to have been, but he has points and points not a few . . .;" in another, he writes that he wants "to speak about the additions to Autolycus. . . . I read it aloud to Anna [his wife] to-day. We liked it a good deal. . . . How bloody good we will make these Autolycus plays!! How damnably the public will like them!!!"[4] It is possible that the draft that Henley read to his wife is Folger MS N.b.31, and that the "additions" are N.b.33.[5] Whether or not the other Autolycus plays mentioned by Henley were ever written is not known. Although Stevenson does not mention the play after 1883, he began writing the novel *Prince Otto* in April of that year, and some of the characters may very well have been quarried from *An April Day*.[6]

H. W.

Louisa May Alcott (1832–1888)

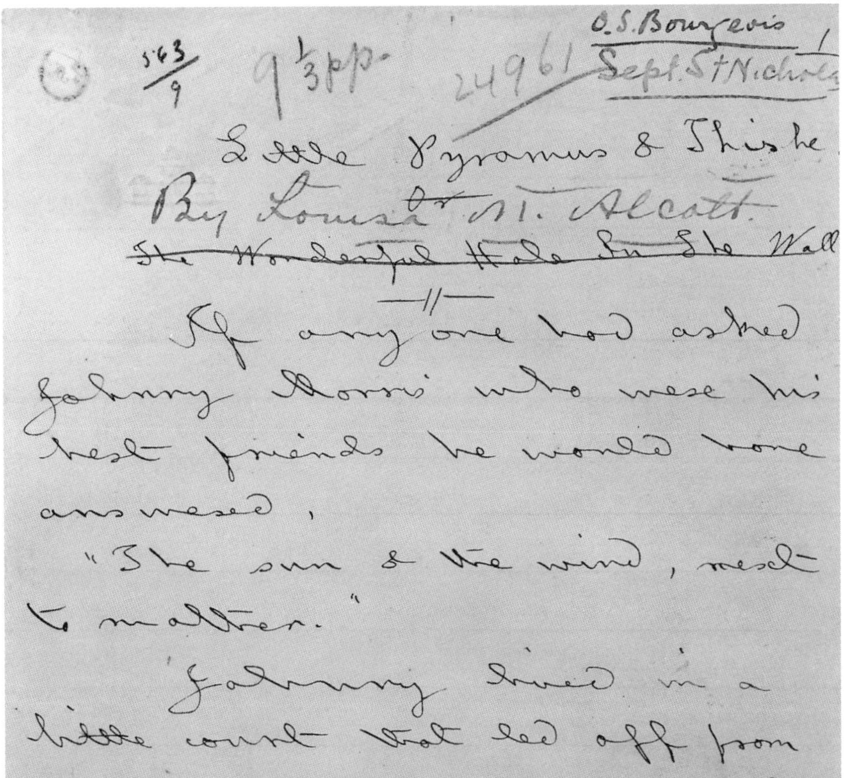
O.S. Bourgeois
Sept. St Nicholas

563/9 9 1/3 pp. 24961

Little Pyramus & Thisbe.
By Louisa M. Alcott.
~~The Wonderful Hole In The Wall~~
—//—

If any one had asked Johnny Morris who were his best friends he would have answered,

"The sun & the wind, next to mother."

Johnny lived in a little court that led off from one of the busiest streets in the city. A noisy street where horse-car bells tinkled & omnibuses rumbled all day long, going & coming from several great depots near by. The court was a dull place, with only two or three shabby houses in it, & a high blank wall at the end. The ~~old~~ people who hurried

"Little Pyramus and Thisbe," N.a.32

"Little Pyramus
and Thisbe"
ca.1883

Autograph manuscript,
initialed, with printing
house markings

65 fols.; 205 x 105 mm.
(mounted on 240 x 160 mm.)

Purchased at the Charles
Romm sale, American
Art Galleries (New York),
March 4, 1921

N.a.32

1. Folger N.a.32, fol. 49.
Quotation from *A Midsummer
Night's Dream*, 5.1.217–218.

2. Many of her shorter works
have only recently been attributed to her, and have been
edited in *Freaks of Genius:
unknown thrillers of Louisa
May Alcott* (New York, 1991),
ed. by Madeleine B. Stern, Joel
Myerson, and Daniel Shealy,
and other collections.

3. It appeared in the September
and October issues of *St.
Nicholas: Scribner's Illustrated
Magazine for Girls and Boys*, 10
(nos. 11, 12):803–7; 885–90. The
characters Pyramus and Thisbe
also briefly appear in Alcott's
novel *Rose in Bloom* (1876).

4. *St. Nicholas*, 5:129.

Fay danced about in the moonlight, like Puck intent upon some pretty prank, and Papa quoted <u>Snout</u> the tinker's parting words, as appropriate to the hour:

> "Thus have I, wall, my part discharged so;
> And, being done, thus wall away doth go."[1]

LITTLE WOMEN (1868–1869) and *Little Men* (1871) represent only a small part of Louisa May Alcott's literary output. In addition to her popular autobiographical novels, she was a prolific writer of thrillers, fairy tales, romance stories, fantasies, plays, and poems, many of them pseudonymously-published.[2] The sixty-five-page manuscript shown here is the story of "Little Pyramus and Thisbe." Written in Alcott's hand and initialed by her on the last page, it was published in two successive issues of the children's magazine *St. Nicholas* (1883).[3] The printer's marks indicate that this was the manuscript copy used for publication. Alcott wrote regularly for *St Nicholas*, whose other contributors included Mark Twain, Frances Hodgson Burnett, Arthur Rackham, and Christina Rossetti. A mini-biography of Alcott that appeared in the December 1877 issue of *St. Nicholas* describes Alcott's value as a writer to the "children readers" of the periodical: "She not only tells you pleasant stories about 'little women' and 'old-fashioned girls,' 'eight cousins,' and children 'under the lilacs,' but she shows you how good it is to be generous and kind, to love others and not to be always caring and working for yourselves."[4]

"Little Pyramus and Thisbe" is a prime example of this observation. As in Ovid's *Metamorphosis* (book IV, lines 55–166) and Shakespeare's *A Midsummer Night's Dream*, the two protagonists are separated by a wall with a small chink through which they see and speak to one another. The similarities end there. In the classical story, Pyramus and Thisbe are lovers forbidden by their parents to marry, who each commits suicide believing that the other had already died. In Alcott's story, a tender friendship ensues. Fay, a wealthy Italian girl living in Boston, pleads with her father to assist poor Johnny, their neighbor, who lost the use of his legs in an accident years earlier. While Johnny is languishing in bed, everyone else conspires to turn the small hole in the wall (where their friendship began) into a beautiful doorway through which the children could freely pass back and forth. Alcott quotes Snout, the actor who plays "the wall" in *Pyramus and Thisbe* as performed in the play within a play in *A Midsummer Night's Dream*, to describe the magical surprise. The story ends with Fay's father painting a garden scene titled "Little Pyramus and Thisbe," depicting Pyramus (Johnny) and Thisbe (Fay) and all the characters in Shakespeare's play. A wealthy woman purchases the painting, and upon hearing of poor Johnny's plight, contributes more money so that Johnny and his mother can go to the country and seek medical help. Johnny and his mother then travel with Fay and her father to the Italian countryside to live in health and happiness.

Alcott's use of Shakepeare is not surprising. An avid theater-goer, she records in her journal her reactions to numerous Shakespearean plays performed by Britain's and America's finest Shakespearean actors, including Edwin Forrest, Fanny Kemble, Henry Irving, Edwin Booth, and Ellen Terry.[5]

H. W.

5. Joel Myerson, et al., eds., *The Journals of Louisa May Alcott* (Boston, 1989).

The Harvest

"And this he meant..." "And that he meant..."
"And this is clear evident..."
"Scene 3, the 2)ᵈ line,
For 'such-and-such' read 'so-and-so'..."
Well, these are wiser heads than mine.
I do not know ... Yet this I know:

He drew his breath, that Stratford clown,
And beauty, free as thistledown
That floats upon an idle wind,
Drifted into the hearts of men,
And grew as tall as Rosalind,
And flowered, sweet as Imogen.

A. A. Milne

"The Harvest," Y.d.517 (1)

A[lan] A[lexander] Milne (1882–1956)

The Harvest.

"And this he meant. . ." "And that he meant. . ."
"And this is clearly evident. . ."
"Scene 3, the 27th line,
For 'such-and-such' read 'so-and-so'. . ."
Well, these are wiser heads than mine.
I do not know . . . Yet this I know:

He drew his breath, that Stratford clown,
And beauty, free as thistle down
That floats upon an idle wind,
Drifted into the hearts of men,
And grew as tall as Rosalind,
And flowered, sweet as Imogen.

THIS MANUSCRIPT VERSE WAS WRITTEN by A. A. Milne in the same year as the publication of *The House at Pooh Corner*. In it, he gently satirizes scholars who are drawn into petty textual arguments concerning Shakespeare's plays at the expense of enjoying the beauty of Shakespeare's words, a beauty that "free as thistle down / that floats upon an idle wind / Drifted into the hearts of men." In the note accompanying the verse, dated September 29, 1928, he wrote, "Dear Watson, I enclose the verses: probably not a bit what you meant, but I hope suitable for your purpose." Milne was most likely addressing Malcolm Watson, the theater critic and playwright who in November 1926 was the Hon. Organiser of the Matinée at the Theatre Royal on Drury Lane. The performance, "To Shakespeare," was attended by the king and queen, and was held to raise money to replace the Shakespeare Memorial Theatre in Stratford-upon-Avon, which had burned to the ground in March. The souvenir program for the event included contributions from Milne and Thomas Hardy, among others.[1] These new verses by Milne, written in 1928, were most likely for another event relating to the rebuilding of the theatre.

As a student at Trinity College, Cambridge, Milne had been elected to the elite Shakespeare Society, and aside from his Pooh series, wrote novels, essays, short stories, poetry, plays, and an autobiography.

H. W.

"The Harvest"
[September 29], 1928

Autograph manuscript, signed
1 fol.; 190 x 140 mm.
Date of purchase unknown
Y.d.517 (1)

1. The Folger has Hardy's correspondence concerning the use of the poem, "To Shakespeare after three hundred years," and the poem itself, for the 1926 event (Folger Y.c.1315 (1–3) and Y.d.585 (1–3)). The performance is described in M. C. Day and J. C. Trewin, *The Shakespeare Memorial Theatre* (London, 1932), 193–96.

Charles Kean (1811?–1868)

Property book
ca.1850

88 pp.; 162 x 95 mm.

Purchased from Baker in 1905

T.a.68

1. *Hamlet, Prince of Denmark. Arranged for representation at the Princess's Theatre, with explanatory notes, by Charles Kean . . . As performed on Monday, January 10th, 1859* (London, n.d.), 40.

2. Folger W.a.10; T.b.15; PROMPT Ham. 19–21.

3. Charles H. Shattuck, *The Shakespeare Promptbooks: A Descriptive Catalogue* (Urbana, IL, 1965), 104. For details of Lloyds, see Alicia Finkel, *Romantic Stages: Set and Costume Design in Victorian England* (London, 1996), 31–58, 180.

4. Fred Belton, *Random Recollections of an Old Actor* (London, 1880), 233: "He left me his immense and valuable wardrobe, chains, crowns, jewels, robes, dresses, and swords."

5. Folger T.a.68, front endleaf.

Polonius: What do you read, my lord?

Hamlet: Words, words, words.

Polonius: What is the matter, my lord?

Hamlet: Between who?

Polonius: I mean, the matter that you read, my lord.

Hamlet: Slanders, sir: for the satirical rogue says here that old men have grey beards; that their Faces are wrinkled; their eyes purging thick amber and plum-tree gum; and that they have a plentiful lack of wit, together with most weak hams.[1]

THIS "ILLUMINATED MANUSCRIPT," bound in purple velvet with eighty-eight pages of crude watercolor sketches and calligraphy, was the property book used by Charles Kean in his role as Hamlet. Charles Kean was actor-manager of the Princess's Theatre in London from 1850–1859, where he staged a number of Shakespearean revivals that were recognized for their historically accurate scenery and costumes.

Kean would have used this book in act 2, scene 2, of *Hamlet,* quoted above. It, or another "Illuminated Book" like it is included in his list of theatrical costumes for plays at the Princess's Theatre, London (ca.1850–1859), under the heading "*Hamlet,* act 2, scene 2." Another manuscript from the Princess's Theatre, titled "Scene Plots, Property Plots, Written Papers, Calls, and Music cues" (ca.1855), also includes a "Handsome Book for Hamlet." Three copies of a souvenir promptbook for Kean's production of the play all list "Hamlet Handsome Book" as the stage prop needed for Act 2.[2]

A note on the endleaf of the book from Fred Belton to Wilson Barrett states that it was the property prayerbook used by Edmund Kean in *Richard III* and Charles Kean in *Hamlet.* Elsewhere it is identified as having been made for Charles Kean in the 1850s, since one of the illuminated pages is initialed "F. L." (possibly the English scene painter, Frederick Lloyds (1818–1894), engaged by Kean from 1848–1858).[3] Belton inherited the book from Kean upon Kean's death in 1868, along with Kean's entire stage wardrobe aside from Hamlet's dress, when he was manager of the Theatre Royal, Exeter.[4] He bequeathed it to Wilson Barrett, then manager of the Princess's Theatre, after meeting him and being "convinced he has the qualities of head & heart to follow worthyly these Illustrious Men."[5]

H.W.

Charles Dickens (1812–1870)

Autograph letter, signed, to Charles Evans, Y.c.771 (9), pp. 2–3

> I have a little difficulty in sending you the exact caste of the Merry Wives, because if Leech should still be unable to come, I shall play Slender, and somebody else will act my present part of Shallow.

ROBERT SHALLOW, the country justice in *The Merry Wives of Windsor*, was one of the characters that Charles Dickens performed best in his "amateur" productions of the play in London and the provinces between May and July 1848. Mary Cowden Clarke, who had recently completed her monumental *Complete Concordance to Shakespeare* and whom Dickens cast as Mrs. Quickly in the production, wrote that Dickens's "impersonation was perfect: the old, stiff limbs, the senile stoop of the shoulders . . . were all assumed and maintained with wonderful accuracy; while the articulation,–part lisp, part thickness of utterance . . . gave consummate effect to his mode of speech."[1]

Autograph letter, signed,
to Charles Evans
June 9, 1848

3 pp. (bifolium); 180 x 115 mm.

Purchased from Pickering and Chatto in 1916

Y.c.771 (9)

"Resolutions of the Amateur Company"
October 14, 1848

Autograph manuscript

2 pp. (bifolium); 323 x 201 mm.

Y.d.341 (43)

1. Charles and Mary Cowden Clarke, *Recollections of writers* (London, 1878), 305-6

2. The house had been purchased by the London Shakespeare Committee in September 1847.

3. For details of Dickens's production of *Merry Wives*, see Valerie L. Gager, *Shakespeare and Dickens: The Dynamic of Influence* (Cambridge, 1996), 106–11.

4. This letter is published in Graham Storey and K. J. Fielding, eds., *The Letters of Charles Dickens*, 5: 1847–1849 (Oxford, 1989), 327–28.

5. *Letters of Charles Dickens*, 5:328.

6. Folger Y.c.341 (45).

7. Folger Y.c.341 (44).

In 1848, Dickens was finishing his novel *Dombey and Son*, publishing the "Cheap Edition" of his works, writing for the *Examiner*, overseeing the "Home for Homeless Women" which he had started with Miss Burdett Coutts, raising six children, and running an amateur theatrical company. Dickens and his company engaged in a series of benefit performances in London, Liverpool, Manchester, Birmingham, Edinburgh, and Glasgow, to endow a curatorship for Sheridan Knowles at Shakespeare's birthplace in Stratford-upon-Avon.[2] Dickens was involved with his theatrical company at every level—in this letter, he discusses the date and time of performance, casting changes, the playbill, the overture, and the afterpiece. Influenced by his close friend William Macready's restorations of Shakespeare plays on the stage, Dickens had professional expectations of his largely amateur cast and placed a strong emphasis on authenticity of performance, both in terms of the text used and in costume and scenery design.[3]

Three days after their first performance in Birmingham, actor-manager Dickens writes here to the head of the Birmingham Theatricals Committee concerning their second Birmingham performance, which took place on June 27, 1848.[4] His cast, which included G. H. Lewes, Mary Cowden Clarke, Mark Lemon, Anne Romer, John Leech, C. A. Cole, Emmeline Montague, John Forster, Frank Stone, Augustus Egg, George Cruikshank, and Miss Kenworthy, played to a full house at Birmingham, and the *Birmingham Journal* had high and enthusiastic praise on both occasions.[5] *Merry Wives* was performed seven other times by Dickens's company, including twice at the Haymarket in London.

Despite the success of the performances, the balance sheet reflected a much smaller sum than they had anticipated.[6] The second document shown in the exhibition, "Resolutions of the Amateur Company," is in Dickens's hand and outlines the company's plan for the disposition of the balance of £557, 11 shillings, and 5 pence. In the covering letter to the Subcommittee of the Shakespeare House, he explains that the small balance was a result of "the immense sums charged by provincial managers for the use of closed Theatres—the great distances to which it has been necessary to convey a large number of persons—and the fact of an actual loss having attended the performances in London (in consequence, chiefly, I conceive, of the arrangements for the sale and distribution of tickets having been very complicated and unintelligible to the Public)."[7]

The Folger has four other letters relating to Dickens's benefit productions of 1848, as well as eleven more autograph letters and three books formerly owned by him.

H. W.

Alfred, Lord Tennyson (1809–1892)

Tennyson 1851- Pub. 1875

Farewell, Macready; since to-night we part.
   Full-handed thunders often have confest
   Thy power, well-used to move the public breast.
We thank thee with one voice, & from the heart.
Farewell, Macready; since this night we part.
   Go, take thine honours home: rank with the best,
   Garrick, & statelier Kemble, & the rest
Who made a nation purer thro' their Art.
Thine is it, that our drama did not die,
   Nor flicker down to brainless Pantomime,
      And those gilt gauds men-children swarm to see.
   Farewell, Macready; moral, grave, sublime.
Our Shakespeare's bland & universal eye
      Dwells pleased, thro' twice a hundred years, on thee.

———

Sonnet on William Charles Macready, Y.d.519 (1)

Autograph sonnet
on William Charles
Macready
1851

1 p.; 186 x 115 mm.

Purchased from Maggs Bros.
in 1943

Y.d.519 (1)

1. Alan S. Downer, *The Eminent Tragedian William Charles Macready* (Cambridge, MA, 1966), 314.

2. William Charles Macready, *The Journal . . . 1832-1851*, abr. and ed. J. C. Trewin (London, 1967), 292–95.

ON FEBRUARY 26, 1851, the English actor, William Charles Macready (1793–1873) made his final appearance on the stage. The theater was Drury Lane, and the play was *Macbeth*, with Macready in the title role. His leave-taking of the stage had begun several years earlier, but this performance was to be his final "last time forever."[1]

Macready's last stage appearance did not go unnoticed. Every seat had been sold days before, and on the evening of the performance, three thousand people gathered outside the theater to see the arrival of those fortunate enough to have secured seats. At Macbeth's first entrance, the audience rose to its feet crying his name and waving hats and handkerchiefs. "Acted Macbeth as I never, never before acted it; with a reality, a vigour, a truth, a dignity that I never before threw into my delineation of this favourite character," Macready wrote in his journal.[2]

A testimonial dinner organized by Macready's closest friend, Charles Dickens, followed on March 1. Among the six hundred people attending were Dickens, Thackeray, Tennyson, Bulwer Lytton, Charles Kemble, and Samuel Phelps. Tennyson, England's Poet Laureate, marked the important occasion with a sonnet:

> Farewell Macready, since to-night we part.
> Full-handed thunders often here confest
> Thy power, well used to move the public heart.

Tennyson goes on to commend Macready's contribution to the English stage and ranks his acting with that of David Garrick and John Philip Kemble:

> Go, take thine honors home; rank with the best,
> Garrick and statelier Kemble, and the rest
> Who made a nation purer through their art.

In the last two lines of the sonnet, Tennyson heaps the highest praise on Macready with his invocation of Shakespeare's spirit, which "Dwells pleased, through twice a hundred years, on thee." This was an accolade indeed for an actor who gained eminence as a tragedian in *King Lear*, *Hamlet*, and *Macbeth*.

Tennyson had entrusted the reading of the sonnet at the testimonial dinner to John Forster, close friend of Macready and editor of the *Examiner*. It was published simultaneously in the March 1851 issues of Charles Dickens's monthly periodical *The Household Narrative*, and *The People's and Howitt's Journal*.

Rosalind Larry
Folger Shakespeare Library

Alfred, Lord Tennyson (1809–1892)
Augustin Daly (1838–1899)
Sir Arthur Seymour Sullivan (1842–1900)

THE **PRODUCTION** of Alfred, Lord Tennyson's *The Foresters* at Daly's Theater in New York in March 1892 is a story of trans-Atlantic collaboration and cooperation. Originally written by Lord Tennyson in 1881 for Sir Henry Irving and Ellen Terry, the play, a rendition of the Robin Hood legend, was then shelved for ten years until Augustin Daly, manager of Daly's Theater, New York City, and Ada Rehan (1857–1916), the leading actress in his company, expressed interest in it while on tour in London in August 1891.[1] Writing from the Lyceum Theatre in London on September 17, Daly informed Lord Tennyson's son Hallam, who was acting as his 82-year-old father's agent, that he would like to enter into an agreement with Tennyson and that "If these terms are agreeable to Lord Tennyson I will at once go over the work and make what suggestions occur to me as to Curtailment &c."[2] Daly made his blue-pencil and brown-ink curtailments to the "stage copy" of the 1890 edition of the play, shown in the exhibition.[3] As the manuscript title page indicates, Daly reduced the play from five acts to four by conflating a number of scenes, tightening the action, and deleting various speeches.[4] Another hand, perhaps Tennyson's later hand, writes over some of the blue-pencil suggestions in brown ink and adds further notes in pencil. In a telegram dated January 25, 1892, Tennyson writes, "Stage Copy approved insert deer speech have you received final report have you signed."[5] The final report to which Tennyson refers is probably the license, also dated January 25, 1892. Daly's copy of the license, with Tennyson's shaky signature, is shown in the exhibition.[6]

At the same time that Daly was negotiating with Tennyson, he was arranging with the composer Sir Arthur Sullivan, of Gilbert and Sullivan fame, to write the music for the production. On October 29, 1891, Tennyson telegraphed Daly in London to ask him, "What have you arranged with Sullivan? We go to Isle of Wight tomorrow and wish you good voyage."[7] In fact, Sullivan had initiated contact with Daly on October 23, and on October 27 wrote that he would be happy to compose the necessary music, but was concerned about the number of songs given to Marian, "for whom a competent singer will rarely be found." He suggested "bright dance tunes with an old English ring" for the forest scenes, and a last chorus that would "send the audience away in good humour."[8] Between October and December 1891 Sullivan reported regularly to Daly, asking him "to guard the music (while it remains in manuscript) from all dishonest efforts to attain & perform it," writing of his concern over a particular scene ("The scene with the fairies has bothered me a good deal as I have had to be in correspondence with Lord Tennyson about certain modifications which were necessary to make it practicable on the stage"), and wishing that Daly "could bring it out in England next season for poor old Lord Tennyson's sake. If it is merely a question of getting a good Theatre I think that might be managed."[9]

ALFRED, LORD TENNYSON
AUGUSTIN DALY

Stage copy for *Under Green Leaves, or The Foresters and Maid Marian* by Alfred, Lord Tennyson (1890) with Augustin Daly's manuscript revisions ca.1892

82 fols.; 210 x 170 mm.

W.a.42

Agreement with Augustin Daly to produce "Robin Hood and Maid Marian" January 25, 1892

3 fols.; 384 x 250 mm.

Y.c.5345 (258)

SIR ARTHUR
SEYMOUR SULLIVAN

Autograph letter, signed, to Augustin Daly October 27, 1891

4 pp. (bifolium); 167 x 107 mm.

Y.c.5047 (3)

1. They learned of it from Joseph Anderson, who wrote to Daly of a play that "would suit your company and Miss Rehan in particular" (Folger Y.c.2603 (1)). In 1888, Anderson's sister, the American actress Mary Anderson, had briefly considered producing the play and performing the role of Maid Marian.

2. Folger Y.c.4173 (38).

3. Folger W.a.42.

4. For the nature of Daly's revisions to the text, see Lois Potter, "The Apotheosis of Maid Marian: Tennyson's *The Foresters* and the Nineteenth-Century Theater," *Playing Robin Hood: The Legend as Performance in Five Centuries*, ed. Lois Potter (Newark, DE, 1998), 182–204. Potter notes that Augustin Daly's brother and biographer, Joseph, was also involved with the play in some way, since he received royalty checks whenever it was produced (194).

5. Folger Y.c.5072 (3).

6. Folger Y.c.5345 (258).

7. Folger Y.c.5072 (1).

8. Folger Y.c.5047 (3).

9. Folger Y.c.5074 (4–6).

10. Folger Y.c.5072 (2); Y.c.5345 (258).

11. Potter, 200, from *New York Times*, March 20, 1892.

12. Folger Y.c.5072 (5).

13. Folger Y.c.5047 (7). He apologizes for writing this letter in pencil, "but as I am still in bed and very weak, I dare not risk the damage which I might do to the sheets if I used ink!" After describing his intense pain, he writes that it is "alleviated a good deal by that priceless and merciful gift to man—hyperdermic injection of morphine."

As opening day approached, Hallam Tennyson telegraphed Daly on his father's behalf from the Isle of Wight concerning the play's title and various costume decisions. In January, Tennyson had telegraphed, "Call play foresters if Robin hood and Maid Marian impossible," and the license for the play referred to it as being "at present called 'Robin Hood and Maid Marian' but the eventual title of which is hereafter to be decided on by the said Lord Tennyson."[10] On February 18, 1892, another telegram requested "My name robin Hood and Maid Marian dress her in bridal white at end if desirable not Countess robes." The stage copy is titled by Daly, "Under Green Leaves or The Foresters and Maid Marian," but the final title was simply, "The Foresters."

Daly's sumptuous production in New York in March 1892 was a huge success. *The New York Times* wrote that "People who see the poetical play once want to go again."[11] Sullivan's music, the costumes, and in particular, the fairy scene (involving wands, headdresses with electric lights, and flying fairies), were praised. On opening day, Hallam telegraphed Daly, "Warmest thanks to yourself and Miss Rehan and all who have taken so much trouble our Congratulations on the splendid success."[12] Sullivan wrote in similar terms from the south of France, where he was suffering from kidney problems—"Author, composer, actors, and last but not least, manager, seemed to have scored a success, and this is always satisfactory . . . I am especially delighted that the fairy scene was so successful."[13] The London production, attended by Tennyson's widow, son, and daughter-in-law, took place in October 1893, shortly after Tennyson's death. The documents at the Folger concerning the play's production are a fascinating and full record of theater production, copyright, and collaboration in the late nineteenth century.

H. W.

William F. Cody ("Buffalo Bill") (1846–1917)

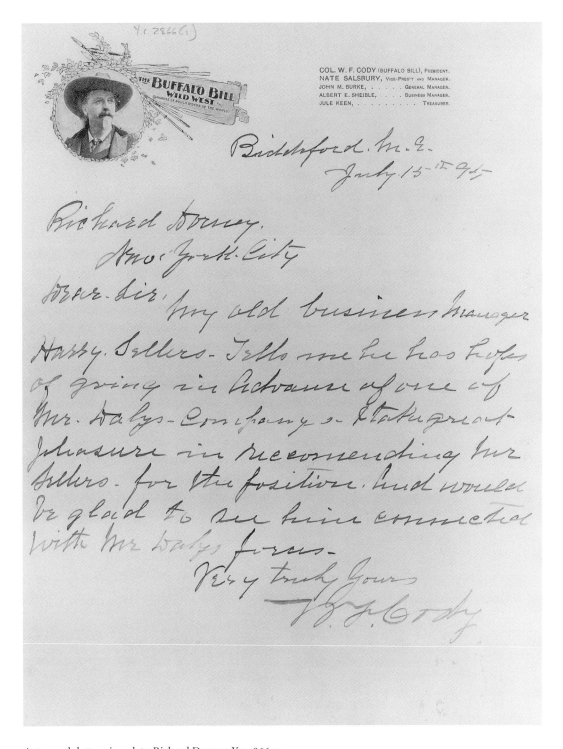

Autograph letter, signed, to Richard Dorney, Y.c.2866 (1)

William F. Cody ("Buffalo Bill")

Autograph letter, signed,
to Richard Dorney
July 15, 1895

1 fol.; 280 x 215 mm.

Daly collection

Y.c.2866 (1)

Dear Sir,

My old business Manager Harry Sellers, Tells me he has hopes of going
in Advance of one of Mr. Dalys Companys. I take great pleasure in
reccomending Mr Sellers. for the position. And would be glad to see
him connected with Mr Dalys forces.

Very truly Yours

W. F. Cody

---

1. Robert A. Carter, *Buffalo
Bill Cody: The Man Behind
the Legend* (New York, 2000),
380–83.

BUFFALO BILL WAS ONE OF AMERICA'S BEST-KNOWN performers and
showmen in the 1890s. In the midst of a 9,000 mile tour involving 131 stops in 190
days, he found time in Biddeford, Maine, to write to Richard Dorney, manager of
Daly's Theatre in New York, on behalf of his former business manager, Harry
Sellers. Sellers apparently hoped to become an advance-man for Augustin Daly,
publicizing Daly's touring shows before they arrived in each town.

In the 1890s, "Buffalo Bill's Wild West" became "The Buffalo Bill Wild West
Congress of Rough Riders of the World," and drew multitudes to their elaborate
performances throughout America and Europe. Buffalo Bill probably became
acquainted with Dorney during the Congress's 1894 season at Ambrose Park in
Brooklyn, New York, where the show was performed twice a day in a covered grand-
stand seating 20,000 people. Poor box office receipts resulted in 1894 being the last
season in which the show remained in one place. In 1895, the year of this letter,
Buffalo Bill joined forces with James A. Bailey (of Barnum and Bailey), who provided him with railway cars and equipment for the exhausting but highly-successful
season of his 700-person "Congress." In the same year, Buffalo Bill created another
enterprise about the history of American slavery, a show called "Black America"
which closed its doors in autumn 1895.[1]

H. W.

Bram Stoker (1847–1912)

Personal Reminiscences of Henry Irving, N.a.66, chap. 74, p. 35

*Personal Reminiscences
of Henry Irving*
1906

Autograph manuscript

1,276 pp.; 230 x 178 mm.

Purchased from Maggs Bros.
in September 1928

N.a.65–66

1. Bram Stoker, *Personal
Reminiscences of Henry Irving*,
2 vols. (New York and London,
1906). Barbara Belford, *Bram
Stoker: A Biography of the
Author of* Dracula (New York,
1996), 308.

2. Belford, 99.

It was almost impossible to believe that he was dead as he lay there with his eyes open. I knelt down by him & felt his heart to ~~see~~ know for myself if it was indeed death. ∧But all was sadly still.∧ His body was still quite warm. Walter Collinson his faithful valet was sitting on the floor beside him, crying. He said to me through his sobs: 'He died in my arms!'

TEN YEARS AFTER writing *Dracula*, Bram Stoker began a biography of the actor Sir Henry Irving (1838–1905), to whom he had devoted twenty-nine years of his life. This 1,276 page autograph manuscript of Stoker's reminiscences was written in intense bursts in the first half of 1906, only three months following Irving's death in Sheffield after a performance of Tennyson's *Becket*. Published in the same year to mixed reviews,[1] the biography is a tender account by a devoted disciple who confesses early on that, "Looking back I cannot honestly find any moment in my life when I failed him." The manuscript contains material not incorporated in the printed version, including the final paragraph of the final page, in which Stoker stands at Irving's grave in Poet's Corner in Westminster Abbey and remembers the particularly apt final lines from Tennyson's poem, "The Silent Voices:"

I stood beside Tennyson's grave in 1892 when the noble words of his "Silent voices," nobly set & nobly sung, seemed like the epitome of the teaching of his life. ∧Years afterwards∧ I heard Irving speak them in the ∧crowded∧ Senate House at Cambridge with a ~~noble~~ fervour which seemed a part of his very life. From his grave, between Garrick and [*blank space*] and in the shelter of the monument of Shakespeare, I seem to hear his voice now:
>"Call me rather, silent voices,
>"Forward to the starry track
>"Shimmering up the heights beyond me
>"On, and always on!

Stoker first met Irving in Dublin in 1876, after Irving, pleased by Stoker's review of his performance of *Hamlet*, invited him to dinner at the Shelbourne Hotel. In 1878, Irving became the lessee and actor-manager of the Lyceum Theatre in London, and Stoker the acting manager. Stoker meticulously oversaw every detail pertaining to the running of the theater and served as Irving's secretary, accountant, speech-writer, and late night friend and listener. Stoker estimates that he wrote at least half a million letters as Irving's secretary.[2] Working for Irving was a sometimes thankless job, and Stoker's alter-ego in *Dracula*, Jonathan Harker, who finally achieves manhood when he slits Dracula's throat, reflects Stoker's ambivalence towards the man who consistently drained him both intellectually and emotionally. None of this ambivalence, however, is reflected in Stoker's biography of Irving. The Folger has numerous letters to and from Stoker, letters from Irving in Stoker's hand, promptbooks belonging to Stoker, and manuscripts relating to Irving.

H. W.

Appendix: Letters of Elizabeth I

SI D'AUENTURE EN Vne Vision M. de beauuois Vous estonne mon treschir frere,
Ne Vous desplaise Que Le desir qu'iL tient de uivre et mourir a Vos pies[1] Ly a
Contrainct de Vous offenser n'en ayant l'authoritie Et m'a prie de grande Instance
que Ie entremele mon Credit pour l'absolution de Ce peche, IL auroit honte de
demourir[2] a son ayse quant[3] son Cher Maistre habite si pres de ses ennemis, Ce qui
Ie trouue si raisonable que plustot Ie prens enuie de son heur en cest endroict que
pour faillir a Vn si fidel Seruiteur Voyre pour Vous mesmes a qui Ie souhaite Le
nombre redouble de teLz qu'il uous est et pour La fidelite, experience, et Valeur
Pourtant Ie m'assure tant de Uostre bonte que ne me nyeras si honorable requeste
Et aussy pour ly auoir impose quelque charge de ma part sans laquelle il n'euct eu
son Conge, C'est pour Vous pencer auec Vn memoriall de moy quant Vous vous
monstreras auoir plus de besoing d'une bride que eperonne, En L'honneur de dieu
Consideres Combien il importe a toute La Cause La Conseruation de uostre persone Vous me pardonneres a Vous dire que se[4] qui se nommeroit Valeur en un aultre
a Vous on l'imputera a temerite et fablte[5] de tel Iugement qui soiet le plus a un grand
Prince, Sy a ceste seuLe heure On feroit preuue de Vostre Courage Ie Vous
souhaiterois plus tot mille dangiers que telle doubte, Car a mon filz si i'en eusse[6] Ie
le Verrois mort plustot que Couard, Mais ^{auec} trop de experien^{ce} en[7] ayant faict
exemplaire assurance de Vostre inVincible magnanimitie[8] Ie Vous ConIure par tout
ce qu'aimes Le mieulx que Vous Vous respectes non Comme priVe Souldait ais[9]
Comme Grand Prince, Peult estre que Vous mespriseres Ce ConseiL comme
Sortant d'un Coeur paoureusx de femme mais[10] Quant il Vous SouViendra par
combien de fois Ie n'ay monstre trop de Craincte a mon sien[11] de Pistols et Espees
qui m'ont este prepare ceste pancee passera estant faulte de que ne ^{me} recognois
Coulpable, Attribues Le pourtant a mon seule affection en Vostre endroict Et
Croyes que n'en pourres recevoir du mal que Ie n'en ay ma part. Cest escript ne
peult passer mes mains sans Vous impartir La grande diligence et estresme Soing
de Ce Gentilhomme qui ne saisse[12] a Soliciter Vos Causes comme un tresfideL
Seruiteur Que dieu vous enVoye de Ces semblables Ly priant aussy de Vous donner
bonsaduis et Vous Conceder La Grace de prendre
tousiours Le meilleur Chemin en tous

Vostre tresassuree fidelle bonne Soeur et Cousine

Vos entreprises et uous Conseruer   Elizabeth R
Comme La prunelle de son OeuL[13]

En l'honneur de dieu rasembles ces faubousiers a quoy sert paris et Le Roy perir, O
que Ie suis en Cholere comme Ce Gentilhomme uous dira de ma parte

Autograph letter, signed,
to Henri IV of France
ca. 1590

V.b.131

Transcription and
translation by
Leah Marcus and
Janel Mueller

1. *pies*, i.e., pieds

2. *demourir*, i.e., demeurer

3. *quant*, i.e., quand

4. *se*, i.e., ce

5. *fablte*, i.e., faibleté

6. *mon filz si i'en eusse*: my son,
if I had had one. Elizabeth's
imagining becomes doubly
suggestive because she addresses a French king twenty years
her junior and because she
places monarchs (herself and
Henri) in a category separate
from their heir(s) (Elizabeth's
presumptive son). A monarch's
highest imperative is to preserve his country's security
by keeping his own life safe.
An heir's highest imperative
is to demonstrate his honoe
by defending his country even
to the death—in her cryptic
phrase, "rather dead than a
coward."

7. *en* added in left margin

8. *magnanimitie*. In her
November 24, 1586, speech
responding to the parliamen-
tary petition calling for the
execution of Mary, Queen of
Scots, Elizabeth identified
magnanimity as one of the
four cardinal political virtues,
substituting it for courage.
The context of her remarks
makes it clear that she
understands magnanimity
as defined by Aristotle,
Nicomachian Ethics 1123b
6–9, as the great-spiritedness
shown in lofty pride that
reaches its ethical heights in
one's concern for one's honor
or dishonor. For the passage
in the speech, see Marcus,
Mueller, and Rose, eds.,
Elizabeth I: Collected Works,
198; for discussion, see Janel
Mueller, "Virtue and
Virtuality: Gender in the Self-
Representations of Elizabeth
I," in *Virtual Gender: Fantasies
of Embodied Space and
Subjectivity*, ed. Mary Ann
O'Farrell and Lynne Vallone
(Ann Arbor, MI, 1999).

9. *ais*, either "mais" or "ains,"
both conjunctions meaning
"but" (the former simply con-
trastive, the latter emphatic).

10. *mais*, added in left margin

11. *sien*, i.e., sein

12. *saisse*, i.e., cesse

13. *Comme . . . OeuL*, as the
pupil of his eye; idiomatic for
a most cherished person or
thing. The last phrases of the
letter are crowded into the left
side of the sheet next to the
closing salutation, as shown. A
postscript follows across a still
lower part of the sheet.

[English translation]
[Addressed] To my dearest good brother and cousin, the most Christian king

IF BY CHANCE in a vision M[onsieur] de Beauvoir astonishes you, my dearest brother, do not be displeased that the desire he has to live and die at your feet has constrained him to offend you, not having the authority to do so; and he has begged me with great earnestness to interpose my credit for the absolution of this offense. He would be ashamed to reside at his ease while his dear master dwells so near his enemies. The which I find so reasonable that I have become desirous rather to use him in this respect than to lack so faithful a servant—indeed to you yourself—to whom I wish the number redoubled of such as he is to you, both for fidelity, expe-rience, and valor. However, I assure myself so much of your goodness that you will not deny me so honorable a request; and also, for my part, I have charged him with a task without which he would not have had his leave.

It is for you to reflect, with a reminder from me, how much you will show your-self in greater need of a bridle than a spur. For the honor of God, consider how much it matters to the whole cause—the preservation of your person! You will par-don me for telling you that what is called valor in another, in you is imputed to temerity and feebleness of such judgment as should be greatest in a great prince. If at this very hour, proof were to be made of your courage, I would rather wish you a thousand dangers than such a doubt. For as to my son, if I had had one, I would rather have seen him dead than a coward. But with too much experience in having made exemplary assurance of your invincible magnanimity, I conjure you by every-thing that you love most that you esteem yourself not as a private soldier but as a great prince.

It may be that you will disdain this advice as coming from the fearful heart of a woman, but when you remember how many times I have not showed my breast too much afraid of pistols and swords that were prepared against me, this thought will pass, being a fault of which I do not acknowledge myself guilty. Attribute it, howev-er, to my singular affection towards you, and believe that you cannot receive harm from it which I have no share of. This writing cannot pass from my hands without imparting to you the great diligence and extreme care of this gentleman, who does not cease to plead your causes like a most faithful servant. May God send you more men like him, praying Him also to give you good instruction and to grant you the grace always to take the best path in all your enterprises, and to preserve you as the darling of His eye.

Your very assured, faithful, good sister and cousin,
Elizabeth R

For the honor of God, assemble those outlying inhabitants together. What use is it for Paris and the king to perish? O how angry I am, as this gentleman will tell you for my part.

Appendix

Autograph letter, signed, to James VI of Scotland ca. March 1593

X.d.397

Transcription by Leah Marcus and Janel Mueller

1. *a noble man* Thomas, Lord Borough, whose commission as special emissary to James took effect with the hand-to-hand delivery of this letter.

2. *slidik dame* slippery woman. Evidently an allusion to the mythic figure of Opportunity, who required to be seized by her forelock and turned out of the oncomer's path, lest she prove an obstacle to success. Elizabeth's writings of the 1590s are marked by a penchant for allegory, most conspicuously on view in her twenty-seven stanzaic verses in French, which feature an array of such personages as the Second Help, Fantasy, Reason, Will, Love, Memory, Justice, Discord, Malice, and Mercy. These verses are printed in modern English translation as Poem 15 in Marcus, Mueller, and Rose, eds., *Elizabeth I: Collected Works*, 413–21; the text of the French original will appear as Poem 15 in Mueller and Marcus, eds., *Elizabeth I: Autograph Originals and Foreign Language Originals*; for discussion of this poem see Constance Jordan, "States of Blindness: Doubt, Justice, and Constancy in Elizabeth I's "Avec l'aveugler si estrange," forthcoming in *Reading Monarch Writing: The Poetry of Henry VIII, Mary Stuart, Elizabeth I, and James VI/I*, ed. Peter C. Herman (Binghamton, NY, 2002), 109–34.

[Addressed] To our deare Brother the Kyng of Scotts.

/ My deare brother /

THE CARE OF YOUR ESTATE with feare of your neglect so afflictz my mynd as I may not ouerslip the sending you a noble man[1] to sarue you for a memorialL of my readinis and desiar of your spide, The slidik dame[2] Who Whan she is turned Leuis no after step to witnis her arriVaL ~~but~~ saue repentance that beareth to soWer a recorde of her short abode may make you so fur awake ~~you~~ that you haue neUer Cause throuwe to Long discoursing, to Loose the bettar knoweLege of hideust[3] tre-son One hoWre bredes a dayes gain to gilefulL spiritz[4] and gilty Conscience skiLs more to shift than ten Wisar hedz ~~to~~ knoWes how to Win Let the Anfild[5] be striken While hit is warme for if hit groWe Colde the Goldsmithe marz his Worke and the oWnar his IuelL hit Vexeth me to Se that thos of Whom the Very filds of SkotLand Could if the mighte spa~~e~~ke truly tel hoW ther banners wer Displaid again your person Who diuers nights did senteneL their actz thos selfe same be but noW bid to a Ward[6] Who Long ago God wot, aught so haue smarted as you nide not noW exa-men ther treachery AL this I say not for my Gaping for any mans bloud God is Witnis but Wische you saVid W∧hereuer the rest Go,[7] and this I must tel you that if the Lands of them that do decerue no brethe Wer made but yours (as ther oWne ~~actz~~ actz haue Caused) you should be a richer prince ∧and than abler of your oWne to defend a kings honor and your oWne Life

Me thinks I frame this Lettar Like to a Lamentation Wiche you Wyl pardon Whan the matter bidz hit so / I can not but beWaile that any LeWd unaduised ~~Varlet of~~ hedsik felowe a subiect of myne[8] shuld make his Soueregn be supposed of Les Gouuernement than mistres of her Word I haue neuer yet dishonored my tonge with a Leasing not to a menar person than a king and Wold be aschamed to desarue so foWLe an infamy I VoWe I neuer kneWe but did forbid that euer he shuld enter my territory that so boLdLy atteinted your dores[9] you knoWe best What I Writ for that and he as I heare ~~as~~ hathe hard hit so muche as hardLy he WyL trust my handz to be his safe refuge Yet you ∧Knowe best What Was offerd and Why he Was not made more desperat If your Long exspectd and neuer had as yet answer had not Lingard I think he WoLd haue gone fur Ynough or noW, Let this suffice be youre doinges as sounde as my profession stanche and I Warrant no spaniard nor ther king shal haue euer footing so nire to you or me / trust I pray you neuer a Conquerar With trust of his kindnis nor neuer raigne precario more

Whan you may ruLe regis regula[10] / your Cumbar to rede suche skribled Lines and pray the almighty to Couer you safely undar his bleased Wings /[11]

Now do I remember
Your most LoVing Sistar
Elizabeth R

3. *hideust*, i.e., hideousest. Laetitia Yeandle has proposed the reading "hidnest," i.e., hiddenest, most hidden. Her equally plausible proposal illustrates very well the difficulty of interpretation caused by Elizabeth's ambiguous "u" and "n" letter forms.

4. *gilefulL spiritz* In the close context of "hideousest treason" at this date, the plural reference can only be to the Scottish Catholic lords led by Angus, Huntly, and Errol.

5. *Anfild* anvil.

6. *bid to a Ward* sent into custody.

7. *Wische you saVid Whereuer the rest Go* Fervent expressions of solicitude for James's safety are a major refrain throughout Elizabeth's twenty-year personal correspondence with the monarch who would succeed to her throne.

8. *any LeWd unaduised hedsik felowe a subiect of myne* Francis Stewart Hepburn, fifth Earl of Bothwell, the violent leader of the Protestant extremists in Scotland.

9. *atteinted your dores* dishonored your doors—an allusion to Bothwell's breaching of James's royal palace in 1591. Additionally, the verb "attaint" plays off the noun, the "attainder" that Bothwell deserves—that is, a judgment of death or outlawry for having committed high treason.

10. *precario more* by way of entreaty. *regis regula* in the manner of a king.

11. *Couer you safely undar his bleased Wings* an allusion to Psalm 63:7. The whole concluding sentence is a manifest addition, crowded into the left corner of the sheet opposite Elizabeth's subscription and signature.

Index

Index of Contributors

Design:
Studio A
Alexandria, Virginia

Printing:
Hagerstown Bookbinding
and Printing
Hagerstown, Maryland